MAMMAL ATLAS OF
NORTH-EAST SCOTLAND AND
THE CAIRNGORMS

Nick Littlewood (Littlewood Ecology), Paul Chapman,
Ian Francis (RSPB Scotland), Glenn Roberts (NESBReC),
Annie Robinson (University of Aberdeen) & Konstantinos Sideris (NESBReC)
(Editors)

FIRST PUBLISHED MARCH 2017 BY NESBReC, ABERDEEN

COPYRIGHT © 2017 NESBReC

ISBN 978-1-5262-0669-5

Image: Mountain Hare, Cairnwell Pass. Harry Scott

FOREWORD

I take my hat off to the coordinators of this impressive project, to all who gathered and organised the mammal records, and to those who crafted the text and produced the illustrations; for collectively they have achieved something rather special. The task must have felt overwhelming at times; but they deserve to feel immensely proud of what they have produced.

Those of us who do our mammal recording in the compact counties of southern Britain - where the network of roads and footpaths provides easy access to the landscape - will find it difficult to appreciate the awesome challenge facing those who produced this atlas. At over 11,500 km² (spread over >140 hectads) the area covered is simply vast: you could fit nearly seven of my home county of Worcestershire inside its boundaries; only the Atlas of Highland Mammals (Scott, 2011) covers a bigger area. Beyond the challenge of size, the area includes five of the six highest mountains in Britain - surely making it our highest and snowiest mammal atlas - where many of the tetrads are accessible only after a long hike from the nearest public road; and the human population - the potential mammal recorders - is predictably low over most of the atlas area. Finally, there is a massive length of coastline that hosts important populations of seals and cetaceans. That is a tough context in which to embark upon a mammal atlas!

In tackling their daunting challenge I applaud the innovative steps taken by the coordinators to maximise the spread and diversity of mammal records as efficiently as possible: through the 'Adopt-a-Square' scheme, for example; and through NESBReC's camera trap loan scheme and a public appeal for small mammal records via the 'Look What the Cat Brought In' scheme. The professionalism of NESBReC is reflected in the superb distribution maps, which show the warp and weft of the landscape so we can imagine its influence on mammal distribution patterns. And talking of innovation, I welcome the inclusion of humans and domestic livestock in the atlas. It is very good for us - the top 'problem mammal' - to see our conservation status and impacts considered objectively alongside our wild relatives with which we share the landscape.

This atlas is important for the baseline it provides for future mammal recording and for the snapshot of nationally important populations that it covers. Notably, the majority of Britain's Mountain Hare population occupies the Cairngorms massif and, lower down the hill, a significant proportion of the beleaguered Wildcat population survives in the forests and plantations alongside important numbers of Pine Martens and Red Squirrels.

Energy, passion and a commitment to improving public understanding of our wildlife shine out of the pages that follow. And if you still need inspiration to get involved, this atlas raises tantalising questions to stimulate future mammal recording: with nowhere higher to go beyond the Cairngorms massif, how will the Mountain Hares respond to the effects of climate change; and, as temperatures rise, will new cetaceans and bats move up from the south? Will escapee Wild Boar establish wild populations as they have elsewhere in Scotland? Might the Pine Marten's impact upon Grey Squirrels be sufficient to help the native Red Squirrel to thrive in perpetuity? And can we turn the Wildcat's fortunes around before it is too late? By all means read on and enjoy this atlas, but don't stay indoors too long!

Dr Johnny Birks

Mammal Society Chair 2009-2015

CONTENTS

2 | **Foreword**

4 | **Survey methods and production of the atlas**

12 | **Mammal habitats, landscape and land use**

34 | **Species accounts**

36   Rodents (squirrels, voles, mice and rats)
52   Lagomorphs (rabbits and hares)
58   Insectivores (hedgehog, mole and shrews)
68   Bats
82   Carnivores (cats, fox and mustelids)
104 Seals
110 Ungulates (wild boar, deer and feral goat)
122 Primates (human)
124 Additional mammal species
126 Cetaceans (porpoises, dolphins and whales)
129 Domestic livestock

132 | **Distribution patterns and species richness**

138 | **Mammal conservation**

160 | **References**

168 | **Annex**

169 1. Acknowledgements and funders
170 2. Recorders' names
174 3. Scientific names of species mentioned in the text
175 4. Glossary of terms
176 5. Gazetteer of sites mentioned in the text
178 6. Atlas facts and figures

179 | **Index**

182 | **Reference map of the atlas area**

Image: Pine Marten, Aboyne. Harry Scott

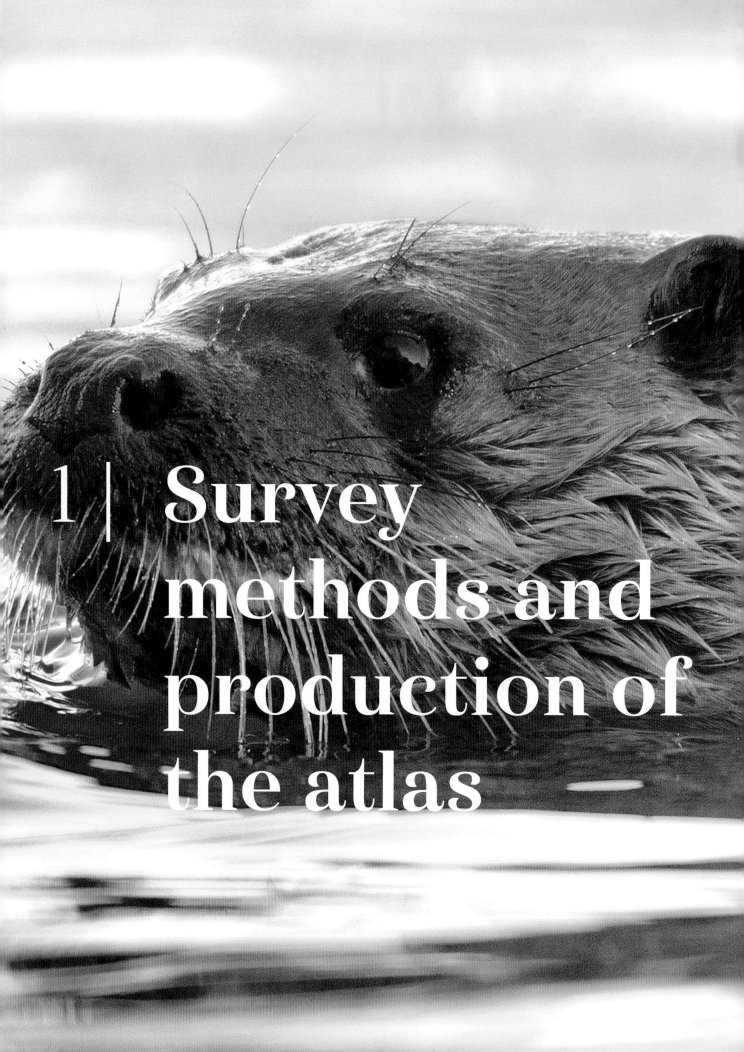

1 | Survey methods and production of the atlas

AIMS OF THE ATLAS

The North-East Scotland and Cairngorms Mammal Atlas project was launched in 2013 in order to increase substantially our understanding of the distribution of mammals in the region. Some wild mammals, such as Rabbit or Mole, are easy for almost anyone to record yet records held on the NESBReC database were thought not to truly represent their range in the region. Others are elusive and can only be recorded by targeted surveying or by a lucky chance encounter. Thus, the project provided an opportunity for engaging with a wide range of people in the region, from those who had never before taken part in a citizen science project, through to experienced biological recorders. In all cases, participants had the potential to generate records that could make a very tangible contribution to our overall understanding of each species.

Molehills are readily identified and provide an easy route for observers to add to our knowledge of species distributions.
Bridge of Don
Bee Smith

The atlas focuses on terrestrial mammals, including seals, since they give birth and haul out on land. Mapping the distribution of dolphins, porpoises and whales in North-East Scotland requires a very different approach. Therefore, they are not given full coverage in the atlas but summary statements about the species that have been seen from our coasts are given on pages 126 to 128. Additionally, in order to make this atlas as complete as possible, Humans are granted a full species account. Further sections briefly describe species that have not been recorded in recent years and those whose occurrence in the region may be due to accidental importation, whilst the status of key livestock species is also described.

SURVEY AREA AND RECORDING UNITS

The atlas covers the NESBReC recording area which encompasses the local authority areas of Aberdeen City, Aberdeenshire and Moray. It also includes the whole of the Cairngorms National Park, which overlaps with Aberdeenshire and Moray and also with Highland, Perth & Kinross and Angus. North of the national park, in the Lochindorb area, the boundary follows the historical Moray vice county boundary. The total area covered is 11,629 km² which is around 15% of Scotland's land area. This region includes approximately 297 km of coast and land up to 1,309 m altitude at the second highest point in the UK.

Records were accepted by NESBReC at any spatial resolution. However, records are mapped at a tetrad resolution and reports received just at hectad resolution were not included in the atlas maps, since these records could not be assigned to a specific tetrad. A tetrad is a 2 km × 2 km square and thus there are 25 tetrads in each hectad (10 km × 10 km square). This has become the standard mapping resolution for most regional distribution atlases. Mapping at this scale, as opposed to at a hectad resolution (as generally used in most national atlas projects) will result in more "false negatives" (squares where a species is present, but not recorded). It does, though, permit better determination of distribution patterns in areas such as along river valleys, around large conifer plantations and in mountainous areas. Ultimately the maps represent where a species has been recorded, rather than the full actual presence, and should act as a prompt for further recording to increase our knowledge of species' distributions across North-East Scotland and the Cairngorms.

Roadkill records account for more than half of reports of Badgers away from setts.
Near Alford
Ian Francis

Footprints of an Otter and cub in silt alongside the River Dee
Lizzie Bacon

7

Water Voles can be recorded by finding their burrows with a distinctive grazed lawn around the entrance.
Invermark
Nick Littlewood

RECORDING METHODS, COVERAGE AND OBSERVER EFFORT

Records were accepted for the atlas project using any recording method by which the species could be confidently identified. The bulk of records were of live sightings or of dead animals such as road casualties. However, some species can be more easily recorded by finding their signs, none more so than Mole, for which reports of molehills made up the overwhelming majority of records. Records of scats (droppings) were frequent for Otter, Fox and Badger while footprint records were also accepted for some species from experienced observers.

Bushnell   06–11–2013   05:22:26

Around half of Pine Marten records for which the method of recording is known were made using camera traps.
Durris Forest
Nick Littlewood

The main atlas period coincided with a substantial increase in the use of camera traps among both amateur and professional naturalists. A camera trap loan scheme was run by NESBReC throughout the fieldwork period and the results from this and from other camera trapping activity contributed substantially to the number of records for some mammals. For some elusive species, such as Pine Marten, they made up a sizeable proportion of records whilst the detection and identification of Scottish Wildcats has been revolutionised recently by camera trapping. Camera traps optimised for recording activity of small mammals were also deployed very effectively in some areas.

Bat records were dominated by those made using ultrasonic bat detectors, which enable the bat's echolocation calls to be heard and in many cases, used to identify the species producing the calls. Bat detectors used include models that are carried in the field by an observer as well as automated detectors that are left on site for a period of time and record just when they detect a bat call. A smaller number of bat records were made from roost visits by licensed bat workers.

At the start of the atlas project, a scheme was devised to ensure at least a very basic level of recording was achieved across the whole of the atlas area. This *Adopt-a-Square* scheme entailed individual recorders committing to visiting a defined hectad to look for mammals and signs of mammals. There was a suggested minimum time commitment of four hours but most observers spent much longer in their adopted square. In some cases, observers adopted the hectad in which they lived, so a much greater level of coverage was achieved. Whilst this scheme in no way resulted in even coverage across the atlas area, it at least increased the likelihood that there would be no large gaps in the maps for common and conspicuous mammals, such as Rabbit and Mole, across traditionally under-recorded regions. Some participants in the *Adopt-a-Square* scheme took on recording in more than one hectad or used the process as a reason for visiting a certain area that was not necessarily familiar to them. Other recorders decided to survey a hectad as a pair or in a group to share the effort and cover more area within it. Participants were supplied with a map of their hectad and encouraged to visit a range of habitats within it. There were 96 participants in the *Adopt-a-Square* scheme, ensuring that all hectads within the area were represented.

A further scheme run by NESBReC, that required less individual time commitment, asked residents to contribute records and photographs of small mammals caught by their pet cats. Entitled *Look What The Cat Brought In*, this scheme helped to ensure a wider spread of records for some of our most common but infrequently recorded small mammal species and also provided a way for more people to take an active role in mammal recording. Some of these cat owners were completely new to the concept of recording wildlife.

The bulk of records collated for the atlas came from reports of mammals or their signs contributed by biological recorders to NESBReC or to other recording schemes. Records ranged from single sightings sent in via the NESBReC website online recording form, through to long lists of records accrued over many years and sent in on spreadsheets, as well as some posted in on sheets of paper in the traditional way. Where possible, datasets from other recording projects or organisations were incorporated into the database and used to produce the maps. These included focused projects looking at the range of one or a small group of species, such as Water Vole and squirrel surveys, as well as records from formal monitoring or research programs, such as deer data collated on behalf of Deer Management Groups or by Scottish Natural Heritage. Records were also extracted from mammal datasets provided by the Highland Biological Recording Group and Perth Museum in order to ensure that peripheral areas to the west and south of the Cairngorms National Park were better represented.

Cat owners were encouraged to contribute records of small mammals through the "Look What the Cat Brought In" project.
Drumoak
Nick Littlewood

COVERAGE OF THE AREA

All hectads with at least some land above sea level within the atlas area were included in the *Adopt-a-Square* scheme. Similarly, records for any tetrad were accepted where the record was made at a sufficiently high resolution to confidently place the record within the atlas area. For tetrads at the edge of the atlas area that spanned a land border, records from that tetrad were not used if they fell outside the atlas area. All hectads were covered through the *Adopt-a-Square* scheme and received at least the minimum coverage as described above. However, given the elusive nature of most mammals, there was an inevitable skew of records towards where recorders live, along roads, in gardens and in commonly visited areas. These include centres of population, especially around Aberdeen, and along the main river valleys, notably Deeside and Speyside. It is not possible from a distribution mapping project that relies on records from a wide variety of sources to determine precise patterns or densities of occurrence. In the case of most species, though, broad inferences based on habitat and altitudinal preference can be made and these, are discussed in the individual species accounts, but variation in observer effort should be considered when interpreting the maps.

ARCHIVING AND AVAILABILITY OF THE ATLAS DATA

Data collated for inclusion in this atlas project will continue to be held by NESBReC and used in its core functions of providing biological records to assist with land management, conservation, planning, education and research. In addition, data underpins NESBReC's aim of promoting and encouraging biological recording and increasing awareness of the biodiversity of North-East Scotland. Data will also be uploaded to the National Biodiversity Network (NBN) Gateway for further use nationally and even globally. However, duplication of data already held on the NBN Gateway will be avoided.

PRODUCING SPECIES ACCOUNTS AND DISTRIBUTION MAPS

The text for the main species accounts was written by 32 authors. Forty species are covered by individual accounts whilst two accounts cover species complexes: Wildcat and Feral Cat; Polecat and Feral Ferret. The authors include those working as researchers and conservation professionals as well as amateur naturalists. Among these authors, we were lucky to be able to call on the services of some nationally acknowledged experts in certain species who live or work in the atlas area. Texts were written to a standard set of instructions. Some leeway was permitted to adapt these, especially the emphasis given to different sections, but the aim in all cases was to provide a readable description of the status of the species in the region and of factors that might affect their distribution and abundance. A contract was issued by NESBReC for collating and editing these texts to ensure adherence with the guidelines and the texts were then reviewed by an atlas editorial group.

The distribution maps are designed to give the reader a good idea of each species' range and were kept quite simple with two different time classes, 1960-2000 and 2001-2015, in order to give an indication of how species distributions may have changed in recent years and to show the general age of the data used. All data were added to the NESBReC database of biological records held in Recorder 6 software from which distribution maps were generated using ESRI ArcGIS 10.1.

PHOTOGRAPHS USED IN THE ATLAS

Photographs were sourced from regular NESBReC contacts and through wider appeals. The intention was, wherever possible, to include a high quality photograph of each species taken in the wild in the atlas area. This was not possible for all species so, in some cases, photographs are included that were taken outside the atlas area. Photographs for the species accounts were selected by the editorial group based on the visibility of various identification features for each species, not just the visual appeal of the composition.

PRODUCTION AND FUNDING OF THE ATLAS

Funding for the atlas was received from Scottish Natural Heritage, Aberdeenshire Council, Forestry Commission Scotland, Cairngorms National Park Authority and the Scottish Ornithologists' Club North-East Scotland Branch. This funding supported awareness raising for the project as well as the design and printing of the book itself.

2 | Mammal habitats, landscape and land use

The area covered by this atlas contains a very wide range of landscapes and habitats - from some of the UK's highest mountains to a spectacular and diverse coastline. It also includes the UK's largest national park. The area holds nationally important concentrations of the UK's arctic-alpine land, native pinewoods, managed coniferous plantations, lowland raised bogs, coastal sand dunes and dune heath. Heather moorland, arable farmland and coastal shingle are also very well-represented in a Scottish context. The plant communities of North-East Scotland and the Cairngorms lie in the Boreal zone of Europe (Polunin & Walters, 1985) and in this differ from much of the rest of Scotland and the UK.

In this atlas, the combination of local authority areas and an overlapping national park means that there is no succinct description or data source that relates to the whole area, so this chapter combines a number of sources to give a portrait of the physical landscape, land cover and habitats. The physical landscape of North-East Scotland was considered within the British Association (1963), RCAHMS (2008) and Merritt & Leslie (2009) while that of Aberdeen City and Aberdeenshire was described in Buckland et al. (1990).

The Cairngorms National Park covers an area of 4,528 km², around 40% of which overlaps with North-East Scotland (see map on pages 182-183). It is dominated in its centre by the Cairngorms, one of the highest, and the most extensive, areas of alpine habitat in the UK, with high summits dropping in all directions to lower moorland, woodland, mixed farmland and large river straths. A full description of the geology, topography and land cover in the Cairngorms area is given in Nethersole-Thompson & Watson (1974, 1981), Watson (1992), Gimingham (2002) and Shaw & Thompson (2006).

PHYSICAL GEOGRAPHY

This atlas covers an area of 11,629 km², approximately 5% of the UK land area and 15% of Scotland, and lies approximately at 57°N, 3°W. It comprises the local authority areas of Moray, Aberdeenshire and Aberdeen City, along with those parts of Angus, Perthshire and Highland that lie within the Cairngorms National Park.

The main Cairngorms massif contains five of the six highest mountains in the British Isles, including the second highest, Ben Macdui, which is the highest point in the atlas area at 1,309 m. To the south there are further high level plateaux extending into Perthshire and east along the Mounth to the Angus glens, including notable peaks such as Beinn a' Ghlo and Lochnagar. To the north-west, the broad, forested strath of the River Spey runs between the Cairngorms and the Monadhliath mountains, with the river flowing north-east through the lower hills and moorlands of Moray to the Moray Firth coast. This coastal area is mostly low-lying with extensive afforested sand dunes and long shingle bars, backed by the fertile, low-lying agricultural land of the Laich of Moray.

The Rivers Dee and Don flow eastwards from the Cairngorms in Aberdeenshire, through moorland and well-forested valleys towards the low-lying farmland along the coast around Aberdeen. To the south, the arable farmland of the Howe of the Mearns is particularly productive, while north of Aberdeen, the open, rolling mixed farmland of Buchan forms the largest lowland area covered by the atlas; it has relatively little woodland but holds many remnants of raised peat bogs (mosses). Extensive semi-natural habitats are largely limited to the south-western and southern fringes of Aberdeenshire. These areas adjoin with the north Angus glens and are formed by the Cairngorms, Lochnagar and the Mounth, where extensive alpine habitat grades down into large moorlands and peatlands. There are some large and important native pinewoods, mainly in Deeside, as well as a high cover of plantation forestry, dominated by Scots Pine. The Aberdeenshire coast is very varied, composed mainly of cliffs which reach up to 150 m high on the north coast, but with extensive sandy beaches backed by dune complexes and coastal heath around Rattray Head and between Collieston and Aberdeen. The City of Aberdeen has much countryside within its boundary and scattered remnants of semi-natural habitat within the built-up area.

Highland Perthshire forms the south-western part of the Cairngorms National Park, with many of the highest mountains here marking the watershed between the Tay, Spey and Dee catchments. Beinn a' Ghlo and Glen Tilt form striking landscape features as the land drops away through deer forest and moorland to Blair Atholl and Glen Garry. This area is characterised by a mix of old plantations, newly-planted woodlands, parkland and some farmland. At the highest, western part of the national park, the hills surrounding the Drumochter Pass form a high level plateau running north-east through Dalnacardoch to Gaick Forest, ultimately rising to central Cairngorms Mountains.

Badenoch & Strathspey runs south-west to north-east along the Spey and its headwaters. This large and diverse area forms the north-western side of the national park, rising to the high hill tops along the Monadhliath Mountains, and its broad strath and associated suite of habitats is one of the most renowned and important areas for nature conservation in the UK. Large areas of interconnected native pine woodlands and largely pine plantations form one of the largest contiguous woodland landscapes in the country, and this is interspersed with a complex network of peatland, moorland, floodplain wetlands and farmland. The land rises up to the northern corries of the Cairngorms and, in a few places, natural tree lines are found. The valley floor holds scattered settlements and farms, along with many new woodlands and marshes and this forms very rich habitat for mammals.

CLIMATE

The climate of the Cairngorms is described in Shaw & Thompson (2006) and that of North-East Scotland was described by the British Association (1963) and the Meteorological Office (1989). Annual precipitation varies between 1,520 mm and 2,250 mm over the Cairngorms to around 650 mm in coastal areas to the north and east that are sheltered from the prevailing south-westerly winds. In winter, precipitation often falls as snow, and the Cairngorms and the North-East is, on average, the snowiest part of the UK; even now, in mid-altitude areas one can expect over 30 days of lying snow each winter, with around 60 days at Braemar and even more on the mountains, where a few snow patches persist through most summers. Temperature inversions can lead to very low temperatures in upland glens, with late frosts well into June. Braemar shares the record for the lowest temperature ever recorded in Britain (-27.2°C on 10 January 1982). Average annual maximum daily temperatures are cool (just over 10°C at both Braemar and Craibstone near Aberdeen), though these have probably increased by up to one degree since 1980. Average annual minimum daily temperatures are 4.5°C at Craibstone and 2.5°C at Braemar. In winter, the Moray coast can be relatively mild due to warming dry winds descending from the Cairngorms with Kinloss and Lossiemouth at times recording the mildest winter temperatures in the UK. In summer, inland parts of Aberdeenshire and Strathspey can record warm temperatures (mid to high 20s Celsius), though coastal areas tend to be cooler and breezier, sometimes with sea fog or 'haar', due to cool temperatures in the North Sea all year round.

HUMAN GEOGRAPHY

The Human species account (pages 122-123) provides further information on aspects of this. Aberdeen City is by far the most populous settlement, with 228,900 inhabitants in 2014 (Aberdeen City Council, 2015). It is Scotland's third largest city and is growing rapidly, with much new development around the urban fringe. Other large towns include Elgin, Forres, Peterhead, Fraserburgh and Inverurie, with locally concentrated settlement around Aviemore. Much of the coast is undeveloped and unpopulated, with many relatively inaccessible and undisturbed areas. The Aberdeen City region is the most prosperous in Scotland and one of the wealthiest in the UK (Scottish Enterprise 2008). Tourism is a major economic force in the Cairngorms National Park, with agriculture, forestry and distilling also playing a part.

LAND COVER AND CHANGES OVER TIME

All summaries of land cover and natural habitats relevant to the atlas area differ in their geographic extent, habitat categorisation, sources and presentation methods. For this reason, and also because of a lack of survey information for some habitats, all figures below should be viewed as approximate; there are few habitats for which accurate extents or precise definitions can be given. The Cairngorms National Park is covered most comprehensively in Shaw & Thompson (2006), but the area considered pre-dates the inclusion of highland Perthshire within the Park. Alexander et al. (1998) summarised habitat information from various sources for the whole of the North-East and Leaper (1999) did the same for the Cairngorms area, as audits of UK Biodiversity Action Plan species and habitats. Prior to that, natural habitats in the former Grampian Region were surveyed and summarised by Grampian Regional Council (1988), many of which are mapped in Buckland et al. (1990), along with agricultural census data for that time.

Changes in land cover classes in Scotland were analysed during the 1980s as part of the National Countryside Monitoring Scheme - NCMS (Mackey et al., 1998). This remains the most detailed regional analysis and, though it is now dated, some clear patterns and trends relevant to today are apparent. For example, some 87% of the land surface of North-East Scotland is made up of just four major habitat types - grassland, arable farmland, heather moorland and coniferous plantation. Compared with Scotland as a whole, all of these are present in higher proportions than the national figures. Conversely, the North-East holds relatively modest extents of blanket mire (though lowland raised mires are well-represented) and less of the land area is occupied by water bodies, with many former wetlands long gone. A more recent national analysis (see below) provides regional land cover totals and the same four major land uses occupied 85.1% of North-East Scotland in 2000 - very similar to the NCMS total. For the Cairngorms National Park, Mackey & Shewry (2006) presented a similar analysis, which used the 'national park area' before the formalisation of the highland Perthshire boundary, and which overlaps with the North-East Scotland data.

LAND COVER CHANGES FROM THE 1940s TO THE 1980s

Between the 1940s and 1980s, in North-East Scotland, the coniferous woodland area expanded greatly, as did the extents of arable farming, urban and developed land. These expansions were largely at the expense of 'smooth' grassland (change from improved grassland to arable crops), heather moorland (losses to grassland and forestry) and broadleaved woodland. Hedgerow length declined greatly while tracks and ditches lengthened. Arable gains were greater than in Scotland as a whole and losses of heather moorland, broadleaved woodland and hedgerows were also higher. The rate of afforestation was less than the Scottish average, probably because parts of North-East Scotland were already well-wooded; the 1980s forest cover was proportionally higher than nationally.

The Cairngorms area shared some of these trends. Significant increases were found in plantation forest, Bracken and built up area, together with rough grassland (change from heather moorland). Significant decreases were found for semi-natural coniferous and broadleaved woodland, often through conversion to coniferous plantation. Blanket mire was reduced by 15% and heather moorland by 11%. Managed grassland was reduced through conversion to arable. Hedgerow length was also reduced.

LAND COVER AND CHANGES SINCE THE 1980s

More recent information is available at the national level on land cover and change but, for almost all habitats, there is little detail for our area that might allow any quantification of these changes. National trends which are probably mirrored in our area include increases in the areas of broadleaved woodland, lowland spruce woodlands in Buchan and new native pinewoods in the uplands. Large scale declines in moorland have probably ceased now. The number of ponds in the UK increased by 11% between 1996 and 2007 but their biological condition deteriorated (likely to be the case in North-East Scotland - many hundreds of new ponds have been constructed recently, often in areas prone to eutrophication). This is less true of the Cairngorms.

TABLE 2-1. LAND COVER TABLE FOR NORTH-EAST SCOTLAND (GRAMPIAN) IN THE 1980s (MACKEY ET AL., 1998) AND THE CAIRNGORMS (PRE-2010 AREA) IN THE 1980s (MACKEY & SHEWRY, 2006)

Note that only terrestrial habitats were considered in the Grampian survey: coastal and marine areas were excluded. The land cover categories use different definitions between the two overlapping areas, so the figures are not directly comparable. In particular, montane habitats were not considered for the North-East Scotland survey as a category distinct from heather moorland or grassland.

LAND COVER / HABITAT TYPE	NORTH-EAST SCOTLAND		CAIRNGORMS NATIONAL PARK	
	AREA (KM²)	% OF NORTH-EAST SCOTLAND LAND AREA (% SCOTTISH LAND AREA IN BRACKETS)	AREA (KM²)	% OF CNP LAND AREA
ARABLE	2,036	23% (11%)	98	1%
BRACKEN AND SCRUB	171	2% (3%)	1	0%
BROADLEAVED WOODLAND	205	2% (1%)	170	3%
BUILT-UP AREAS	343	4% (4%)	10	0%
CONIFEROUS PLANTATION	1,228	14% (12%)	622	10%
GRASSLAND	2,650	31% (28%)	1,022	16%
HEATHER MOORLAND	1,647	19% (15%)	2,738	42%
LOCHS AND RIVERS (INCLUDING WET GROUND)	50	1% (3%)	31	0%
MIRE (UPLAND & LOWLAND)	357	4% (23%)	118	2%
MONTANE HABITATS			1,655	25%
INLAND ROCK			51	1%

MAIN LAND COVER, HABITAT CHANGES AND KEY MAMMAL SPECIES

The main habitats of North-East Scotland and the Cairngorms are outlined and illustrated below, with some indication of mammals that might be found in each (though the list of examples is not exclusive). Further information for habitat subdivisions in the north-eastern section of the atlas area can be found in Francis & Cook (2011).

ALPINE HABITATS AND UPLAND BOGS

MAMMALS: Water Vole, Mountain Hare, Pygmy Shrew, Red Deer

Scors Burn, Blackwater Forest, 1997
Ian Francis

Descriptions of the 'high tops', their alpine habitats and wildlife are found in Nethersole-Thompson & Watson (1974, 1981), Buckland et al. (1990), Watson (1992), Gimingham (2002) and Shaw & Thompson (2006). The atlas area has some of the most extensive and diverse high altitude habitats in the UK, with considerable areas of alpine plateaux, steep mountain sides, large corries, boulder fields and large areas of summit heath and grassland. Snow lies in many areas for two-thirds of the year with a few snow patches lasting through most summers. Although recreation levels are locally high, most parts are less disturbed. There is little evidence of significant large-scale change in habitat extent or quality in recent decades, but some local factors, such as the development of ski areas, have caused changes in areas nearby. High-level deer grazing and atmospheric pollution may also have influenced vegetation communities (Scottish Natural Heritage, 2002).

Areas of blanket bog extend across the Cairngorms and into North-East Scotland. Much is relatively dry and has been affected by centuries of burning, grazing, drainage and peat cutting. Nevertheless, there are scattered areas of bog pools and active peat-forming plant communities. The vegetation is dominated largely by Heather, Hare's-tail Cottongrass and Deergrass with various mosses depending on site conditions.

Cairn Toul from Sgor an Lochain Uaine, 2015
Paul Chapman

MOORLAND AND UPLAND GRASSLANDS

MAMMALS: Mountain Hare, Common Shrew, Pygmy Shrew, Stoat, Weasel, Red Deer

North-East Scotland and the Cairngorms have very large areas of heather moorland, which is often mixed with, or lies adjacent to, upland acid grassland. Many moorlands and grasslands are grazed by sheep (increasingly on grouse moors to act as a method of controlling ticks) and occasionally cattle too. Where moorland is not managed, scrub and trees often regenerate. On most eastern moorlands, management for Red Grouse shooting is intensive with very frequent burning, short Heather and, increasingly, new tracks which have been created to facilitate shooting and management.

Muirburn at Invercauld, 2015
Ian Francis

Upland heathland/grassland mosaic, Invermark, 2015
Nick Littlewood

Western Cairngorms moors are generally less intensively managed. Heather moorland decreased in extent between the 1940s and 1980s, principally due to the expansion of afforestation and conversion to grassland; this has largely ceased now.

CALEDONIAN PINEWOODS

MAMMALS: Red Squirrel, Bank Vole, Wood Mouse, Scottish Wildcat, Fox, Badger, Pine Marten, Red Deer, Roe Deer

Glen Quoich pinewood, Mar Lodge, 2010
Ian Francis

The Cairngorms National Park holds a very high proportion of the remaining native Caledonian pinewoods, and they are of very high nature conservation interest. While Scots Pine is dominant, the woodlands contain varying amounts of broadleaved trees (principally Birch) and juniper scrub. There are 20 officially-listed native pinewood remnants in the atlas area (Jones, 1999) but also numerous other stands of self-sown pine of native

Pine woodland alongside Loch Garten, 2016
Nick Littlewood

origin, some of which are quite large. The list includes the well-known forests of Glen Tanar, Ballochbuie, Mar, Abernethy and Rothiemurchus. Historically, there have been some large losses in extent and quality of native pinewoods in Scotland, but this trend has probably now reversed. However, all sites have been managed to some extent, affecting the woodland structure, and most may contain some trees of non-local origin. Several areas of 'New Native Pinewoods' were planted on moorland in the 1990s, especially in Moray and Strathspey; these are only now becoming established, due to slow growth rates.

UPLAND BROADLEAVED WOODLANDS, SCRUB AND BRACKEN

MAMMALS: Bank Vole, Wood Mouse, Red Squirrel, Roe Deer, Feral Goat

Birch woodland with Bracken, Dinnet, 2005
Ian Francis

Much of the upland broadleaved woodland in the area is dominated by Birch, covering large extents of national significance which, along with Scots Pine, characterise the 'Scandinavian' feel of parts of the Cairngorms. In some areas, Birch colonisation of moorland fringes has occurred, forming quite extensive regenerating young woodland, such as at Muir of Dinnet. Some nationally important patches of Aspen woodland are also found, particularly in Strathspey. Oak woodlands are few in number and although Ash trees are widespread in farmland and riparian woodland, they rarely dominate woodlands. Beech woodland is found as small planted patches, as shelterbelts and as fringes to larger woods. Many small broadleaved woodlands have been planted on marginal farmland in recent decades, especially along watercourses.

Gorse, north of Rhynie, 2009
Ian Francis

There are also many areas of dense scrub, composed primarily of Gorse (Whin) and Broom, and ranging in size from small patches and hedge lines to whole hillsides. Juniper scrub also can form nationally important concentrations in the uplands. Willow scrub, however, is rare and localised. Bracken is less widespread compared with milder areas further west in Scotland, but has increased in extent, especially in the Cairngorms National Park.

CONIFEROUS PLANTATIONS

MAMMALS: Red Squirrel, Wood Mouse, Scottish Wildcat, Badger, Pine Marten, Roe Deer

The early history of plantations in the area was described by Edlin (1963), which remains the only published general account of all forests in North-East Scotland. Conifer plantations now cover around 14% of North-East Scotland and the Cairngorms National Park and their area has increased over three-fold since the 1940s. The plantations are dominated by extensive Scots Pine on drier soils and Sitka Spruce on wetter sites, with smaller amounts of Norway Spruce, Lodgepole Pine, European and Japanese Larch, Douglas Fir and, in the coastal plantations of Moray, Corsican Pine. Many of the older Scots Pine plantations are well-spaced with well-developed ground vegetation and these can be diverse habitats. Clear-felling is the most common

system of management, but increasingly alternative systems are being used in a move towards 'continuous cover' forestry. As plantations are harvested and replanted, they are increasing in diversity, with more mixtures of species, a higher proportion of broadleaves and more open space.

Sitka Spruce-dominated plantation and clear-felled areas, Alltcailleach, Glen Muick, 2010
Ian Francis

LOCHS, RESERVOIRS, PONDS, RIVERS AND BURNS

MAMMALS: Water Vole, Brown Rat, Water Shrew, Daubenton's Bat, Natterer's Bat, Soprano Pipistrelle, Nathusius' Pipistrelle, Otter, American Mink

Lochs cover less than 1% of the atlas area and there are few reservoirs (mainly hydro-electric dams in Badenoch). There are probably fewer than 150 water bodies of more than c.2-3 ha in size, and only three larger than 200 ha (Loch Muick, Lochindorb and Loch of Strathbeg). Most standing water is held in a few large upland oligotrophic lochs such as Loch Muick (the largest

Uath Lochans, Inshriach, 2008
Paul Chapman

loch by area and volume in the atlas area). Some of these are among the highest in the UK, including Loch Etchachan at 900 m. At lower altitudes, moderately nutrient rich or mesotrophic lochs include the Dinnet lochs and Loch Insh. Richer, eutrophic lochs include the Loch of Strathbeg and Loch Spynie. Many new ponds have been created in recent years, frequently under agri-environment schemes. Some of the new ponds are stocked with fish, which may have benefited Otters.

River Spey, Insh Marshes, 2010
Ian Francis

The main rivers draining the area are the Garry (Tay catchment), Spey, Dee, Don, Deveron, Ythan, Ugie, Lossie and the North and South Esk. The Spey, Tay and Dee are among the largest rivers in Scotland and the Dee has the highest source, at 1,220 m, higher than any other British river. Most rivers in the area have good water quality and the Dee is oligotrophic from source to mouth. The Ythan, by contrast, has poorer water quality, rising entirely in an intensively farmed landscape. The Dee, Tay, Spey and South Esk are designated as being of European importance for nature conservation. Detailed information about the Dee can be found in Jenkins (1985), the Spey in Jenkins (1988) and the Ythan in Gorman (1997).

LOWLAND FARMLAND, GRASSLANDS AND BOUNDARY FEATURES

MAMMALS: Bank Vole, Field Vole, Wood Mouse, Brown Rat, Rabbit, Brown Hare, Hedgehog, Mole, Common Shrew, Leisler's Bat, Common Pipistrelle, Fox, Badger, Stoat, Weasel, Roe Deer

Farmland (arable and grassland) accounts for over half the land surface of North-East Scotland and retains a more traditional mix of livestock and cropping that has been lost from most other parts of the UK. There is no detailed analysis for the whole of the land covered here, but the state of agriculture in Aberdeenshire in 2007 was reviewed by Cook et al. (2008); Aberdeenshire contains 9% of Scotland's agricultural land. However, almost all agricultural activity is disproportionately higher than this: cereals (27% of Scottish area, much grown for cattle feed); Oil-seed Rape (35%); potatoes (16%); beef breeding herd (15%); feeding cattle (26%); pigs (57%); poultry (14%); full time labour (15%). Only sheep (6%) and dairy cattle (5%) are under-represented by proportion and are declining. The proportion of

Farmland, Mearns, 2011
Paul Chapman

cereals that are autumn sown increased during the latter part of the 20th century (32% of the total) but Aberdeenshire is still dominated by spring barley, a growing proportion of which is sold for malting. Specialist fruit and vegetable crops have increased sharply recently.

Improved grassland and hay crop, near Leslie, Insch, 2009
Ian Francis

Aberdeenshire is intensively farmed by Scottish standards. Almost half the grass is mowed and stocking rates can be locally very high. Formartine along with Kincardine and the Mearns are the most heavily cropped parts (60-63% of the arable area), which almost certainly influences mammal distributions, with large 'gaps' in ranges for several species coincident with these areas. However, comparing Aberdeenshire with some other parts of the UK, the mixed farming, pockets of unimproved land, spring cropping and many small farms operating at lower intensity benefits some mammals. There are also small but important areas managed under agri-environment schemes, producing good mammal habitats such as field margins, hedges and wild bird cover crops.

The atlas area is not traditionally rich in hedges, but dry stone dykes and drainage ditches are common, and often associated with a line of Broom or Gorse. These are important features for mammals in farmland, providing breeding sites and feeding areas. Hedges and dykes decreased in the latter half of the 20th century, but some new hedges have been planted under agri-environment schemes.

There are no available combined figures for the extent of all lowland grasslands in the area. They form part of the farmland landscape but also extend into other, more semi-natural habitats and are important for open country mammals such as Brown Hares. Less intensively managed grass, with light grazing levels or a single cut of hay or silage taken in late June or July are likely to provide more valuable mammal habitat than grass that receives high fertiliser inputs and which is cut twice or more each year or heavily grazed.

LOWLAND RAISED BOGS AND LOWLAND HEATHLAND

MAMMALS: Field Vole, Pygmy Shrew, Water Shrew, Weasel

Red Moss of Netherley, 2016
Nick Littlewood

Found mostly in the north-east of the atlas area, lowland heathlands occur on shallow acid soils, often linked with acid grassland or cliff-top heathland areas. They also overlap in nature with heather moorland extending down from higher altitudes. Raised bogs are formed from thick peat and, when intact, their only water source is rainfall, so plant communities are those tolerant of acid and nutrient-poor conditions. However, most raised bogs in North-East Scotland have been damaged by drainage, cutting and burning or conversion to agriculture and forestry. Nevertheless, they are an important resource in a national context, covering 54 km^2 (depending on definitions), and forming 19% of the Scottish and 8% of the UK totals. There are also intergrades between raised and blanket bogs in the North-East ("intermediate bogs"). Within Scotland, the central lowlands and the North-East are the main centres of raised bog development. About half of our remaining raised bog area is sufficiently undamaged to be considered of conservation interest (Scottish Wildlife Trust data). Most of the extant sites are in Aberdeenshire, where there are several hundred remnants of various sizes; 45 of these have some primary (uncut) open bog surface.

FENS AND REED-BEDS

MAMMALS: Water Shrew, Otter

Reed-bed at Loch Kinord, Dinnet, 2007
Ian Francis

Both of these habitat types are scarce, especially reed-beds, and most are very small. The largest three reed-beds (Loch Spynie, Loch of Strathbeg and the Dinnet Lochs) between them hold over half of the reed-bed area. Common Reed dominates at all these sites, with willow scrub encroachment. Fens are more widespread but, with the exception of the nationally important Insh Marshes in Speyside, most are less well known and there are problems of ecological definition and inter-gradation, especially at the margins of raised bogs and with reed swamps and wet grassland. Typically, fens contain high levels of sedge and rush cover, with tall herb communities dominated by Meadowsweet and Flag Iris. Willow scrub is often frequent and water tables are high all year. Many sites are completely unmanaged and undergoing gradual vegetation succession to wet woodland or drier marshy grassland. They often form areas of rank habitat within wider farmed landscapes and are an important part of the habitat matrix in the atlas area.

LOWLAND BROADLEAVED WOODLAND, WET WOODLANDS AND PARKLAND

MAMMALS: Red Squirrel, Grey Squirrel, Natterer's Bat, Common Pipistrelle, Soprano Pipistrelle, Brown Long-eared Bat, Fox, Badger, Pine Marten

Wet Alder - Ash woodland, near Alford, 2005
Ian Francis

Lowland woodlands are very varied and are not always clearly distinguishable from upland woodlands. There are many areas of long-established broadleaved woodland, often on 'ancient woodland' sites though these are individually usually small in extent. More common are planted broadleaved woodlands, often containing Sycamore or Beech; some of these are well-established, and can be found in urban areas, but there has also been much recent planting on farmland. The area recorded as 'parkland' by the NCMS in the late 1980s was 2,200 ha, but, within this, grazed wood pasture is likely to be rare. There are some fine veteran trees within parkland and country house policy woodlands in the area. Some of these are now within arable farmland, but the main characteristic of this habitat is the presence of large trees. The surrounding grassland or farmland can also provide good feeding habitat.

Wet and riparian woodland is difficult to measure and ecological definitions vary. It includes woodland growing in a fairly thin strip along rivers and burns, usually where land is either wet and inundated, or on steep river banks which are difficult to cultivate and influenced by the humidity of the river. In some areas, such as the lower Spey, it may occupy open flood plains and braided shingle, which can be frequently flooded. Wet woodlands can grade into fen and raised bog, as well as marshy grassland. Their humidity and wet ground produces abundant invertebrates, as well as holes for roosting bats in such species as Alder, and since it is difficult to use such land for other purposes (except for grazing), they may be relatively unmanaged and often form a network of wooded habitat within more intensively managed farmland. Their total extent is small compared with other woodland types.

URBAN, GARDENS, INDUSTRY, QUARRIES AND RECREATION AREAS

MAMMALS: Red Squirrel, Grey Squirrel, Wood Mouse, House Mouse, Brown Rat, Hedgehog, Common Pipistrelle, Soprano Pipistrelle, Fox, Roe Deer

In North-East Scotland, there were 343 km² of built up and related bare land in the 1980s, 4% of the land area; this will have risen considerably since then. The mix of buildings, gardens, open spaces and urban woodlands is probably typical of settlements elsewhere in the country and they provide habitat for a range of mammals. The wildlife and habitats within Aberdeen City were summarised by Marren (1982). Much smaller settlements are found in the Cairngorms National Park. There are no available figures for the extent of quarried land, but there are numerous granite quarries across the area, both active and disused, and a wide range of other small quarries and borrow pits, often used as excavation sites for track construction and building material. Some of these are very old. In north Moray and the Howe of the Mearns, there are active sand and gravel quarries, where the dynamic habitat provides suitable breeding sites for some mammals. Within and around the urban areas, and also well out in the countryside, are open recreation areas, typified by golf courses. There are already 70 of these in North-East Scotland, and additional courses in the western Cairngorms, with more planned. There is no accurate figure for the total land area occupied, but the 53 courses with 18 holes (at c. 50 ha each) and 17 with 9 to 12 holes (at c. 25 ha each) equate to at least 3,075 ha (see Visit Scotland, 2005 for numbers and SAC area data).

Aberdeen suburbs from the air, 2010
Ian Francis

Ballater golf course, 2010
Ian Francis

COASTAL CLIFFS AND MARITIME HEATHS

MAMMALS: Field Vole, Rabbit, Common Shrew, Stoat

High seabird cliffs at Troup Head, 2009
Duncan Goulder

A description of our coastal habitats was given in Buckland et al. (1990). Hard rock cliffs extend to around 108 km in length of the North-East Scotland coast (Barne et al., 1996), which is some 6% of the Scottish and 3% of the UK total. Much of this has only a narrow fringe of cliff-top vegetation, usually grassland, but there are small patches of coastal/maritime heath, amounting to around 3.5 km², a figure that is insignificant nationally. The coastal cliffs themselves probably hold few mammal species, perhaps mainly small rodents, but cliff tops are likely to be more diverse. Our cliffs are among the most natural of the habitats we have.

ROCKY SHORES, COASTAL SHINGLE AND SAND DUNES

MAMMALS: Rabbit, Common Shrew, Fox, Otter, Stoat, Grey Seal

No figures are available for the extent of rocky shore in North-East Scotland, but it is quite extensive with some large areas on the Moray coast between Burghead and Lossiemouth and, in Aberdeenshire, between Rosehearty and Fraserburgh and between Gourdon and Inverbervie. Parts are tidally inundated but above this, there is suitable habitat for some mammals. Moray has impressive extents of bare shingle, and although vegetated shingle accounts for only 1.5 km^2, we have some of the best examples in Britain at Culbin and Kingston, with 19% of the Scottish and 2.5% of the UK total. Some rocky shore areas are important haul out sites for seals.

Sand dunes, Inverugie, Peterhead, 2011
Ian Francis

Rocky intertidal shore, Cruden Bay, 2011
Ian Francis

The North-East holds a significant concentration of sand dunes, amounting to around 70 km², with some of the largest extents and best examples in the country. Most ecological types are present, from mobile fore dunes to more stable vegetated dunes with their associated dune slack wetlands. On stable acid sand, dune heath may develop (a habitat also present in nationally important concentrations), and dune scrub and woodland are also found. Apart from at St Cyrus in the very south, most sand dunes are found along the central and northern east coast. There are scattered sites in Moray, including Culbin Sands, once the largest mobile sand system in Britain, but now stabilised by decades of conifer afforestation. Although sand dunes can be amongst the least modified of all terrestrial habitats, there has been loss or degradation due to a variety of human activities.

ESTUARIES, SALTMARSH AND THE SEA

MAMMALS: Otter, Grey Seal, Common Seal, Harbour Porpoise, Common Bottlenose Dolphin

The Ythan estuary, 2012
Paul Chapman

There are few estuaries in North-East Scotland and little saltmarsh. Estuaries cover around 14 km², around 0.3% of the UK total, divided between nine main sites. Findhorn Bay is by far the largest, with the Ythan estuary and St Cyrus next in size. They provide rich bird feeding habitats, but mammal use is probably limited to seals and Otters, though they inter-grade into sand dunes and other coastal habitats suitable for foraging by Foxes. The small total area of saltmarsh in North-East Scotland is found mainly at Culbin Sands, Findhorn Bay, Spey Bay, the Loch of Strathbeg and within the Ythan estuary. Saltmarshes probably hold similarly limited mammal communities.

Aberdeen Harbour entrance, 2016
Ian Francis

Most of the open coast of the North-East is classed as 'exposed' or 'moderately exposed', with sheltered shores confined to the estuaries. Sand is the commonest intertidal sediment and most of the inshore area has a coarse sandy seabed, with gravel or sandy gravel extending from Spey Bay to Rattray Head. Our seas include part of the Moray Firth and part of the open North Sea, which is influenced both by oceanic water from the North Atlantic and by freshwater from several major rivers. Offshore, water becomes thermally stratified in summer but closer to the coast, the water remains well-mixed throughout the year. The stratification extends into the Moray Firth but off the Aberdeenshire coast there is a tidal front (the Buchan front), in the transition zone between stratified and well-mixed water masses. This area is rich in plankton and of great importance to feeding seabirds (Doody et al., 1993; see also Barne et al., 1996), as well as Grey and Common Seals, along with a range of cetaceans, including the widely known and frequently seen groups of Common Bottlenose Dolphins (see page 127).

3 | Species accounts

SPECIES ORDER AND TAXONOMY

The species sequence and grouping of species into mammal orders follows Harris & Yalden (2008). The Human species account is placed at the end of the main species accounts section. Scientific names follow Wilson & Reeder (2005). English names are those used by the Mammal Society (2014) which tend to be the names in common usage among naturalists in the British Isles. Two accounts each combine two species into a single expanded account. These are Feral Ferret combined with Polecat and Feral Cat combined with Wildcat. In both cases, hybrids occur widely, complicating attempts to understand the distribution of either species.

SPECIES TEXTS

Full texts are included for 44 species (including the two species pairs referred to above). All texts follow a uniform format though the emphasis placed on different sections varies, depending on the information available to present. Content is referenced where it has been sourced from specific publications, though widely available information, such as the physical appearance of the mammal, is not referenced. References from all species account texts (and elsewhere in the book) are combined on pages 161 - 167.

PHOTOGRAPHS

Each species account is accompanied by a photograph. Where possible, these were taken in the atlas area, though photographs from elsewhere have been sourced for a few species. All photographs are of wild mammals except for that which illustrates the Feral Ferret account, which is of a working animal of the type that sometimes forms feral populations. Location and photographer is included for each photograph. Photographs of some species also appear in other sections of the book and reference should be made to the Index (pages 179-181) to locate these.

SPECIES DISTRIBUTION MAPS

Maps show records of presence of each mammal species in North-East Scotland and the Cairngorms National Park between 1960 and 2015. Two symbol types are used so that records from 1960 to 1999 are shown differently to those from 2000 to 2015. The symbols are both visible in cases where there are records from both time periods. The mapping unit is the tetrad, a square measuring 2 km × 2 km, such that there are 25 tetrads in a hectad (a 10 km × 10 km square). A key to the symbols is included in each map. The inclusion of a symbol in a tetrad shows that there is at least one record in that tetrad within the respective time period. No inference can be made about relative abundance; a single record of a wandering individual briefly visiting and being recorded in a tetrad is shown in the same way on the map as a large and permanently established population.

Place names mentioned in the species accounts can be located by reference to the gazetteer in Annex 5. Similar but subtly different place names may be used to mean different things; for example, citing a 1974 publication, Morayshire is referred to in the Badger account. The county at that time had different boundaries to the current administrative region of Moray.

The background used in the distribution maps shows basic geographical information that may be useful in interpreting patterns in species' distributions. High ground in the Cairngorms National Park, in the south-west of the map, is clearly displayed as are the major river valleys and the lowest ground around the coasts. Names of some settlements are featured whilst inclusion of 10 km grid lines and line numbers aid location of specific Ordnance Survey grid references on the map.

SPECIES GROUPS

RODENTS
SQUIRRELS, VOLES, MICE AND RATS

LAGOMORPHS
RABBITS AND HARES

INSECTIVORES
HEDGEHOG, MOLE AND SHREWS

BATS

CARNIVORES
CATS, FOX AND MUSTELIDS (WEASEL FAMILY)

SEALS

UNGULATES
WILD BOAR, DEER AND FERAL GOAT

PRIMATES
HUMAN

CETACEANS
PORPOISES, DOLPHINS AND WHALES

DOMESTIC LIVESTOCK

RED SQUIRREL

(Sciurus vulgaris)

HABITAT AND ECOLOGY

Red Squirrels are most frequently found in large coniferous woodlands, where they feed on the seeds of a range of tree species. A small proportion of their diet is made up of fungi, buds, flowers, fruit, insects and, occasionally, birds' eggs or young (Gurnell, 1987; Gurnell, 1994). In absence of competition from the non-native Grey Squirrel, Red Squirrels can be found in broadleaved woodlands although coniferous woodland provides the best habitat. Extensive commercial forestry plantations can be of great benefit, particularly where Scots Pine, Norway Spruce, or Larch are planted. Sitka Spruce, with its sporadic coning cycle, rarely offers much food for squirrels.

MANAGEMENT AND CONSERVATION

The Red Squirrel is listed on Schedule 5 of the Wildlife and Countryside Act 1981 (as amended). The key threat to the native Red Squirrel is the presence of the non-native Grey Squirrel. The Grey Squirrel outcompetes the Red Squirrel for resources in most types of woodland and this can lead to localised extinctions. The Grey Squirrel also carries the Squirrelpox virus which is fatal to Red Squirrels. Although this disease is not yet present in the atlas area, it has spread through southern Scotland to the Central Belt and may spread northwards in coming years (White & Lurz, 2014). Red Squirrel management is, therefore, primarily concerned with reducing Grey Squirrel numbers, and is coordinated in the region by the Saving Scotland's Red Squirrels (SSRS) project.

Ongoing habitat fragmentation and development (particularly roads) threaten the viability of some Red Squirrel populations. Rope bridges and traffic warning signs have been erected at some locations but, sadly, there is no evidence to show that either of these initiatives reduces road mortality.

RECORDS

Reports of Red Squirrels are submitted via the SSRS website (scottishsquirrels.org.uk), directly to NESBReC and from formal survey by SSRS. The majority of records are of live animals, with a known bias towards gardens, roads, and well-used woodland sites. Roadkill animals are also recorded. Camera traps have proved useful for detecting Red Squirrels, especially in commercial forestry plantations.

BRITISH ISLES DISTRIBUTION, POPULATION AND TRENDS

Although once widespread, with declining woodland cover Red Squirrels had almost become extinct in Scotland by the 18th century, though a few may have survived in Speyside. Reintroductions, using English and Scandinavian squirrels, took place from late that century, initially in central Scotland and then at a wider range of sites, with most of the atlas area being reoccupied from the mid to late 19th century (Yalden, 1999).

The most recent estimate of the British Red Squirrel population was of 160,000 animals, with 75% thought to live in Scotland (Harris et al., 1995). The Red Squirrel remains a widespread animal across many of the wooded areas of Scotland. They can also still be found in suitable habitat in parts of Cumbria, Northumberland, and other areas in northern England with restricted ranges elsewhere. Islands, such as the Isle of Wight, Brownsea Island, and Anglesey, likely offer long-term strongholds, easily defended from Grey Squirrels. Red Squirrels are also present through large parts of Ireland.

The species is known to experience population fluctuations based on food availability. Following good mast years or cone crops, females will produce more young. Whilst Red Squirrels are an extremely challenging animal to census, there is evidence that populations are at least stable, if not expanding in Scotland.

NORTH-EAST SCOTLAND AND CAIRNGORMS DISTRIBUTION AND TRENDS

Red Squirrels occupy a vast part of the atlas area. In wooded parts of the lowlands to the edges of the Grampians, Red Squirrels occupy most of the available suitable habitat. Remnant Caledonian Pine Forest in Deeside, Donside, and Strathspey hold nationally significant populations. The Red Squirrel is found throughout the wooded areas of the Cairngorms National Park but lowland agricultural areas of The Mearns and Buchan have more scattered populations. Away from semi-natural native woodlands, large tracts of commercial forestry can provide a refuge for Red Squirrels.

Populations in Moray and all across the Cairngorms National Park live far from the threat of the Grey Squirrel. Ongoing management of the non-native Grey Squirrel in Aberdeenshire and Aberdeen City has resulted in increases of Red Squirrels. Annual spring surveys around Aberdeen are showing expansion of the Red Squirrel back into the suburbs, parks, and gardens of the city (Brassey & Tonkin, 2014).

OBSERVING RED SQUIRRELS

Red Squirrels are smaller than Grey Squirrels and have prominent ear tufts in winter. Their usual reddish-brown coat is very different from that of a Grey Squirrel though a degree of variation in colour does exist in both species. A visit to a quiet conifer wood early in the morning almost anywhere in the region could yield a Red Squirrel sighting. Viewing facilities can be found at Glenmore, Abernethy, Bennachie Centre and Haddo Country Park. Red Squirrels are active all year round, will readily visit gardens and can become quite tame.

Image: Aviemore, Raymond Leinster
Author: Stephen Willis

DISTRIBUTION IN NORTH-EAST SCOTLAND AND THE CAIRNGORMS

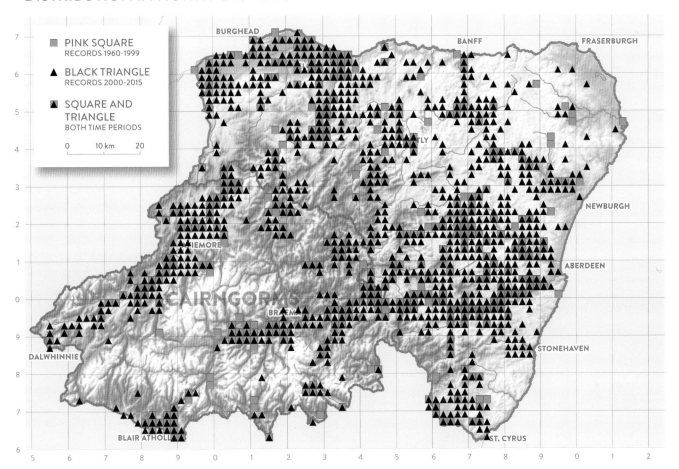

GREY SQUIRREL

(Sciurus carolinensis)

HABITAT AND ECOLOGY

The Grey Squirrel has a broad diet including acorns, beech nuts, hazel nuts, berries, fungi and even bark, buds and shoots. It is particularly well adapted to living in broadleaved woodlands but also thrives in parks and gardens.

Grey Squirrels are the single biggest threat to the native Red Squirrel. They can live at higher densities than the Red Squirrel and compete for food where the two species occur together. This can depress both the Red Squirrel's breeding productivity and juvenile survival leading ultimately to the loss of Red Squirrel populations (Gurnell et al., 2004; Lurz, 2010). In most of Britain, Grey Squirrels also carry Squirrelpox virus, which is fatal to Red Squirrels, but this is not present among the Grey Squirrel population in the atlas area.

MANAGEMENT AND CONSERVATION

Grey Squirrels are not formally protected (other than under animal welfare legislation). Due to their non-native status and impact on the native Red Squirrel and on hardwood plantations, it is an offence to release a Grey Squirrel into the wild (under the Wildlife and Countryside Act, 1981).

The Grey Squirrel is the subject of intensive control in North-East Scotland, largely by the Saving Scotland's Red Squirrels (SSRS) project. Established in 2009, SSRS has project staff in Aberdeen, Aberdeenshire, Angus, Tayside and southern Scotland. Control work involves the use of live-capture cage traps and is carried out by private individuals, estates and SSRS project staff.

RECORDS

Records of Grey Squirrels come via submissions to the SSRS website and to NESBReC as well as from formal surveys by SSRS. There is known to be a bias in sightings from the public towards roads, gardens and easily accessible woodlands. Most reports are of live animals, but others come from roadkill and camera trapping. Capture locations of trapped Grey Squirrels also form some of the records though, as these animals are removed, the species may no longer persist in some mapped locations.

BRITISH ISLES DISTRIBUTION, POPULATION AND TRENDS

Since its introduction to the British Isles from North America in the late 19th century, the Grey Squirrel has spread across most of England and Wales, much of the eastern half of Ireland and parts of Scotland. As it has spread, it has displaced the Red Squirrel. The UK population has previously been estimated to be around 2.5 million with around 200,000 in Scotland (Harris et al., 1995). They are actively managed across large areas of Northern England, Wales and Scotland (outside the

Central Belt). In 2015 the island of Anglesey, in Wales, was declared free of Grey Squirrels, after over 18 years of management (Shuttleworth et al., 2015). SSRS has a long-term aim of eradicating Grey Squirrels from North-East Scotland.

NORTH-EAST SCOTLAND DISTRIBUTION AND TRENDS

The Grey Squirrel population in the atlas area is centred on Aberdeen City, where a release took place in the 1970s. The wooded corridors of the Dee and Don facilitated dispersal and, by the mid-2000s, the species was found along the coast from Stonehaven to Balmedie and west to Alford and, occasionally, Aboyne. Records in Moray and Buchan were generally one-off sightings, many dating back 30 years. These older records have been impossible to verify though, given the much more restricted range of the species currently, it seems unlikely that Grey Squirrels will naturally disperse into these areas again. However, the population is expanding in Angus and could spread into south Aberdeenshire.

Crucially, from a management perspective, the Grey Squirrel population in the North-East is isolated from that in the rest of the UK. This has been confirmed by public sightings, formal surveys and even genetic analysis (Signorile et al., 2014). This isolation strengthens the case for aiming to eradicate the Grey Squirrel from North-East Scotland and it is vital to maintain the current distribution gap between Angus and Aberdeen. If eradication can be achieved, it would significantly reduce the threat of Grey Squirrels spreading beyond Aberdeenshire and colonising Red Squirrel strongholds in Moray, the Cairngorms National Park, and the Highlands. Occasional individual Grey Squirrels are recorded around Blair Atholl, on the southern edge of Cairngorms National Park. These are trapped and removed when located.

As a result of live trapping by SSRS and others, the current Grey Squirrel population in North-East Scotland is much reduced from its historic peak in around 2005. By 2015, just tiny populations persisted around Banchory, just west of Inverurie, south to the southern edges of Aberdeen and north to Balmedie (see also map on page 149).

OBSERVING GREY SQUIRRELS

Grey Squirrels are slightly larger than Red Squirrels and, as the name implies, have a generally grey coat, though they can sometimes acquire a reddish tinge. Like Red Squirrels, they are superb climbers and can be seen moving quickly through trees. However, they also regularly spend time at ground level and, especially in autumn, can be seen foraging on the ground and storing seeds.

Image: Near Kemnay, Sandy Main
Author: Stephen Willis

DISTRIBUTION IN NORTH-EAST SCOTLAND AND THE CAIRNGORMS

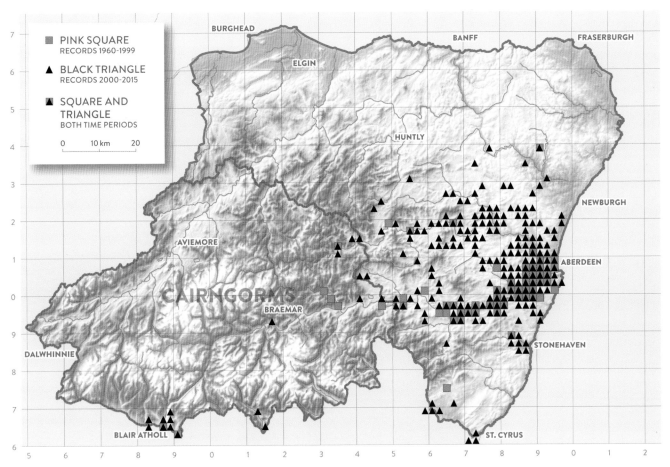

BANK VOLE

(Myodes glareolus)

HABITAT AND ECOLOGY

Like other voles, Bank Voles are herbivorous and eat leafy vegetation and grass stems and will occasionally cache these (Shore & Hare, 2008). Bank Voles are active both during the night and day but become proportionally more active during daytime in winter, probably to conserve heat during colder winter nights. Home range sizes vary with food availability, habitat quality and gender but night movements are generally within a few hundred metres from their burrow (Wolton & Flowerdew, 1985).

Bank Voles will occupy mixed and deciduous mature woodland, grasslands, deciduous and coniferous plantations, hedgerows, riparian habitat and woodland edges (Shore & Hare, 2008). In farmland they show a preference for uncultivated areas of arable landscapes but will forage in cropped parts when the crop is fully grown (Wilson et al., 2014).

MANAGEMENT AND CONSERVATION

Management to increase Bank Vole numbers is rare since they are abundant and widespread. At high densities, and more so in the temperate climates of mainland Europe, they can become crop pests by consuming seedlings and older crops (Shore & Hare, 2008). To control numbers, snap traps, rodenticides, live traps and rehoming have been used.

RECORDS

All small mammal species, including Bank Voles, are traditionally under-recorded. In the atlas area, at least 33% of all records held appear to be obtained using camera traps. Some are also recorded when household pets bring home dead individuals. Incidental live sightings have also been recorded when Bank Voles are active during the day, especially in winter. Typically they are seen shuffling quickly across a path or road. On such occasions, it can be difficult to distinguish Bank Voles from Field Voles but tail length is the best feature to differentiate between the species. Live trapping projects also provide some records.

BRITISH ISLES DISTRIBUTION, POPULATION AND TRENDS

The Bank Vole population size in Great Britain was last estimated to be in the region of 23 million, including 3.5 million in Scotland (Harris et al., 1995). Bank Voles are ubiquitous on the British mainland but, in Ireland, are restricted to the south where they were probably introduced in the 1920s (Shore & Hare, 2008). They are not found in Northern Ireland as yet, although their distribution in Ireland is thought to be rapidly expanding (Montgomery et al., 2015). They are absent from many Scottish islands, including Orkney and Shetland, but have been recorded on Scalpay, Ulva, Raasay, Mull, Arran, Bute, Handa and possibly

Islay (Shore & Hare, 2008). There is no evidence of population cycles in Britain but three to five year population fluctuations do occur elsewhere (Hansson & Henttonen, 1985).

NORTH-EAST SCOTLAND AND CAIRNGORMS DISTRIBUTION AND TRENDS

Records are scattered and scarce in general but the species is probably seriously under-recorded, so it is difficult to obtain a reliable impression of the Bank Vole's distribution. That said, they are likely to occur widely across the atlas area and be present in many vegetated areas that have sufficient cover at ground level. Records suggest that they are mostly absent from the more mountainous regions but this may to some extent represent recorder bias rather than a real trend. Extrapolations from research carried out in Tayside would suggest that they are probably not numerous in urban areas or within cropped habitat (Wilson et al., 2014).

OBSERVING BANK VOLES

It is more usual to only see the signs of Bank Voles, such as grazed vegetation, tunnels through vegetation and latrines, than live animals. These signs can be supported by live trapping projects and groups conducting these in grassland or riparian habitats, outside of urban areas, are likely to encounter Bank Voles. Care should be taken to distinguish Bank Voles from Field Voles. Bank Voles have proportionally longer tails and more of a chestnut-brown coat compared to the short tail and greyish-brown coats of Field Voles.

Image: Near Stonehaven, Genevieve Leaper
Author: Amanda Wilson

DISTRIBUTION IN NORTH-EAST SCOTLAND AND THE CAIRNGORMS

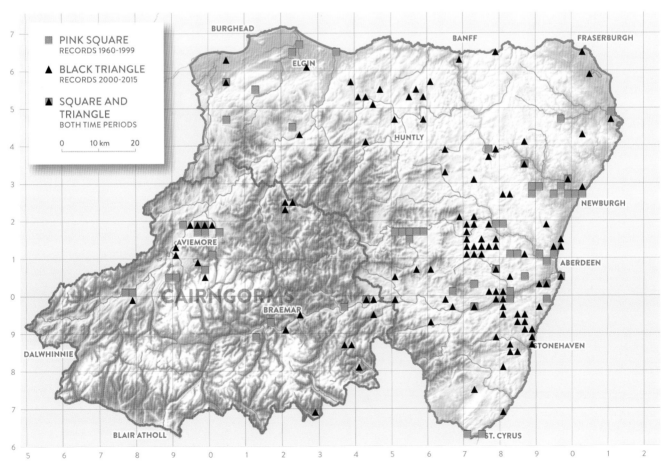

FIELD VOLE

(Microtus agrestis)

HABITAT AND ECOLOGY

Field Voles, also known as Short-tailed Voles, are a very common small mammal species in Britain. They are supposedly slightly more abundant than Bank Voles, although there are anecdotal reports to the contrary and more research is needed. They are a herbivorous species and mainly feed on leafy vegetation and grass stems, occasionally caching short chewed grass stems (Lambin, 2008). As with other voles, they defecate in latrines and these can be found by looking carefully at the base of leafy vegetation alongside food caches (Lambin, 2008). Although they do show considerable nocturnal activity, their activity peaks at dawn and dusk and they tend to be more active during daytime in winter to minimise heat loss during the coldest parts of the day (Baumler, 1975). Home range sizes vary with food availability, habitat quality and gender but in general, nightly movements are within a few hundred metres from their nest site (Agrell, 1995).

Field Voles are most often found in grassland habitats but will also occupy field margins, riparian habitat, and woodland edge, sand dunes, blanket bogs and moorland (Lambin, 2008). They occasionally venture into arable fields when crops are fully grown (Wilson et al., 2014).

MANAGEMENT AND CONSERVATION

Management for Field Voles is rare but there are occasional instances of management of grassland for Field Voles to support birds of prey that have declined, such as various species of owl. Such management might include sowing with a grass seed mix, cutting annually and leaving set-aside in place for at least two years (Tattersall, et al., 2000).

Field Vole densities fluctuate and they can increase dramatically following winter snowfall, which protects them from predators and provides insulation from cold temperatures (Lambin, 2008). At high densities they can become a pest, when they damage young plantations and valued plant species in grassland habitat.

RECORDS

All small mammal species are traditionally under-recorded and Field Voles are no exception. At least 29% of the records come from cat owners whose pets bring home dead individuals. Other records come from bird pellets or are of animals found dead of unknown cause. Incidental live sightings are possible because Field Voles show some diurnal activity in winter and are active around dawn and dusk. However, they move quickly when disturbed and it can be difficult to distinguish them from Bank Voles on superficial examination. Live trapping projects also provide some records.

BRITISH ISLES DISTRIBUTION, POPULATION AND TRENDS

Most recent estimates suggest that the British Isles has a Field Vole population in the region of 75 million (Harris et al, 1995). Field Voles are ubiquitous on the British mainland but are not found in Ireland or on the Isle of Man, the Isles of Scilly or the Channel Islands. They occur on most Hebridean islands but are absent from Orkney and Shetland (Lambin, 2008). Although numbers show cyclic patterns, with a peak population every three to four years (Lambin et al., 2000), there is no evidence to suggest any longer-term population decline or increase.

NORTH-EAST SCOTLAND AND CAIRNGORMS DISTRIBUTION AND TRENDS

Field Voles are under-recorded in the region relative to their likely abundance and records of the species are scattered and scarce in some areas. It is, therefore, difficult to obtain a reliable impression of its distribution. However, records appear to be spread across the atlas area, which is in line with the thinking that this species is ubiquitous. There are some records from mountainous areas and, indeed, this species has been found higher than 1,300 m in the Cairngorms National Park (Lambin, 2008).

OBSERVING FIELD VOLES

Field Voles are one of the small mammal species brought in by cats and they are easily identified and recorded in this way. They can also be spotted running across a path during the day in winter or around dawn and dusk at other times, especially during times of high population. It is more usual to only see the signs of Field Voles, such as grazed grass stalks and caches, tunnels through vegetation and latrines. These signs can be supported by live trapping projects and groups conducting these in grassland habitats are likely to encounter Field Voles. Care should be taken to distinguish Field Voles from Bank Voles, the latter having a longer tail and a more chestnut-brown coat rather than the greyish-brown coat of Field Voles.

Image: Cambridgeshire, Mark Howes
Author: Amanda Wilson

DISTRIBUTION IN NORTH-EAST SCOTLAND AND THE CAIRNGORMS

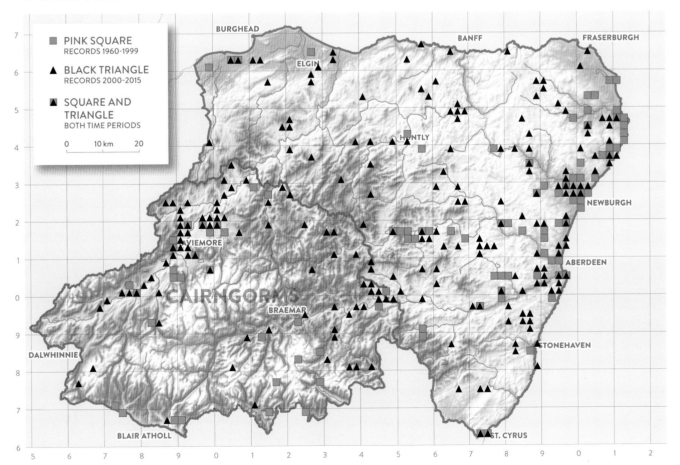

WATER VOLE

(Arvicola amphibius)

HABITAT AND ECOLOGY

Water Voles are large amphibious rodents. They are associated with grass-rich, non-wooded river banks with uncompacted soils in which they can dig extensive burrow systems (Aars et al., 2001; Telfer et al., 2001). They can be found wherever these habitat requirements are met including in wet dune systems, lowland farm ditches, heather moorland and montane areas. Water Voles typically exist in networks of small colonies, made of one or a few family groups and around 15-20% of colonies suffer extinction each year (Aars et al., 2001; Telfer et al., 2001). In healthy Water Vole networks, a similar number of new colonies is formed annually owing to the exceptional ability of Water Voles to disperse. Dispersers routinely travel more than 2 km along watercourses and overland, with some individuals tracked for over 12 km in one month (Telfer et al., 2003, Lambin et al., 2004).

MANAGEMENT AND CONSERVATION

Water Voles have experienced an alarming UK-wide decline, largely attributable to predation by American Mink and, locally, to habitat loss (Strachan & Jefferies, 1993; Strachan et al., 2000). The species is listed on Schedule 5 of the Wildlife & Countryside Act 1981 (as amended). Legal protection in Scotland is restricted to the "Water Vole's places of shelter" though there is no suggestion that disturbance has contributed to

the decline of the species. Vacant habitat (rivers and streams) is plentiful but much of it is also occupied by American Mink, though partnership working by organisations and volunteers has ensured that most of the atlas area is now free of resident breeding mink (Bryce et al., 2011).

RECORDS

Most records are of the distinctive signs, namely latrines and burrows but some are of sightings, including of dead voles. Records from structured surveys in defined sampling areas account for 87 % of the 1784 records (mostly from surveys performed by staff or students from the University of Aberdeen). These surveys were often centred on known surviving Water Vole colony networks. Thus, extreme care must be used when making any inference from the maps as the apparent distribution is likely to strongly reflect survey effort.

BRITISH ISLES DISTRIBUTION, POPULATION AND TRENDS

Once found throughout much of Britain (though absent from Ireland), the Water Vole is now said to be the fastest declining British mammal. Stratified randomised surveys provide the startling statistic that, by 1998, Water Voles had declined UK-wide by 98.7 % relative to a 1939 baseline (Strachan & Jefferies, 1993;

Strachan et al., 2000; summarised in Moorhouse et al., 2015). Numerous conservation efforts are focusing on maintaining strongholds in England or on reintroducing Water Voles, both with mixed success because of the challenge of removing mink on a sufficiently large scale. Indeed recent, less rigorously structured, mapping exercises suggest that there is a continuing decline this century (Anon, 2013).

NORTH-EAST SCOTLAND AND CAIRNGORMS DISTRIBUTION AND TRENDS

The map confirms that widespread networks of Water Vole colonies still persist in upland moorland and montane areas, where most structured surveys take place. Indeed they are recorded on Lochnagar and Ben Avon plateaux at over 1,000 m altitude. These upland areas did not experience the catastrophic collapse seen in lowland sites, presumably reflecting less frequent or shorter incursion by mink into gamekeepered areas. Nevertheless, there was evidence of a steady, if slower, decline from 1996-2004 in the eastern part of the Cairngorms National Park (Aars et al., 2001; Capreolus Wildlife Consultancy, 2005) which has now been arrested and reversed.

The map shows that the catchment of the River Ythan, where initial conservation efforts were focused, remains well occupied. The scattering of localised sightings in the Buchan plain and in the Deveron catchment is encouraging. They may reflect colony persistence or recolonisation. It is important to note that many thousands of km of rivers, burns and ditches are suitable for Water Voles and any map is guaranteed to under-record the true distribution. The cluster of occupied tetrads north of the River Dee between Banchory and Drumoak, many of which are based on recent sightings, is potentially evidence of natural recolonisation given that the area lacked Water Voles in the 1990s.

OBSERVING WATER VOLES

Water Voles approach twice the length of the more common Bank and Field Voles and weigh up to 300 g. They are more likely to be confused with Brown Rats, which can also be found along waterways, though Water Voles have blunter muzzles, less conspicuous ears and furrier tails. Most Water Voles in the atlas area are largely black in colour though some are dark brown. Whilst Water Vole signs, latrines, cropped "lawns" and burrow entrances are readily visible, seeing an actual individual requires patience or luck. Anglers and hill walkers are most likely to encounter Water Voles but the ongoing recolonisation, aided with a local reintroduction in the Tarland area, is likely to offer new opportunities to enjoy this species on the riverbank.

Image: Upland NE Scotland, Alan Ross
Author: Xavier Lambin

45

DISTRIBUTION IN NORTH-EAST SCOTLAND AND THE CAIRNGORMS

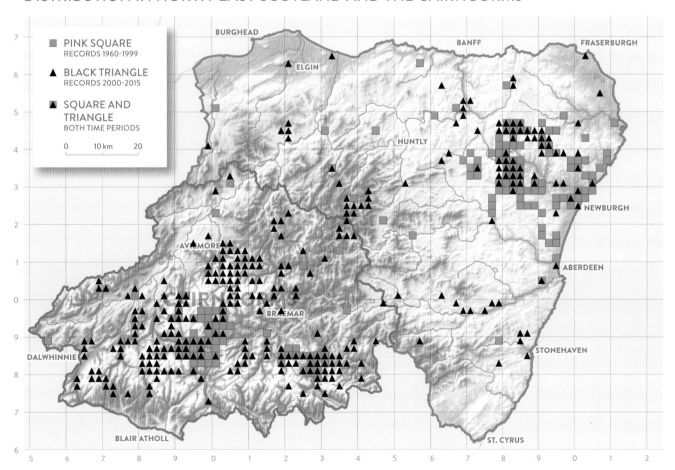

PINK SQUARE RECORDS 1960-1999

BLACK TRIANGLE RECORDS 2000-2015

SQUARE AND TRIANGLE BOTH TIME PERIODS

0   10 km   20

BURGHEAD
BANFF
FRASERBURGH
ELGIN
HUNTLY
NEWBURGH
AVIEMORE
ABERDEEN
CAIRNGORMS
BRAEMAR
STONEHAVEN
DALWHINNIE
BLAIR ATHOLL
ST. CYRUS

WOOD MOUSE

(Apodemus sylvaticus)

HABITAT AND ECOLOGY

The Wood Mouse is one of the most abundant and probably the most ubiquitous of mammal species in the British Isles (Flowerdew & Tattersall, 2008). They are a generalist species in many senses and consume a wide variety of foods, although their diet largely comprises seeds and grains when these are available. They will also consume leafy vegetation, larger invertebrates such as beetles and even feast on fruits, like Blackberries (Flowerdew & Tattersall, 2008). Wood Mouse home range size varies, but estimates suggest that individuals can travel as far as 1 km from their nest site (Macdonald et al., 2000).

Wood Mice can be found in high numbers in broadleaved woodland, especially over winter, but coniferous woodland is less favourable because the forest floor has little suitable food and less cover in comparison (Flowerdew & Tattersall, 2008). In Britain, Wood Mice make substantial use of arable fields in spring and summer, where they feed on crop seeds and vegetation and are also provided with a thick canopy cover (Wilson et al., 2014). They commonly use grassland, heath, reed-beds and will even live in sand dunes, despite burrowing to make a nest being rather tricky (Flowerdew & Tattersall, 2008)! They are also common in urban areas and will use parks, cemeteries, allotments and gardens, but they usually stick to areas with vegetation overhead to protect them from predators (Baker et al., 2003) and generally avoid gardens that have cats (Baker et al., 2005).

MANAGEMENT AND CONSERVATION

In general, Wood Mice populations receive very little management. There are occasional reports of management to increase Wood Mouse numbers in order to help reinstate populations of their predators, for example Pine Martens and Wildcats. However, where management does take place it is mainly in the form of population control. Wood Mice are considered a pest species as they consume crop seeds, food intended for human consumption, building insulation and even plastic cable coverings. They can also carry various disease-causing pathogens such as salmonella and *E. coli*, but reports of Wood Mice being linked to these illnesses in Humans in recent times are scarce (Meerburg & Kijlstra, 2007). When these issues are a concern, control is carried out using snap-traps, rodenticides and live trapping with relocation.

RECORDS

Wood Mice are small, nocturnal and move quickly when disturbed so the chance of identifying them in the wild is low, although a small proportion of records was of incidental live sightings. A larger proportion of records (24%) came from camera trapping projects. Around 16% of records were obtained when Wood Mice were brought in by cats. A small number of records came from small mammal live-trapping studies and university student projects.

BRITISH ISLES DISTRIBUTION, POPULATION AND TRENDS

There are few good estimates of population density but total numbers for Britain are almost certainly in the tens of millions (Harris et al., 1995). Wood Mice are ubiquitous across the British Isles, being found throughout England, Scotland, Wales and Ireland, including on most islands around our coastline (Flowerdew & Tattersall, 2008). Although the occasional harsh winter can delay seasonal population increases, there is no reason to believe that Wood Mouse populations are anything other than stable and live trapping studies yield very healthy numbers in most years (Flowerdew & Tattersall, 2008).

NORTH-EAST SCOTLAND AND CAIRNGORMS DISTRIBUTION AND TRENDS

Wood Mice are widespread in the atlas area and though records are scattered, they are larger in number than for most other small mammal species. They are, nonetheless, significantly under-recorded in most parts of the region though targeted surveying using adapted camera traps in the hectad centred on Kemnay, north-west of Aberdeen, demonstrated there that Wood Mice were present in every tetrad. There is some suggestion of a patchier distribution in the mountainous areas of

the Cairngorms National Park, which may be a true pattern or may reflect some recording bias. There is no reason to believe that populations are anything other than stable.

OBSERVING WOOD MICE

Mice have proportionally larger ears and longer tails than voles. Wood Mouse is the more frequently encountered of the two mouse species, being more abundant than House Mouse even, usually, inside buildings. They are generally paler brown with a whitish stomach, compared to the more uniform greyish-brown of House Mice. If in doubt, the teeth provide diagnostic evidence as to the species. Many live sightings will be in the form of household invaders but it is also possible to record Wood Mice on camera traps feeding at bait stations (peanut butter is a favourite!). Plastic traps for live trapping of small mammals can be purchased in DIY stores for a few pounds and are simple to use. However, it would be advisable to seek training in their safe and humane use prior to taking on such a venture. Seasoned mammalogists may wish to purchase more robust live traps, such as Longworth traps, for capture-release projects.

Image: Aboyne, Harry Scott
Author: Amanda Wilson

47

DISTRIBUTION IN NORTH-EAST SCOTLAND AND THE CAIRNGORMS

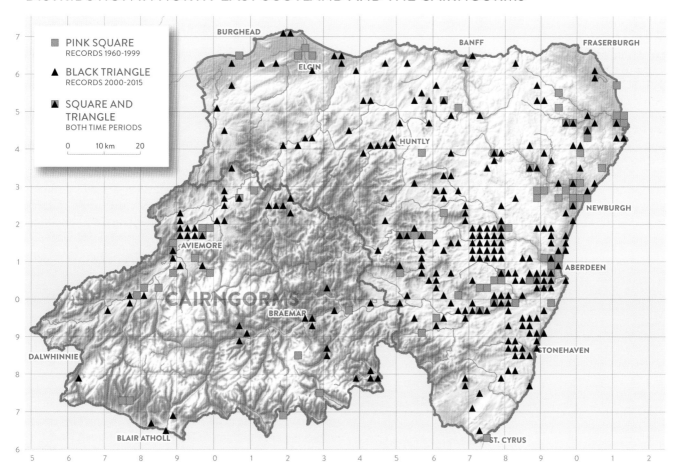

PINK SQUARE
RECORDS 1960-1999

BLACK TRIANGLE
RECORDS 2000-2015

SQUARE AND TRIANGLE
BOTH TIME PERIODS

0   10 km   20

HOUSE MOUSE

(Mus musculus)

HABITAT AND ECOLOGY

Species of the genus *Mus* originated in Asia and spread globally, travelling alongside their Human colonisers, among food sacks and possessions (Boursot et al., 1993). Our species, the House Mouse, still lives closely alongside Humans, making use of a wide variety of food sources such as stored grains in farms and human foods, but also insects and vegetation (Berry et al., 2008). Where House Mice live indoors, they can breed throughout the year and each litter has between five and eight young (Berry et al., 2008). Home range sizes can vary dramatically depending on food sources and habitats available. For example, they may remain within a single barn complex when food is plentiful but will roam several hundred metres from their nest when they occupy stone walls in farmland habitat (Pocock et al., 2005).

In Britain, House Mice make use of buildings where they use structural gaps, such as cavity walls, to nest within. In urban areas, they can use houses, flats, restaurants, shops and factories and in farmland habitat they make use of barns, grain silos and pig or chicken houses where food is plentiful (Berry et al., 2008). There are also reports of House Mice using zoo buildings, which have the benefit of a topped-up food source and warmth, as well as lower levels of Human disturbance. Other stone structures can be used by House Mice, such as dry stone dykes, but such reports in the atlas area are scarce.

MANAGEMENT AND CONSERVATION

Management, when it occurs, is predominantly population control. Globally, other species of *Mus* feature within lists of the world's 100 most invasive species (Invasive Species Specialist Group, 2015). In Britain, House Mice are considered a pest species because they consume stored grains and human foods and, although they only consume around 4 g of food per day, they can produce up to 50 droppings per day (Goldenberg & Rand, 1971). Their gnawing behaviours can also cause damage to insulation and cables within buildings. Control is typically via rodenticide, snap trapping or occasionally live trapping followed by relocation, but given the specialist habitat requirements of House Mice, relocation away from buildings is likely to be unsuccessful.

RECORDS

Small mammals are traditionally under-recorded and very few reliable records of House Mice exist for the atlas area. There are 41 records in the dataset for this atlas, of which 16 are from prior to 2000. Records come from sightings, mainly within houses or outbuildings, trapping projects and the occasional camera trap record. Records of House Mice generally require verification because of the potential for confusion with Wood Mice. The latter is often found in houses but the two species are readily distinguished by examining the fur colour on the underside of specimens. Wood Mice have very white stomach fur whereas House Mice are more uniformly grey (Berry et al., 2008).

BRITISH ISLES DISTRIBUTION, POPULATION AND TRENDS

Most recent estimates tentatively suggest that there are in the region of five million House Mice in Britain (Harris et al., 1995). House Mice are reported to have a widespread, though patchy, distribution across England, Scotland and Wales. They are also found throughout Ireland and on many of our offshore islands (Berry et al., 2008). They are thought to have declined in modern times because of better mouse-proofing of buildings, tidier storage of farm and food products and better control methods (Berry et al., 2008). House Mice also appear to be outcompeted by the more abundant Wood Mice, which also make use of buildings when the opportunity arises (Tattersall et al., 1997). Nevertheless, any decline in abundance does not appear to have had ecological consequences and no concerns have been raised about their numbers.

NORTH-EAST SCOTLAND AND CAIRNGORMS DISTRIBUTION AND TRENDS

The few records available for the atlas area show a scattered distribution. Some distribution maps suggest that the species should be widespread (Berry et al., 2008) but others, such as Arnold (1993), show a similarly sparse and scattered distribution. A widespread distribution in the region seems unlikely, given the sparsity of records and the very low trapping rate of House Mice in live trapping projects, though the species is doubtless more widely distributed than is indicated by the map.

OBSERVING HOUSE MICE

Most live sightings will be in the form of building invaders but camera-trapping projects also provide some potential for observing House Mice. Care should be taken to distinguish between House Mice and Wood Mice, which are by far the more common of the two species - if in doubt, animals should be photographed and expert opinion sought. Plastic live small mammal traps can be purchased in DIY stores for a few pounds and are simple to use, but it would be advisable to seek training prior to taking on such a venture. Seasoned mammalogists may wish to purchase more robust live traps, such as Longworth traps, for capture-release projects.

Image: Drumoak, Nick Littlewood
Author: Amanda Wilson

DISTRIBUTION IN NORTH-EAST SCOTLAND AND THE CAIRNGORMS

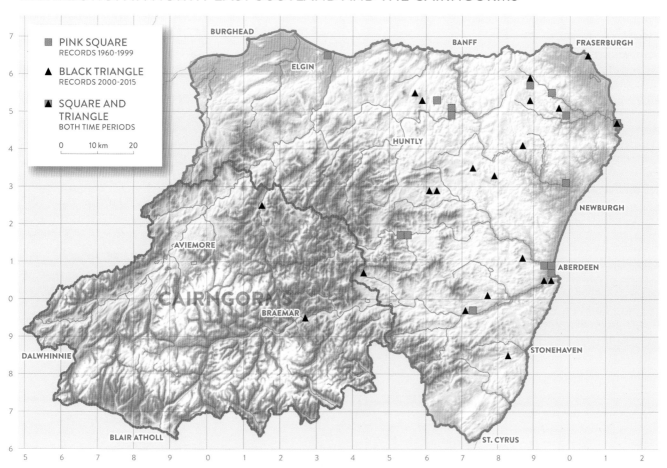

BROWN RAT

(Rattus norvegicus)

HABITAT AND ECOLOGY

Brown Rats are much larger than mice. They have a head and body length of around 280 mm, with the tail a little shorter than this, and can weigh over half a kilogram. They eat a wide variety of food, though their diet is often dominated by cereals (Quy & Macdonald, 2008). They can reproduce at just six weeks old and can potentially have six litters of 12 young each year (Hull, 2007). Research is being carried out on the ultrasonic capabilities of Brown Rats, which they seem to use for communication (Vaughan et al., 2015).

Brown Rats can be found wherever Humans live. They are good diggers and can construct complex tunnel routes underground, through sewer walls or in haystacks (Morris et al., 1989; Brown et al., 2004). Causes of mortality of Brown Rats include predation, parasites, disease, starvation and bad weather. It is believed that only 1% of Brown Rats reach one year old (Quy & Macdonald, 2008) but adults can then live to be around 3 years old (Hull, 2007).

MANAGEMENT AND CONSERVATION

Brown Rats are commonly classed as pests and can be exterminated legally as long as there is no unnecessary, prolonged suffering. Pest controllers use rodenticides and traps to catch Brown Rats, including 'tunnel traps' which involve a lethal spring trap that must, by law, be set inside a tunnel (Stewart, 2012). These are designed to catch small mammals, though rats may avoid strange objects and suspiciously placed baits for up to two days (Quy & Macdonald, 2008).

Damage caused by Brown Rats can be extensive, especially when the gregarious nature of the species is taken into consideration. They can eat huge quantities of food in a short time and damage sewer walls by digging burrows through the brickwork (Morris et al., 1989). Uneaten food spoiled by Brown Rats is destroyed, as the risk of transmission of diseases carried by the rats is considered to be too great for the food to be consumed by Humans. Financial losses to agriculture and other businesses that store food can, therefore, be large. Brown Rats have been known to carry diseases that are harmful to Humans, pets and livestock, such as Weil's disease and jaundice (Hull, 2007).

RECORDS

There are relatively few records of Brown Rat in the NESBReC database when compared with much rarer mammals, such as Pine Marten. However, Brown Rats frequently live in areas where they are unlikely to come into contact with people (especially in sewers) and being largely nocturnal may further reduce the likelihood of sightings (Brown et al., 2004). Hence only 18% of records for which the circumstances are known are of live sightings and a similar proportion is of animals found dead. A greater proportion (46%) is from signs, with footprints on Mink rafts providing most of these.

BRITISH ISLES DISTRIBUTION, POPULATION AND TRENDS

Originating from Asia (Alderton, 1999; Yalden, 1999) the adaptable Brown Rat spread to the British Isles as a stowaway on ships, appearing from around the 1730s (Hull, 2007). The species can now be found almost throughout the British Isles, being absent from only a few small islands and mountain peaks (Harris et al., 1995).

It is thought that the population of Brown Rats in Britain is just under 7 million before the breeding season. However, this figure does not take account of many urban habitats, including sewers, which means that the true population could be much larger (Harris et al., 1995).

NORTH-EAST SCOTLAND AND CAIRNGORMS DISTRIBUTION AND TRENDS

The distribution map may give the misleading impression that the Brown Rat is a sparsely distributed mammal, with an extremely fragmented range. Being a pest species, most people's instincts would be to exterminate the rat rather than to record its location, and it is likely that the species is significantly under-recorded. The available records do, however, show that the Brown Rat is fairly widely distributed across the atlas area. Most records are from in or around towns and villages. Predictably, the city of Aberdeen holds quite a few records, though smaller clusters of records are evident by Newburgh, Alford and Oldmeldrum.

OBSERVING BROWN RATS

Many sightings are perhaps 'chance encounters' when the rat has been glimpsed by someone who is not actively seeking them. There are, however, some clues to their whereabouts. Brown Rats often lay their droppings in a few selected spots and can form runs (trails) up to 10 cm wide in vegetation, but rarely far from shelter (Brown et al., 2004). Runs inside buildings can appear as smudge marks (Quy & Macdonald, 2008). Being strong swimmers, it is possible to see Brown Rats crossing rivers and streams.

Image: Aboyne, Harry Scott
Author: Mike Sedakat

51

DISTRIBUTION IN NORTH-EAST SCOTLAND AND THE CAIRNGORMS

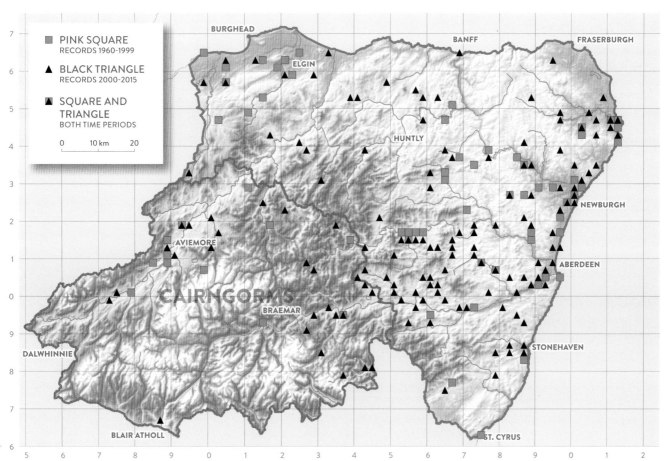

RABBIT

(Oryctolagus cuniculus)

HABITAT AND ECOLOGY

Rabbits are herbivores. Their relatively small size means they can be highly selective in what they graze and they favour plant species with low levels of fibre and high levels of protein in their leaf tissue (Somers et al., 2008). They also remove seeds from some plant species. Some dung pellets are re-ingested, which facilitates prolonged microbial digestion of the plant material.

Rabbits are mainly species of grassland and heathland, but they are also found along the edges of arable fields and woodlands. They depend upon seeing predators to avoid them and so are more frequently found in shorter grasslands, even to the extent of reducing their food intake (Cowan & Hartley, 2008). Their need for suitable soil for burrowing means they are mainly restricted to drier habitats.

MANAGEMENT AND CONSERVATION

Rabbits are not protected in the UK although they are in their native range in Portugal and Spain. Instead they are generally seen as vermin because they are a serious pest of cereal crops and grassland, as well as causing damage to small trees. Control methods include shooting, trapping, lamping with dogs and ferreting, as well as gassing. Rabbit-proof fences are an added cost for tree planting schemes and rural gardens.

However, Rabbits are important for the conservation of species-rich grasslands since, without their continual grazing, such habitats can revert to coarser, species-poor grassland, scrub and even woodland. Elsewhere in the British Isles, Rabbit grazing can have beneficial impacts on the conservation of species such as Large Blue butterfly, Stone-curlew, Chough and Woodlark. They are also important as prey for predators including Fox, Stoat, Polecat, Scottish Wildcat, Red Kite and Buzzard (Lees & Bell, 2008).

RECORDS

Sightings of live Rabbits make up the majority of records (53.2%), with only a small proportion of records being of roadkill (6.3%) or of dead animals in other situations (5.4%). A small number of records were of live and dead animals brought in by cats (mainly) and dogs (2.6%). Records of Rabbit pellets (22.2%) and of burrows and warrens in use (6.9%) are also common. Camera traps have added a small number of more recent records (3.4%).

BRITISH ISLES DISTRIBUTION, POPULATION AND TRENDS

Rabbits were introduced into Britain and Ireland in the 12th century by the Normans but they became common as a result of land management changes in the 19th century, such as planting of winter crops, hedgerow creation and predator control (Sheail, 1971). Numbers peaked in the 1950s at between 60 and 100 million. Myxomatosis was released in 1953 as a biological control agent and reduced populations by up to 99%. Recovery has occurred, but numbers are generally less than 40% of pre-1950s levels (Harris et al., 1995).

Rabbits are near ubiquitous across the British Isles. The exceptions are the high mountains of Scotland, extensive blanket bogs and some outlying islands, notably Rum, Tiree and the Isles of Scilly. They were also the most frequently observed mammal in the Breeding Bird Survey (Wright et al., 2014). This survey revealed a decrease in population of 48% between 1995 and 2015 for the United Kingdom, but a fall of 78% for Scotland. It is possible that Rabbit Haemorrhagic Disease is responsible for part of this fall (Wright et al., 2014) but, apart from this, the reasons for this recent decline in numbers are unknown.

NORTH-EAST SCOTLAND AND CAIRNGORMS DISTRIBUTION AND TRENDS

The distribution map highlights some areas where Rabbits are unrecorded. Some of these gaps are likely to be true absences, such as the high tops of the Cairngorms and, possibly, some of the intensively managed farmland in Buchan. However, many of the other gaps are likely a result of under-recording.

Records are most frequent from the North Sea coastal strip, probably reflecting the association of Rabbits with sand dune systems. They are also frequent along the main river valleys (especially the Dee) and in less intensively farmed areas at moderate altitude, where grassland is the main land cover. The increase in records for 2000-2015 compared to 1960-1999 suggests increased recorder effort but also reflects more frequent records from upland areas in the centre of the region.

There are no local data on population trends, though the recent fall in numbers for Scotland appears to be reflected across the atlas area.

OBSERVING RABBITS

The Rabbit is the most common of the three lagomorph (rabbits and hares) species in the atlas area. Rabbits are about two thirds the size of either hare species and have proportionally shorter ears. The recent falls in numbers seen across the area means that sightings may not be as frequent as in the past though most grassland areas should still harbour Rabbits. The best opportunities for observing them are on well drained grasslands and dune systems such as the National Nature Reserves at Sands of Forvie and St Cyrus.

Image: Fowlsheugh, Harry Scott
Author: Robin Pakeman

DISTRIBUTION IN NORTH-EAST SCOTLAND AND THE CAIRNGORMS

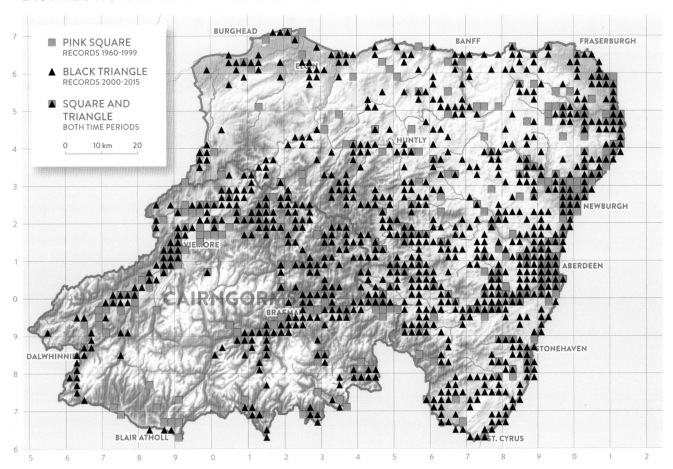

54

BROWN HARE

(Lepus europaeus)

HABITAT AND ECOLOGY

Brown Hares are most commonly found on arable farmland and grassland (Hutchings & Harris, 1996). They also need some permanent cover and will often rest in woods, hedgerows, and shelterbelts during the day. Farms with smaller fields and year-round food and shelter are more suitable for Brown Hares than are large-scale monocultures (Tapper & Barnes, 1986). In some areas they spend the winter in woodland, moving to arable land as crops start growing (Scott, 2011).

Diet mainly consists of grasses and wild plants but may include arable crops, especially young cereals (Frylestam, 1986). They also browse woody plants, and will eat their own soft droppings to extract maximum nutrition from them.

Brown Hares are largely nocturnal and rest during the day in a form, a depression or scrape in the ground. In North-East Scotland they may travel up to 1.7 km between their resting and feeding areas (Hewson & Taylor, 1968).

MANAGEMENT AND CONSERVATION

Brown Hares have limited legal protection in the UK and they may be killed as game or when causing crop damage. However, there is legislation affording some protection and, in Scotland, they cannot be taken or killed from 1st February to 30th September.

While Brown Hares can cause damage to crops and young forestry plantations (Harris et al., 1995), they have little long-term economic impact on forestry in southern and central Scotland, and none in northern Scotland (Wray & Harris, 1994).

Threats to Brown Hares include modernisation of agriculture (which has reduced the availability of year-round food and shelter), agricultural machinery, pesticides, disease and predation by Foxes (Jennings, 2008). Other causes of mortality include traffic, driven shooting, poaching and illegal hare coursing by using greyhounds or lurchers to chase hares.

RECORDS

Most Brown Hare records (87% of those where the circumstances are known) are of direct sightings, which peak in spring, probably because they are easier to see before crops are fully grown (Arnold, 1993). Roadkill animals form 7% of the records, with camera trap images and records from field signs currently making up a much smaller proportion of records.

BRITISH ISLES DISTRIBUTION, POPULATION AND TRENDS

Brown Hares were probably introduced to Britain as early as the Iron Age (Yalden, 1999). They are widely distributed across large parts of Britain and are present on some islands, including Skye, although they are absent from the West and North-West Highlands (Arnold, 1993; Scott, 2011). There have also been small numbers in Northern Ireland since the mid-19th Century (Jennings, 2008).

The Brown Hare population declined by roughly 80% during the 20th Century to an estimated 817,500 animals, including 187,250 in Scotland (Harris et al., 1995). There has also been a significant reduction in the numbers recorded in game bags since the 1960s (MacDonald & Barrett, 1993). However, numbers may have more recently stabilised. Breeding Bird Survey data, which also incorporate mammal sightings, indicate that there has been no overall decline between 1995 and 2014 (Harris et al., 2015) although there is evidence of regional trends, with the distribution having reduced in Scotland between 1995 and 2002 (Battersby et al., 2005).

NORTH-EAST SCOTLAND AND CAIRNGORMS DISTRIBUTION AND TRENDS

In the atlas area, Brown Hares occur largely in the lowlands, with few present in mountainous areas. This is typical of Brown Hare habitat selection in Scotland and they are largely replaced by Mountain Hare above 300 m, where farmland gives way to heather moor (Harris et al., 1995; Jennings, 2008). A visual comparison of the Brown Hare and Mountain Hare distribution maps shows little overlap.

Dense clusters of records, along with apparent gaps or low densities, may reflect recording effort in some areas. Some of the gaps in the lowland areas, for example along the lower reaches of the River Spey, may be due to extensive plantation forestry and Brown Hares are also absent from Aberdeen, the most urbanised area in the region. A substantial number of records from 2000 to 2015 are in areas in which there were no records prior to 2000. It is likely, but not certain, that this is due to increased observer effort.

Coursing (which is illegal) has a significant presence in Moray and some landowners are reported to cull Brown Hares in order to reduce the presence of coursers, and associated criminal activity, on their land (Douglas Darling, pers. comms. 2015). The extent to which this may have affected Brown Hare distribution in the region is not clear.

OBSERVING BROWN HARES

Brown Hares are larger than Rabbits, with proportionally longer ears. They may also be confused with Mountain Hares in their summer coat, but are deeper brown and usually occupy lower ground. While the breeding season is quite long, the Brown Hare's 'boxing' behaviour, when unreceptive females fend off males, is best observed in early spring (especially at dawn and dusk), as the vegetation is still low.

Image: Muir of Dinnet, Harry Scott
Author: Dan Puplett

DISTRIBUTION IN NORTH-EAST SCOTLAND AND THE CAIRNGORMS

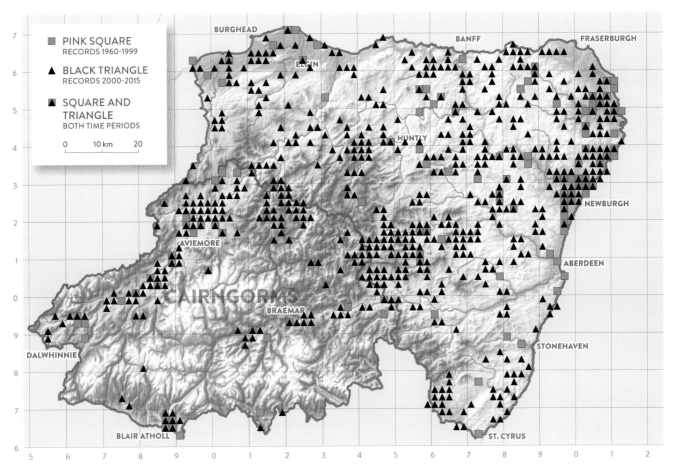

MOUNTAIN HARE

(Lepus timidus)

HABITAT AND ECOLOGY

In the atlas area, Mountain Hares occur mainly above 300 m altitude with highest densities on managed heather moorland. They are found at a range of elevations elsewhere in their range including Ireland, where Brown Hares are largely absent. In more fragmented landscapes, Mountain Hares prefer either grass mires in summer (Rao et al., 2003b), or upland pastures or woodland habitats (Hulbert et al., 1996). In all habitats they eat mainly woody plants during the winter months, notably Heather on moorland, and grasses and herbs during the summer when they are available (Iason & Waterman, 1988; Hulbert et al., 2001). They are mostly active from dusk to dawn, resting during the day, mainly in sheltered depressions in the ground, known as 'forms'.

MANAGEMENT AND CONSERVATION

Mountain Hares can be legally controlled but The Wildlife & Countryside Act 1981 (as amended) prohibits or restricts certain methods of capture, including unselective live-trapping or night shooting. They are listed in Annex V of the EC Habitats Directive (1992) and member states must ensure that management is *"compatible with their being maintained at a favourable conservation status"*. The Wildlife and Natural Environment (Scotland) Act 2011 introduced a close season (March-July inclusive) when killing of Mountain Hares is not permitted.

High local densities can damage agricultural crops (Flux, 1970) and the establishment of young trees (Rao et al., 2003a). On some estates, large numbers of hares are killed as part of controversial and scientifically questionable culls to control ticks and tick borne diseases, for the benefit of Red Grouse (Harrison et al., 2010; Patton et al., 2010; Watson, 2013).

Mountain Hares may be threatened by climate change. Milder conditions may permit Brown Hares to expand their range uphill and to out-compete Mountain Hares (Thulin, 2003).

RECORDS

The majority of the 3,111 records are of sightings of living animals. Numbers reported vary from single animals in 80% of cases where a count is given up to 70 live individuals at one time. About 175 observations were of dead animals with other records being of larger numbers (up to 15) counted as 'roadkill' on a particular stretch of road on a single day. Roadkills comprise 50% of the Mountain Hares recorded as dead. Fifty-nine records were of images from camera traps.

BRITISH ISLES DISTRIBUTION, POPULATION AND TRENDS

Mountain Hares occur naturally through most of upland mainland Scotland. They have been introduced in the Peak District and on some Scottish islands including Jura, Mull, Skye, Shetland mainland and Hoy in Orkney (Arnold, 1993). They are also native throughout Ireland.

Estimates of the Mountain Hare population in Scotland vary between 300,000 and 360,000 (plus or minus 50%) (Harris et al., 1995). The large variation in estimates may be an effect of different survey techniques and/or fluctuations in numbers, as around half of Mountain Hare populations demonstrate large fluctuations or population cycles with an average periodicity of nine years (range four to fifteen years). Population density can change more than tenfold over such a cycle (Newey et al., 2007). The highest densities in Scotland can reach 200 per km² although, more usually, 30 to 69 per km² occur in the atlas area on heather moors overlying base-rich rocks, while the lowest densities (2 to 5 per km²) occur in West Scotland on low lying moors over acidic rocks (Watson & Hewson, 1973). Numbers are considered to be declining in the long-term (Battersby et al., 2005; Watson, 2013) possibly due to reductions in moorland area, afforestation, long-term decline in habitat quality and reduced gamekeeper activity leading to increased predation. In some areas, the decline may be driven by killing of Mountain Hares for tick control (50% of hares killed), sport (40%) or forest protection (10%) (Patton et al., 2010).

NORTH-EAST SCOTLAND AND CAIRNGORMS DISTRIBUTION AND TRENDS

Mountain Hares are indigenous in the atlas area and are found mainly in or close to the Cairngorms. The region probably contains the majority of the British population due to the widespread extent of heather moorland managed for Red Grouse. Their distribution is patchy elsewhere in Scotland and at lower altitudes in the atlas area, with Mountain Hares being absent from lowland agricultural areas. A recent study of Mountain Hare distribution showed no major changes between 1995-96 and 2006-07 in any region, including North-East Scotland (Patton et al., 2010).

OBSERVING MOUNTAIN HARES

Mountain Hares are slightly smaller than Brown Hares, with proportionally shorter ears. In summer, their fur is greyish-brown though they turn white in winter. This helps to camouflage them against snow though when snow is lacking, they can be easily spotted against the darker background. They can be watched most clearly from a vantage point, moving soon after sunset. Groups of Mountain Hares are particularly visible as they aggregate on leeward hill slopes during snow cover. The roads over the Cairnwell Pass and the Lecht provide accessible areas where Mountain Hares can often be seen.

Image: Cairnwell Pass, Harry Scott
Authors: Glenn R Iason & Scott Newey

DISTRIBUTION IN NORTH-EAST SCOTLAND AND THE CAIRNGORMS

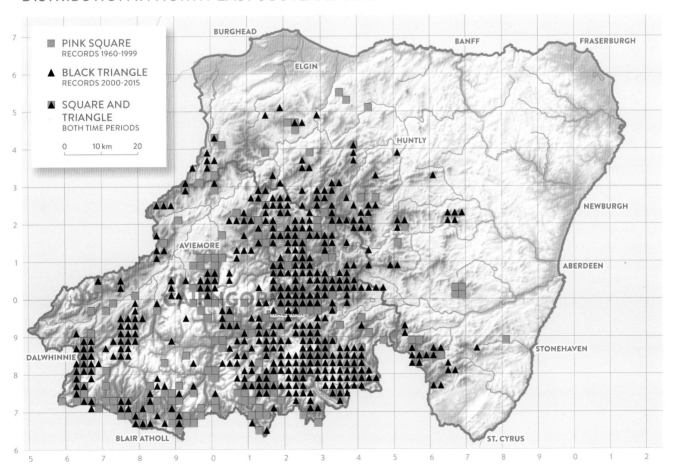

HEDGEHOG

(Erinaceus europaeus)

HABITAT AND ECOLOGY

Hedgehogs are common in parks, gardens and farmland. They are also found in mixed woodland, favouring woodland edge habitat in particular. They favour grazed or short-mown grassland for foraging and feed on ground-living invertebrates including beetles, worms, caterpillars, slugs and other insects. They will also take eggs and chicks of ground nesting birds.

Hibernation usually begins in November and ends in late March, but is weather dependent. They make a winter nest of leaves, positioned under a bush, logpile, garden shed or other structure offering shelter. Hedgehogs can wake up several times during the winter and may even build a new nest. In spring, they become active, though will re-enter hibernation if the weather turns colder.

Hedgehogs are nocturnal. They typically travel one to two kilometres each night to feed and then return to the same daytime nest for a few days in a row before making a new nest. Females have a litter of four to five young between April and September. Young born late in the season are often too weak and have insufficient fat reserves to survive hibernation.

MANAGEMENT AND CONSERVATION

Hedgehogs are partially protected under the Wildlife & Countryside Act and may not be trapped without a license from Scottish Natural Heritage.

Hedgehogs are declining in number (Battersby et al., 2005). Habitat loss, with a change to more intensive agriculture, may be a factor in this. In addition, an increased use of chemicals in gardens and on arable land may be reducing the supply of invertebrates that they feed on. 'Tidy' gardens are generally not Hedgehog-friendly. Development may carve up suitable habitat, so that small populations can become isolated and more vulnerable to local extinction. Road deaths may also be a cause of decline locally.

Spines protect against most predators, except for Badgers. Hedgehogs have been shown to actively avoid sites where Badgers are present in high numbers and a study in Oxfordshire found that the local distribution and abundance of Hedgehogs correlated inversely with the distribution of Badgers (Micol et al., 1994).

Gardens with piles of brash or leaves provide good winter hibernation sites. Hedgehogs can be encouraged into gardens by these habitat piles. They also benefit from non-use of garden pesticides. A focus on developing 'green corridors' and on sensible planning of new development, to prevent isolating blocks of suitable habitat for Hedgehogs, is key.

RECORDS

The circumstances in which the record was made are known for around half of the 1,067 records. Of these, the majority (72%) were of animals found dead, mostly as roadkill and 23% were live sightings. The distribution of records through the year, being high in spring and summer and tailing off in autumn (November) is typical of a hibernating animal.

BRITISH ISLES DISTRIBUTION, POPULATION AND TRENDS

Hedgehogs are found throughout the British Isles, except on some offshore islands (Morris & Reeve, 2008). The pre-breeding Scottish Hedgehog population has been estimated at 310,000 animals (Harris et al., 1995) but this was based on very limited information. Analysis of data from five national surveys of Hedgehog abundance undertaken between 1996 and 2010 indicated a significant decline during this period. This includes wider countryside surveys in addition to those focused on gardens (Roos et al., 2012).

NORTH-EAST SCOTLAND AND CAIRNGORMS DISTRIBUTION AND TRENDS

The distribution of records in the atlas area follows that of suitable woodland edge, parkland and suburban habitat. It may be biased by recorder activity and it is unlikely that Hedgehogs are as sparsely distributed in the north of the region as the records might suggest. Hedgehogs do tend to be scarce, though, in intensively farmed arable areas, wetlands, pine/conifer woodlands and heathland. There are a few records from the uplands of North-East Scotland and the Cairngorms, consistent with occasional previous records at higher altitude (Arnold, 1993). Anecdotal evidence from local naturalists suggests that, mirroring the national situation, Hedgehogs have declined in number in the atlas region over the last 10 to 15 years.

OBSERVING HEDGEHOGS

Hedgehogs have an unmistakable coat of several thousand spines along the back. With acute senses of smell and hearing, they erect their spines at the first sign of danger, rolling up tightly to protect their head and extremities completely. They are speckled brown and cream with a darker brown pointed snout and black eyes and nose.

Attracting animals to one's garden with suitable habitat piles of logs or garden clippings is a good way to observe Hedgehogs, though any supplementary feeding of garden Hedgehogs should be limited and should be of Hedgehog-friendly foods.

Image: Aboyne, Harry Scott
Author: Emma Williams

DISTRIBUTION IN NORTH-EAST SCOTLAND AND THE CAIRNGORMS

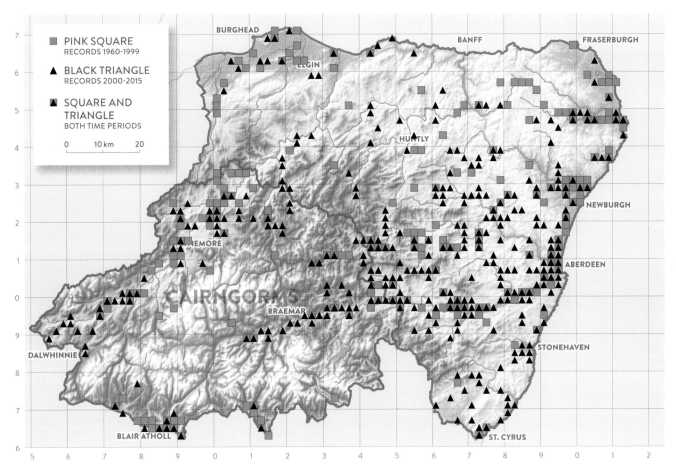

PINK SQUARE RECORDS 1960-1999

BLACK TRIANGLE RECORDS 2000-2015

SQUARE AND TRIANGLE BOTH TIME PERIODS

0   10 km   20

MOLE

(Talpa europaea)

HABITAT AND ECOLOGY

Moles are native to Britain. Originally a species of deciduous woodland, they thrive on pastures and arable land (Yalden, 1999). They live at lower densities in most other habitats, including coniferous forest, moorland and even sand-dune systems (Gorman, 2008). Population densities of 8/ha in winter and 16/ha in summer have been reported for English pastures (Larkin, 1948) while, in North-East Scotland, summer densities of 4-5/ha have been measured in deciduous woodland and pasture (Gorman & Stone, 1990).

Moles have limbs that are specially adapted for digging. They occupy individual territories in which they dig an extensive and elaborate system of permanent tunnels, creating molehills. Moles have very small eyes and use smell to locate prey. They eat soil invertebrates including earthworms, with *Lumbricus terrestris* being the most important. In North-East Scotland, litters of three to four young are born in May or June. Lactation lasts for four to five weeks and then the young disperse, generally above ground. Dispersing juveniles suffer high mortality from starvation and predation by Tawny Owls, Buzzards, Stoats, domestic cats and dogs, and from vehicles. Once established, the mortality rate of adult Moles is constant at 50-60% per annum. Consequently, most Moles are aged one year or less and few live beyond three years, although some can live to be six (Gorman & Stone, 1990; Gorman, 2008).

MANAGEMENT AND CONSERVATION

In the past, Moles were trapped for their skins and, in 1905, more than a million skins were traded in London for the fashion market. Today moleskins are not in demand but Moles are culled as a pest of agricultural land, golf courses and other amenity land. In a questionnaire study, Atkinson et al. (1994) revealed that most farmers perceived the Mole as a pest, but that damage was slight on most farms. Silage pollution by soil from molehills was the biggest problem. Mole control is now mainly by trapping, with poisoning with strychnine being illegal since 2006.

RECORDS

Of the 4,618 submitted records, 3,231 provided the evidential basis of the record. Molehills accounted for 97.1% of these, dead Moles above ground 1.5%, live Moles above ground 0.5%, Moles caught or killed by cats 0.7%, and evidence from work of mole-catchers 0.2%. There was also a single record of a Mole in a house. It is likely that the other 1,387 records were also of Molehills, giving a probable total of 97.9% in that category.

BRITISH ISLES DISTRIBUTION, POPULATION AND TRENDS

In mainland Britain, Moles occur wherever the soil is sufficiently deep for burrowing. There are records at 930 m in Scotland (Arnold, 1993) and 1,000 m in Wales (Milner & Ball, 1970). They are absent from Ireland, the Isle of Man, the Outer and the Northern Isles but are present on some larger islands such as Mull and Skye (Arnold, 1993; Gorman, 2008). The total pre-breeding population has been estimated at 31,000,000; 19,750,000 in England, 8,000,000 in Scotland and 3,250,000 in Wales (Harris et al., 1995).

There is little information on population trends but they are thought to be stable (Harris et al., 1995; Battersby et al., 2005).

NORTH-EAST SCOTLAND AND CAIRNGORMS DISTRIBUTION AND TRENDS

Moles occur wherever the soil is deep enough for digging, albeit at different densities related to food supply, and there are records from throughout the area. Apparent absences will usually be the result of observer bias. With molehills being the most common form of encounter, it is unsurprising that records are concentrated where people are most likely to see them, such as along transport routes and in areas of higher density of Human presence. However, gaps in records in agricultural areas may be the result of modern agricultural practice. Deep ploughing, re-seeding and insecticides significantly reduce populations of earthworms and other soil invertebrates and may affect Moles indirectly or directly (Edwards & Lofty, 1972).

OBSERVING MOLES

Moles are rarely seen alive, the best evidence for their presence being molehills, surface tunnels and fortresses, which are large mounds with one or more nests that can also house food stores. Careful and patient observation of an active molehill may provide a fleeting glimpse of the Mole. Moles, alive or dead, are sometimes found above ground during droughts and when the young are dispersing.

Image: Aboyne, Harry Scott
Author: Martyn Gorman

61

DISTRIBUTION IN NORTH-EAST SCOTLAND AND THE CAIRNGORMS

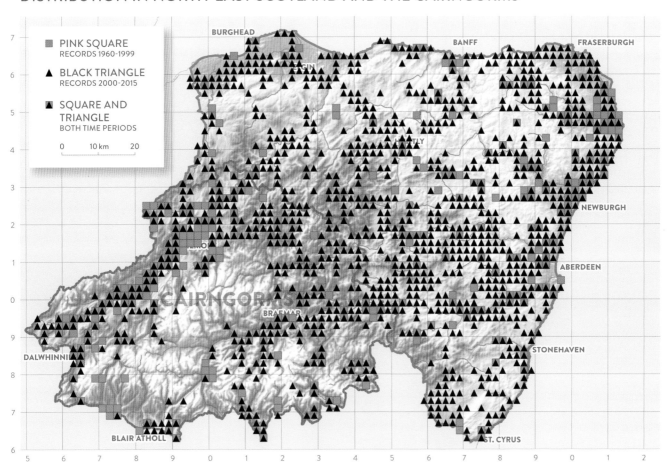

PINK SQUARE
RECORDS 1960-1999

BLACK TRIANGLE
RECORDS 2000-2015

SQUARE AND TRIANGLE
BOTH TIME PERIODS

0   10 km   20

COMMON SHREW

(Sorex araneus)

HABITAT AND ECOLOGY

The Common Shrew is a small, ubiquitous, mainly terrestrial mammal found in a range of habitats including hedgerows, scrub, grasslands and deciduous woodlands. It travels through surface vegetation using runways and burrows, either self-made or those created by other species such as voles and mice.

One of three native shrew species found on mainland Britain, the Common Shrew can easily be distinguished from the Water Shrew, which has a black upper coat. The Common Shrew's tri-coloured markings, usually including a dark brown upper coat, a pale brown flank and greyish white undersides, distinguish it from its close relative, the Pygmy Shrew. In addition, the Common Shrew has a slightly longer head and body though its tail is proportionally thinner and shorter.

With a markedly high metabolic rate, the Common Shrew is active throughout the day and night in search of prey, though this activity peaks during darkness hours. It feeds on a range of items, largely insects, but also small vertebrates, earthworms, carrion and seeds. It can consume its own bodyweight in food over a 24 hour period and, depending on the composition of its diet, the Common Shrew may need to make more than six hundred prey captures each day (Churchfield, 2002). Few Common Shrews live for longer than 18 months.

In winter, the Common Shrew shrinks in size, with the brain and other organs becoming smaller. This adaptation, known as Dehnel's Phenomenon (Dehnel, 1949) relates not only to seasonal prey availability, but also the ability of shrews to forage for certain types of food within frozen soil and leaf litter (Churchfield et al., 2012).

MANAGEMENT AND CONSERVATION

Under Schedule 6 of the Wildlife and Countryside Act 1981, Common Shrews are afforded some degree of legal protection. Certain types of trapping and killing are prohibited and licences must be applied for to intentionally capture any animals.

As one of the most widespread mammal species in the British Isles, found in a range of habitats, Common Shrews do not currently require any conservation action. They are not viewed either as an agricultural or garden pest. Indeed, with an invertebrate-rich diet, they may possibly be viewed as beneficial to gardeners (Churchfield et al., 1991) and they are also an important food item for some predators, such as Kestrels and Barn Owls.

RECORDS

Despite the ubiquitous nature of the species, there are relatively few records in the atlas area (421). Of those records where methodology was cited, dead animals formed the greatest proportion (54%) which included a number brought in by cats. Camera traps, especially those modified for recording small mammals, accounted for 29% of records. There were relatively few chance sightings of live animals (7%) and 6% of records were of animals caught alive using small mammal traps. There were single records each of one caught by a Weasel and of one identified by call.

BRITISH ISLES DISTRIBUTION, POPULATION AND TRENDS

Common Shrews are native to Britain. They occur widely across most of the mainland at all altitudes though are apparently less common in the Scottish Highlands than elsewhere (Churchfield & Searle, 2008a). They are absent from Ireland and many offshore islands, including Orkney, Shetland and the Outer Hebrides, but have been recorded from most of the larger islands of the Inner Hebrides (Arnold, 1993).

The British population has been estimated at 41,700,000, with 11,500,000 of these in Scotland, making Common Shrew the second most abundant British mammal (discounting Humans) and the third most abundant in Scotland (Harris et al., 1995). Population trends in Britain are not known (Battersby et al., 2005).

NORTH-EAST SCOTLAND AND CAIRNGORMS DISTRIBUTION AND TRENDS

Common Shrews probably occur in every 10 km square and most tetrads in the atlas region though, due to difficulties in recording this species, mapped records are scattered more sparsely. The largest concentrations of records are within the Dee, Don and Ythan catchments though these may simply reflect recorder activity. Although Common Shrews may be less numerous in upland environments, they have been seen at over 1,000 m altitude on the Mounth plateau (Watson, 2013). Nothing is known about population trends for this species in the atlas area.

OBSERVING COMMON SHREWS

Viewing Common Shrews in the wild can be rather difficult; they make use of vegetation cover to move through the landscape and are generally most active at night. However, the growing popularity in camera trapping by conservationists and amateur naturalists has led to increased opportunities to view these animals in their natural habitat. Although rarely seen, they may more readily be heard, particularly in spring, when they call more frequently, though the high pitch of the call is inaudible to some.

Image: Cambridgeshire, Mark Howes
Author: Rose Toney

63

DISTRIBUTION IN NORTH-EAST SCOTLAND AND THE CAIRNGORMS

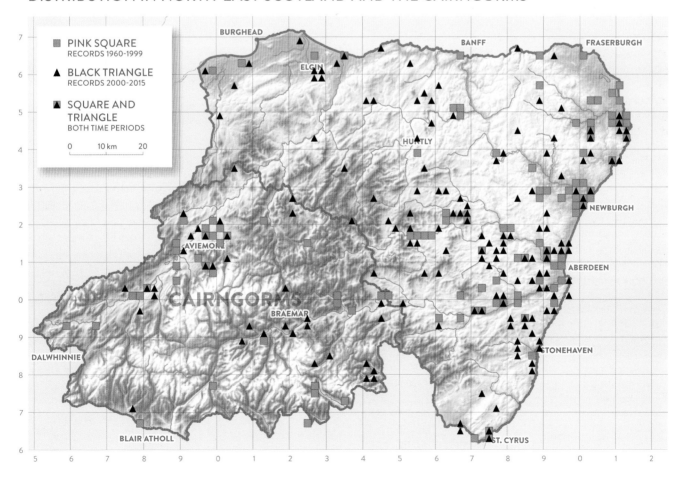

PYGMY SHREW

(Sorex minutus)

HABITAT AND ECOLOGY

The Pygmy Shrew is one of the smallest mammal species found in the British Isles. With a combined head and body length measuring typically between 40 and 60 mm and weighing less than 10 g (often considerably less), the only other British mammals of comparable size are the pipistrelle bats.

There is considerable overlap between Pygmy Shrew habitat and that occupied by its close relative, the Common Shrew. Pygmy Shrews are less abundant than Common Shrews in areas such as woodland, grassland and hedgerow but are more numerous, relative to Common Shrews, in acidic habitats and upland environments such as moorland and bog (e.g. Shore et al., 1995). They use burrows created solely by other animals and forage for food above ground as they do not display an aptitude for digging, unlike the Common Shrew. Hence, although the Pygmy Shrew has a wide, mainly insectivorous diet, earthworms do not form part of it. This may enable the Pygmy Shrew to escape competition from the Common Shrew as earthworms tend to be scarce in the Pygmy Shrew's most favoured habitats. As with other shrew species, the Pygmy Shrew is a rather solitary animal outside of the breeding season. It will defend its territory aggressively, emitting short, high-pitched noises and making swiping movements with its tail when confronted with another of its species.

MANAGEMENT AND CONSERVATION

Pygmy Shrews are provided with partial protection under the umbrella of Schedule 6 of the Wildlife and Countryside Act 1981. It is illegal to employ certain methods to trap or kill the species, with licences required for intentional trapping for purposes such as research.

Ubiquitous and widespread, with negligible impact on human activities, Pygmy Shrews are not currently thought to require any specific conservation action.

RECORDS

Not surprisingly, due to their cryptic nature, there is a paucity of reports of this species in the region. With just 165 records, the Pygmy Shrew is one of the least well mapped species in the atlas area, comparative to its likely population size.

The recording methodology is known for fewer than half of the records. Of these, 49% were of dead animals. Most were simply found in the open but records also included remains found in owl pellets, by-catch in pest-control devices and animals brought in by cats. Camera traps modified to record small mammals accounted for 44% of records. Three animals were also spotted opportunistically and two records refer to live-trapping for research.

BRITISH ISLES DISTRIBUTION, POPULATION AND TRENDS

Pygmy Shrews are native to Britain and also occur throughout Ireland, where they were probably introduced (Yalden, 1999). They occur widely from sea level up into mountains and have been recorded at the highest point in Britain, on the summit of Ben Nevis (Arnold, 1993). Of islands larger than 10 km², they are absent only from Shetland, Lewis and the Isles of Scilly. They are also present on many of the smaller islands (Churchfield & Searle, 2008b).

The British population has been estimated at 8,600,000, with 2,300,000 of these in Scotland although the degree of confidence in this estimate was considered to be low (Harris et al., 1995). Population trends in the British Isles are not known (Battersby et al., 2005).

NORTH-EAST SCOTLAND AND CAIRNGORMS DISTRIBUTION AND TRENDS

Pygmy Shrews are likely to occur across most of the atlas area. However, due to the difficulty of accurately recording the species, this is not at all well represented on the map, which shows a very thin scatter of records across much of the region. The apparent higher number of records in lowland parts of the region could simply be an artefact caused by recorder activity and the species has indeed been found on the highest parts of the Cairngorm plateau (Watson, 2013). Nothing is known about Pygmy Shrew population or distribution trends in the atlas area.

OBSERVING PYGMY SHREWS

It is rare to catch a glimpse of these animals in open ground and it is even less frequent that views sufficient to confidently identify the species are obtained. They can be difficult to differentiate in the field from the Common Shrew and although generally smaller, there may be an overlap in size between the two species. However, the Pygmy Shrew has a proportionally longer tail (around two thirds the length of their head and body), which is also thicker and hairier. The upper pelage is more uniform in colour (medium brown), lacking the paler flank of the Common Shrew.

Dead animals are sometimes found, as some predators find shrews to be distasteful and discard those that they catch. Camera traps optimised for recording small mammals provide the best opportunity for finding this species.

Image: Cambridgeshire, Mark Howes
Author: Rose Toney

DISTRIBUTION IN NORTH-EAST SCOTLAND AND THE CAIRNGORMS

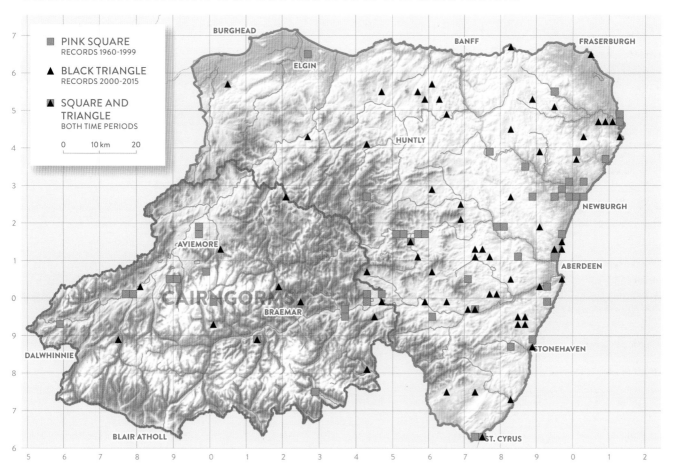

WATER SHREW

(Neomys fodiens)

HABITAT AND ECOLOGY

Water Shrews are small, highly active, semi-aquatic insectivores. They are predominately associated with freshwater habitats including fast flowing streams, rivers, ponds, fens and reedbeds. They are considered to favour waterbodies with dense patches of emergent and adjacent vegetation (Churchfield, 1998; French et al., 2001). However, they also utilise terrestrial habitats and individuals have been recorded up to 6 km from water (Churchfield, 1998).

Water Shrews have a broad diet, consuming both terrestrial and aquatic prey. Invertebrates predominate but they also take fish and amphibians (Churchfield, 1984; Kuvikova, 1985). Adaptions to a semi-aquatic lifestyle include having stiff hairs on their feet and tail to aid swimming (Churchfield, 1988), highly effective insulating fur (Vogel et al., 1998) and a large proportion of heat-producing brown fat (Hyvarinen, 1994). Perhaps one of the most surprising features is that the Water Shrew is Britain's only venomous mammal species. Their saliva contains a neurotoxin that is thought to enable them to subdue larger prey items (Churchfield, 1988).

MANAGEMENT AND CONSERVATION

Water Shrews are protected under Schedule 6 of the Wildlife and Countryside Act 1981, which means that they are protected from certain methods of killing and trapping. As a result, intentional trapping for Water Shrews (and other native UK shrew species) requires a licence.

The Water Shrew's diet of invertebrates, coupled with its assumed preference for well vegetated waterbodies, means that pollution and habitat modification of freshwaters could impact on the population. This, though, has never been systematically assessed.

RECORDS

Of the 70 records, the circumstances are known for 39. Animals found dead account for 44% of records, 38% came from camera trapping, particularly from camera traps set to target small mammals, and 18% were live sightings. Analysis of droppings left in baited tubes set specifically to target this species is a commonly used survey method (Churchfield et al., 2000) but was not known to account for any of the records mapped here.

BRITISH ISLES DISTRIBUTION, POPULATION AND TRENDS

The Water Shrew is native to Britain but has always been absent from Ireland (Churchfield, 1988). It is found throughout much of the mainland and is also found on many islands, including Skye, Mull, Arran and Hoy, but is thought to be relatively common only in England, Wales and southern Scotland (Carter & Churchfield, 2006).

The British population has been estimated to be 1.9 million in spring, with 400,000 of those in Scotland (Harris et al., 1995). Data on the population are not robust enough to assess trends.

NORTH-EAST SCOTLAND AND CAIRNGORMS DISTRIBUTION AND TRENDS

The map shows a relatively small number of records for Water Shrew distributed across the region. Although thought to be less common in this area than further south in Britain, it is likely that they are more numerous than local records might indicate. Being small, elusive and semi-aquatic they are not frequently encountered. Recent dedicated survey effort in the atlas area and beyond using baited tubes and camera traps has indicated that, where the habitat is suitable, the species is likely to be present. Hence large gaps on the map probably represent a lack of records rather than a lack of Water Shrews. However, it is clear that the species never reaches the densities of some other small mammals.

OBSERVING WATER SHREWS

The Water Shrew is the largest shrew species in the British Isles, weighing up to 18 g and with a head/body length of up to 97 mm. It has a pointy nose, black dorsal fur and a white belly (melanistic forms do occur) making it highly distinctive. The species is patchily distributed and is predominately active at dawn, dusk and during the hours of darkness. Hence, it is not an easy mammal to observe, with chance encounters being the most frequent means by which people see them. However, camera traps set up to record small mammals in areas of good Water Shrew habitat have been shown to be successful in the region.

Image: Red Moss of Netherley, Nick Littlewood
Author: James Davidson

DISTRIBUTION IN NORTH-EAST SCOTLAND AND THE CAIRNGORMS

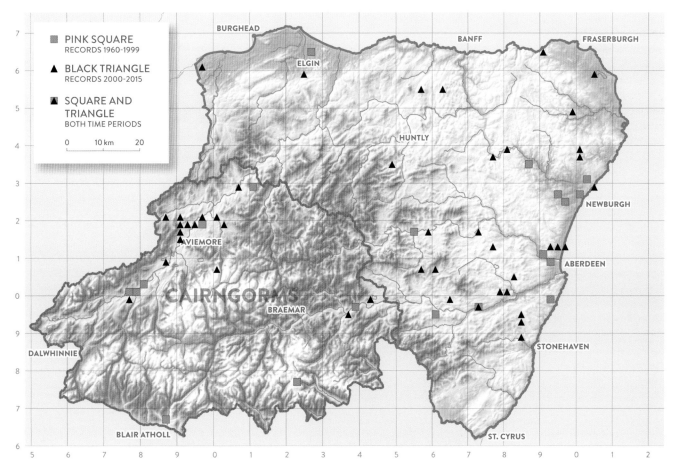

DAUBENTON'S BAT

(Myotis daubentonii)

HABITAT AND ECOLOGY

Daubenton's Bats are medium-sized bats with even, mole-like fur and very large hairy feet. They are darker brown on their dorsal surface and dirty white or grey below. They are most easily recognised by their habit of flying very low over fresh water, often flying only centimetres above the water surface, from where they hunt their prey, finding insects by echolocation.

Maternity roost sites, in which larger numbers of bats can be seen in one place, form in the summer months. In England and Wales, Daubenton's Bats form summer maternity roosts in crevices in bridges, tunnels and trees near to water and very occasionally in buildings. In northern England, the mean size of maternity roosts has been found to be 16 bats (Jones et al., 1996) though up to 100 bats can occupy a single maternity roost (Nyholm, 1965; Swift & Racey, 1983). In Scotland, maternity roosts have been more often found in buildings, in old stone houses or in churches with big roof spaces. In buildings the bats tend to roost in the open, along the ridge beam or on ledges and the buildings are always near to water or a short flight away along a suitable tree or hedge-lined flyway (Susan Swift pers. comm.). In winter, Daubenton's Bats hibernate underground in caves, mines, tunnels and cellars (Bat Conservation Trust, 2010b). Daubenton's Bats are long-lived, with some surviving for up to 20 years (Richardson et al., 2008).

MANAGEMENT AND CONSERVATION

All species of bats and their roosts (both, summer and winter roosts), are protected under the Conservation (Natural Habitats, &c.) Regulations 1994 (as amended).

The condition and management of inland wetlands and waterways are important to Daubenton's Bats. Trees are also important for a number of reasons. Trees surrounding favoured feeding sites increase insect diversity and shelter. Those with elevated and insulated cavities may also be used as summer maternity roosts and temporary night roosts during rain or weather that is otherwise unsuitable for hunting. The bats can be noisy in their summer roost sites during the day, which can be a good way to locate the trees that are being used. The removal of these waterside trees could pose a threat to Daubenton's Bat populations. Another potential threat is disturbance at their hibernation sites (Bat Conservation Trust, 2010b).

Daubenton's Bat is the main species in Britain harbouring the rabies-related European Bat Lyssavirus, which led to the death of a bat worker in Scotland in 2002, after he was bitten by a Daubenton's Bat.

RECORDS

Records of the presence of Daubenton's Bats in the atlas area have recently increased with the use of bat detectors, especially static detectors, which account for 88% of records for which the method of recording is known. Daubenton's Bats have mainly been recorded in the past by observers watching rivers or water bodies or looking for roosts in bridges or structures near water.

BRITISH ISLES DISTRIBUTION, POPULATION AND TRENDS

Daubenton's Bats are one of our most widespread bat species. They are found through most of the British Isles, although are rare in the far north-west of Scotland and absent in some of the Western Isles, Orkney and Shetland (Altringham, 2003). The British population of Daubenton's Bats is cautiously estimated at 150,000 with 40,000 in Scotland, 95,000 in England and 15,000 in Wales. (Harris et al., 1995). They occur at similar densities in Ireland, giving a population estimate there of 62,000 (Richardson et al., 2008).

Hibernation Surveys, as part of the Bat Conservation Trust's (BCT) National Bat Monitoring Programme, show a significantly increasing population trend for Daubenton's Bats. A similar, but non-significant, increase is apparent in the BCT Waterways Survey (Barlow et al., 2015). Possible reasons for this increase may include the growth in Britain in the number of artificial water bodies, reservoirs, flooded gravel pits and quarries. An increase in the bats' insect prey,

especially Chironomid midges, associated with reduced levels of pollution in water sources may also be a factor (Racey et al., 1998).

NORTH-EAST SCOTLAND AND CAIRNGORMS DISTRIBUTION AND TRENDS

The map reflects the Daubenton's Bat's foraging habits by showing the bats occurring along major waterways in the atlas area. They have been recorded all along the length of the Spey, and the Dee. There are also records from the other rivers including the Deveron, Ugie, Ythan and Don. The distribution of records of Daubenton's Bats is also influenced by recorder effort and further surveys are likely to reveal the species to be present in many more tetrads.

OBSERVING DAUBENTON'S BATS

Daubenton's Bats are fairly easy to observe in the atlas area. The bats emerge to feed approximately 45 minutes to an hour after dusk so are best observed on a moonlit night from an open vantage point, overlooking a quiet stretch of slow moving, tree-lined inland water.

Image: Mosset Burn near Forres, Mark Shewry
Author: Toni Watt

69

DISTRIBUTION IN NORTH-EAST SCOTLAND AND THE CAIRNGORMS

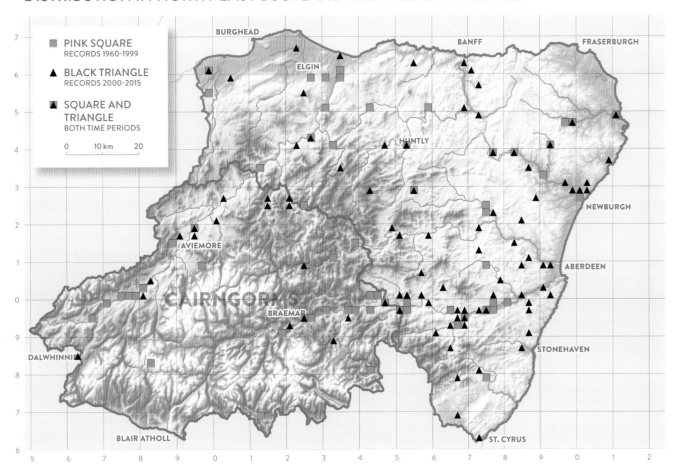

NATTERER'S BAT

(Myotis nattereri)

HABITAT AND ECOLOGY

Natterer's Bats are medium-sized bats that feed mainly on flies, caddisflies, spiders, harvestmen and beetles, caught in flight or picked off vegetation (Swift, 1997). They forage in woodland, parkland and near water using echolocation to catch their prey and may use a feeding perch to eat it. In the summer they mainly roost in trees but are most likely to be encountered where they roost in old buildings, such as farm steadings or large houses. Natterer's Bats will use gaps in walls and sometimes openly roost in attics. They are known to use bat boxes and to change roosts frequently (Smith & Rivers, 2008; Dodds & Bilston, 2013). Females roost together in maternity colonies in summer, while males roost in smaller numbers elsewhere. They leave the roost to forage approximately one hour after sunset. From December to February there is a lack of food and they need to hibernate, usually in cool cave-like sites such as tunnels.

MANAGEMENT AND CONSERVATION

The UK population is internationally significant (Smith & Rivers, 2008) and, as with all UK species of bats, is legally protected under the Conservation (Natural Habitats, &c.) Regulations 1994 (as amended). It is an offence to disturb, take or kill the species and also to damage or destroy its roosts. In the atlas area, Natterer's Bats are towards the northern limit of their range which may make them more vulnerable to changes in environmental conditions. The main risks to roosts are conversions of old buildings, inappropriate timber treatments and felling of trees that contain roosts. Bat surveys are often carried out where planning permission is sought for building conversions or where trees with potential to hold roosts are to be felled. Collins (2016) provides guidance on best practice for surveying.

RECORDS

Since 2000, there are 17 sites with records for Natterer's Bats in the atlas region. A quarter of these are non-breeding roosts in traditional farm steadings. There is a record of a maternity roost in a house in Speyside and one pre-2000 hibernation roost record of a single bat in a tunnel in the Angus Glens. The remainder of records are of foraging bats or dead bats. DNA analysis of bat droppings is sometimes used to provide a definitive species identification where *Myotis* sp. bats are present in a building.

BRITISH ISLES DISTRIBUTION, POPULATION AND TRENDS

Natterer's Bats are found widely across Britain and Ireland with the exception of the North-West Highlands and the Hebrides. However, they are relatively uncommon, especially towards the northern part of the range into the central Highlands. The British population has been estimated at 100,000 with 17,500 of these in Scotland (Harris et al., 1995) but this is based on limited information (Battersby et al., 2005; Smith & Rivers, 2008).

Bat Conservation Trust (BCT) volunteers carry out bat monitoring at Natterer's Bat roost and hibernation sites, as part of the National Bat Monitoring Programme. The hibernation count has shown an overall positive trend in numbers since the survey started in 1998. The colony count started in 2000 but has shown no significant trend. The increase in hibernation records could represent an increase in the number of Natterer's Bats but could also reflect other influences on the way that the bats use hibernation sites. A longer monitoring period will be required to establish if this is a sustained trend or due to yearly fluctuations (BCT/JNCC, 2014).

NORTH-EAST SCOTLAND AND CAIRNGORMS DISTRIBUTION AND TRENDS

Natterer's Bats appear to be scarce in the atlas area. Most records come from mid- to lower-Deeside, with additional records in Grantown, Morayshire and the Angus Glens. This possibly indicates an association with wooded river valleys. However, this is a difficult species to locate without the use of specialist survey techniques so the dearth of records may under-represent the species' true status. It is likely that more will be found with improvements in sound recording equipment and that surveyor bias will be reduced over time.

OBSERVING NATTERER'S BATS

Natterer's Bats are difficult to identify in the field as they are active in full darkness and their quiet calls are difficult to separate from Daubenton's and Brown Long-eared Bats without the use of specialist bat detectors. The North East Scotland Bat Group (NESBATS) organises bat walks and talks for those wishing to learn more about this and other bat species.

Image: Aberfoyle, Stirling, John Haddow
Author: Aileen Salway

71

DISTRIBUTION IN NORTH-EAST SCOTLAND AND THE CAIRNGORMS

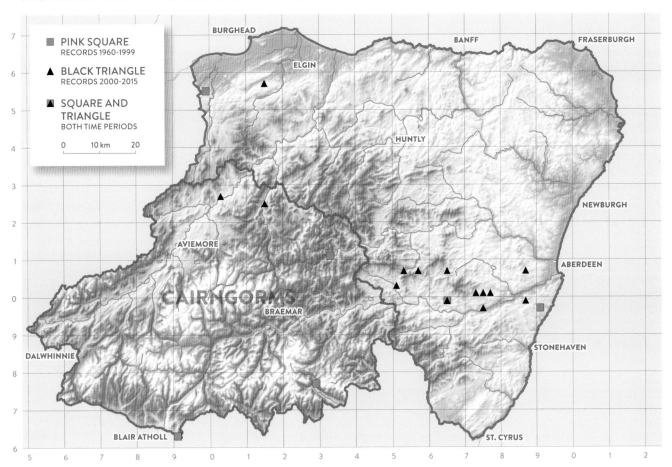

■ PINK SQUARE
RECORDS 1960-1999

▲ BLACK TRIANGLE
RECORDS 2000-2015

◣ SQUARE AND TRIANGLE
BOTH TIME PERIODS

0   10 km   20

LEISLER'S BAT

(Nyctalus leisleri)

HABITAT AND ECOLOGY

Leisler's Bats are large compared to other bat species in the atlas area, with a wingspan of around 30 cm. They emerge from their roosts rather early compared to many other species, typically 10 to 15 minutes after sunset. They fly fast and high, foraging along woodland edges, over pasture and over water bodies, where insect prey is caught and eaten in flight. In Britain and Ireland, known maternity roosts are mainly in the roof spaces of houses, with non-maternity roosts found in tree cavities and bat boxes (Shiel et al., 2008). In Scotland, known Leisler's Bat roosts are largely in trees. In Europe, long distance seasonal migrations have been described for Leisler's Bats but this has not been recorded in Britain or Ireland to date (Shiel et al., 2008).

MANAGEMENT AND CONSERVATION

Leisler's Bats are protected under the Conservation (Natural Habitats, &c.) Regulations 1994 (as amended). It is an offence to disturb, take or kill the species and also to damage or destroy its roosts. Roosts may be threatened by tree felling, tree surgery, building work on houses and inappropriate timber treatment. Given the importance of pasture to foraging Leisler's Bats, they may be particularly affected by the use of Ivermectin, a treatment used to control parasites of livestock, which can reduce the availability of insect prey (Floate et al., 2005; Shiel et al., 2008).

RECORDS

There are records from two sites in the atlas area which come from active bat detector use and bat detector recordings. Both records are from 2006 onwards.

BRITISH ISLES DISTRIBUTION, POPULATION AND TRENDS

Leisler's Bats are widespread and common in Ireland, but uncommon in Britain. Their known British range is primarily across central and southern parts of England so the atlas area falls well to the north of this. Recent survey effort has, though, shown them to be present across central and south-western Scotland (John Haddow, pers. comm.). The pre-breeding population has been estimated at 9,750 in England and 250 in Scotland (Harris et al., 1995) and may be increasing (Battersby et al., 2005). There are currently insufficient data to identify population trends (BCT/JNCC, 2014) and it is likely that the species has been under-recorded.

NORTH-EAST SCOTLAND AND CAIRNGORMS DISTRIBUTION AND TRENDS

There are records of Leisler's Bats from two sites in the atlas area. One or more were heard on a bat detector in the summer of 2006, flying near Maryculter in lower Deeside and foraging bats were recorded over several nights in September 2015 at Sand Loch near Collieston. Previously, in 1993, likely (but unconfirmed) Leisler's Bats were heard in Aberdeen and the lower reaches of the River Dee (Rydell et al., 1993). Further surveys are required to establish if the records are from resident, migrant or vagrant individuals.

OBSERVING LEISLER'S BATS

Bat detector recordings are the most likely means of identification. Sites of interest for further survey may be identified if larger bats with fast, high and direct flying characteristics are seen in the early evening and have "chip-chop" calls peaking around 23 kHz in the open, or 27 kHz in cluttered environments (Russ, 2012). They may resemble Noctules in flight and by sound though that species is not known to be present in the atlas area (but see page 125). They may be associated with water bodies near woodland and will sometimes make use of bat boxes.

Image: Wood of Cree, Dumfries and Galloway, John Haddow
Author: Aileen Salway

DISTRIBUTION IN NORTH-EAST SCOTLAND AND THE CAIRNGORMS

PINK SQUARE
RECORDS 1960-1999

BLACK TRIANGLE
RECORDS 2000-2015

SQUARE AND TRIANGLE
BOTH TIME PERIODS

0   10 km   20

COMMON PIPISTRELLE

(Pipistrellus pipistrellus)

HABITAT AND ECOLOGY

Common Pipistrelle and Soprano Pipistrelle are very similar in morphology and habit. They were considered to be a single species until the 1990s when they were separated into the two species that we now recognise (Jones & van Parijs, 1993) and this was later confirmed by genetic evidence (Racey et al., 2007). Of the two species, Common Pipistrelle is thought to be more generalist in terms of habitat requirements. However, they are broadly associated with woodlands and also with unimproved grassland and cattle pasture (Vaughan et al., 1997).

Common Pipistrelles roost in small crevices such as under slates, behind fascia boards, or in tree holes. They feed on a wide range of small insects. The bats use echolocation to navigate and catch their prey, which is usually consumed in flight. Common Pipistrelles are largely nocturnal and leave their roosts approximately 20 minutes after sunset, although may be seen during the day on occasions. They will feed all night if the temperature is high enough for insects to be flying. They occupy different roost types depending on the season and the gender of the bats. During the summer months, female Common Pipistrelles will gather together in maternity or nursery roosts which vary in size. Maternity roost size is significantly smaller than for Soprano Pipistrelle (Barlow & Jones, 1999). Males roost singly or in small numbers away from the maternity roosts. In winter, Common Pipistrelles hibernate in cool, damp locations such as cold buildings.

MANAGEMENT AND CONSERVATION

Common Pipistrelle populations have significantly declined in Britain since the mid-1900s, probably due to loss of roosting and feeding habitat (Stebbings, 1995), reductions in food availability caused by increased use of insecticides and the use of toxic timber treatments (Racey & Swift, 1986). As a result of this, all British bats and their roosts are protected by law.

Historical loss of elevated tree cavities has driven Common Pipistrelles to set up roosts in houses and other buildings that provide comparable conditions. This has inevitably brought them into some conflict with people using these buildings. However, they do not use any nesting materials, do not chew wires and, in many cases, have no significant impact on the buildings that they occupy.

RECORDS

Bats are very difficult to identify to species level without the use of a bat detector and it is perhaps because of this that most species are under-recorded. However, any records of 'Bat' (Chiroptera) provided by members of the public can be useful in supporting or targeting bat survey effort. Whilst the use of bat detectors by enthusiasts and professionals is thought to account for the majority of Common Pipistrelle reports in the atlas area, the method of recording and degree of rigour employed in identification is not known with certainty for a substantial proportion of the records that are mapped. Records have also been obtained by licensed professionals visiting roosts and identifying the bats in the hand. Bats are preyed upon by various predators, including the domestic cat, and this has provided a small number of records.

BRITISH ISLES DISTRIBUTION, POPULATION AND TRENDS

The Common Pipistrelle is native to the British Isles and is the most common of the British bats, occurring throughout mainland Britain and Ireland and on some islands. Although populations have declined significantly since the mid-1900s, the National Bat Monitoring Programme, run by the Bat Conservation Trust, indicates that there has been an upward trend since 1998 (Bat Conservation Trust, 2016a). It is difficult to place a number on the current population, due to very limited population data being available, but it is cautiously estimated to be 2,430,000 in the UK (Battersby et al., 2005).

NORTH-EAST SCOTLAND AND CAIRNGORMS DISTRIBUTION AND TRENDS

Common Pipistrelle is the most widely reported bat species in the atlas area though it remains under-recorded in some regions. There appear to be concentrations of records associated with some of the main areas of human habitation, such as Aberdeen, Stonehaven and Banchory. This may be due to increased roosting potential within buildings or a higher number of recorders. Few records come from upland areas, where suitable habitat is less common and climatic conditions less favourable. Records are also fewer in more arable areas in the north and east of the atlas area where large expanses of treeless habitat is likely to be a factor.

OBSERVING COMMON PIPISTRELLES

British bats are rarely seen during daylight. Common and Soprano Pipistrelles are among the earliest bats to leave their roosts at night, so are likely to be the most easily seen. The presence of droppings beneath roosts may also be evident. Echolocation calls are at a frequency above that normally heard by Humans. Social calls can sometimes be heard when close to a roost though it is difficult to identify these to species level without use of a bat detector and sound analysis software.

Image: East Sussex, © Hugh Clark/www.bats.org.uk
Author: Rachael Thwaites

DISTRIBUTION IN NORTH-EAST SCOTLAND AND THE CAIRNGORMS

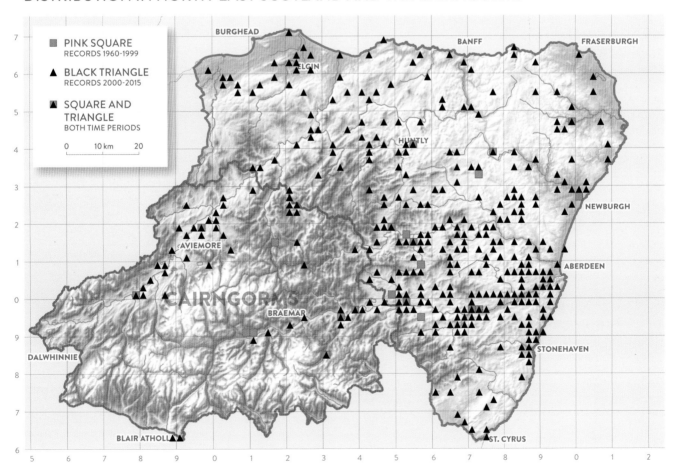

SOPRANO PIPISTRELLE

(Pipistrellus pygmaeus)

HABITAT AND ECOLOGY

Soprano Pipistrelle and Common Pipistrelle are very similar in morphology and habit. They were, until relatively recently, considered to be a single species, before being separated into two recognised species during the 1990s (Jones & van Parijs, 1993) with genetic evidence subsequently supporting this treatment (Racey et al., 2007). Both species evolved in woodland habitats, although Soprano Pipistrelle is now also more closely associated with riparian habitats than is Common Pipistrelle (Vaughan et al., 1997).

Soprano Pipistrelles roost in small crevices such as under slates, behind fascia boards, or in tree holes. They feed on a wide range of small insects, especially species associated with freshwater, using echolocation to navigate and catch their prey. Soprano Pipistrelles leave their roosts approximately 20 minutes after sunset and feed all night if the temperature is high enough for insects to be flying. They hibernate over the winter, when food resources are largely unavailable, in cool damp situations such as cold buildings. They occupy different roost types depending on the season and the gender of the bats. During the summer months, females gather together in maternity or nursery roosts that vary in size, but maternity roost size is significantly larger than that of Common Pipistrelle (Barlow & Jones, 1999). Males roost singly or in small numbers away from the maternity roosts.

MANAGEMENT AND CONSERVATION

Soprano Pipistrelle populations have significantly declined since the mid-1900s, probably due to a loss of roosting and feeding habitat (Stebbings, 1995), reductions in food availability due to increased use of insecticides and the use of toxic timber treatments (Racey & Swift, 1986). As a result of these factors, all British bats and their roosts are protected by law.

With a historical loss of elevated tree cavities, Soprano Pipistrelles have opportunistically exploited roost sites in houses and other buildings. This has inevitably brought some conflict with the people using these buildings. However, they do not use any nesting materials, the bats do not chew wires and, in many cases, they do not have a significant impact on the buildings that they occupy.

RECORDS

Bats are very difficult to identify to species level without the use of a bat detector. Whilst the use of bat detectors by enthusiasts and professionals is thought to account for most Soprano Pipistrelle reports in the atlas area, the method of recording and degree of rigour employed in identification is not know with certainty for a substantial proportion of the records that are mapped. In addition to bat detector records, some records have also been obtained by licensed professionals visiting roosts and identifying the bats in the hand. Bats are preyed upon by various predators, including the domestic cat, and this has provided a small number of records.

BRITISH ISLES DISTRIBUTION, POPULATION AND TRENDS

The Soprano Pipistrelle is native to the British Isles and is one of the most common of our bats, occurring throughout mainland Britain and Ireland and on some of the smaller islands. Populations of pipistrelle bats (Common and Soprano Pipistrelle combined) declined significantly since the mid-1900s. However, the National Bat Monitoring Programme, run by the Bat Conservation Trust, indicates that there has been an upward trend for Soprano Pipistrelle since 1998 (Bat Conservation Trust, 2016b). It is difficult to determine the current population, due to very limited data being available, but it is cautiously estimated to be 1,300,000 in the UK (Battersby et al., 2005).

NORTH-EAST SCOTLAND AND CAIRNGORMS DISTRIBUTION AND TRENDS

Soprano Pipistrelle is the second most widely recorded bat species in the atlas area, after Common Pipistrelle. There are concentrations of records around settlements such as Aberdeen, Banchory, Alford and Inverurie which may be due to increased roosting potential within buildings or a higher number of recorders in these areas. Few records come from upland areas. Compared with Common Pipistrelle, records in some areas are perhaps slightly more associated with waterways with, in particular, a concentration along mid- and lower-Deeside. Records are fewer in more arable areas in the north and east of the atlas area, where the large expanse of treeless habitat is likely to limit bat numbers. As with all bat species, Soprano Pipistrelle is likely to be under-recorded within the atlas area.

OBSERVING SOPRANO PIPISTRELLES

Soprano Pipistrelles are usually distinguished from Common Pipistrelles by differences in their echolocation calls. These calls are at a frequency above that normally heard by Humans though they can be picked up using a bat detector. Social calls can sometimes be heard when close to a roost and can also be identified to species using a bat detector and sound analysis software. The two species are very similar in appearance. Soprano Pipistrelles are usually slightly smaller with a dark 'mask' over the eyes. There are slight differences in wing venation. They leave their roosts before complete darkness and consequently are more easily seen than other, later-emerging, bats.

Image: Birkhall, Toni Watt
Author: Rachael Thwaites

DISTRIBUTION IN NORTH-EAST SCOTLAND AND THE CAIRNGORMS

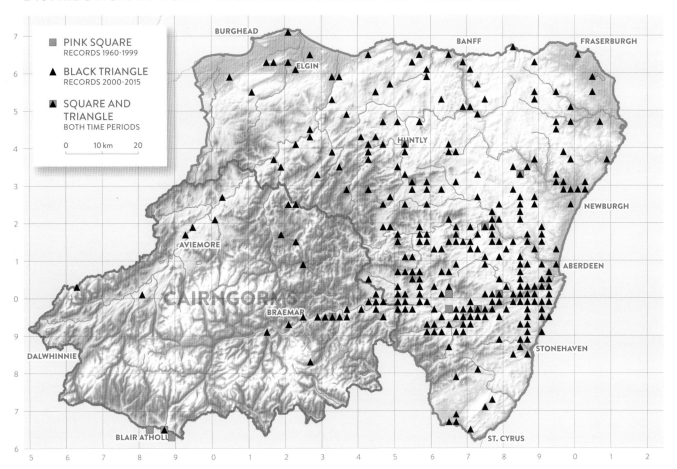

NATHUSIUS' PIPISTRELLE

(Pipistrellus nathusii)

HABITAT AND ECOLOGY

Nathusius' Pipistrelle is similar in appearance to the Common and Soprano Pipistrelles but is slightly larger with longer dorsal fur giving it a 'shaggy' appearance. Well studied in Continental Europe and Scandinavia, much less is known about the species in Britain and particularly in the atlas area.

The species is strongly associated with large areas of open water (Judes, 1989; Kapteyn, 1993; Vaughan et al., 1997). Its diet is predominantly composed of small fly species, often those with aquatic larval stages such as Chironomid midges, which it takes in the air (Beck, 1995; Vaughan, 1997).

MANAGEMENT AND CONSERVATION

Nathusius' Pipistrelles are protected by both domestic and international legislation. It is an offence to disturb, take or kill the species and also to damage or destroy its roosts.

As a migratory species (see below), collisions with wind turbines, especially coastal or offshore turbines, are a risk (Voigt et al., 2012). Where maternity roosts are located in trees or buildings, they can be damaged or destroyed by development/building works and land management activities.

RECORDS

The majority of UK records of the species come from surveys using acoustic bat detectors and 21 of the 22 records in the atlas are from this source. It is thought that the British Isles population peaks in September, boosted by incoming migrants, and so dedicated surveys for the species have taken place on open waterbodies close to the coast at that time of year. The species is also occasionally encountered on North Sea oil rigs.

BRITISH ISLES DITRIBUTION, POPULATION AND TRENDS

Nathusius' Pipistrelles are known to be migratory in Europe and Scandinavia, moving from their breeding areas in north-eastern parts of the continent in a generally south-westerly direction in autumn and returning in the spring (Roer, 1995). Furthermore, records from North Sea oil rigs and from waterbodies adjacent to coastal areas in the east in September suggest migration to Britain. However, it is known also to be a resident breeding species in parts of England and Ireland (Hutson, 1995; Russ et al., 1998; Russ et al., 2001).

The UK population is estimated to be 16,000 by Battersby et al. (2005). Population data are not robust enough to describe trends.

NORTH-EAST SCOTLAND AND CAIRNGORMS DISTRIBUTION AND TRENDS

The distribution map shows that there are five tetrads with records of Nathusius' Pipistrelle in the atlas area. All are close to the east coast and most records come from open bodies of water. The species has been predominantly recorded in late summer and autumn, however there are also records from mid-summer. This suggests that the species may be a year-round resident in the atlas area with a population boosted by autumn migrants. Due to the difficulties involved in detecting

this species, it is likely to be under-recorded in the region, though it is clearly the least common of the three pipistrelle species.

OBSERVING NATHUSIUS' PIPISTRELLES

Nathusius' Pipistrelles are small, nocturnal bats that are strongly associated with large waterbodies and are likely to be present in the atlas area in relatively low densities, though numbers might locally be higher if there are maternity roosts in the area. Due to this, it is a difficult species to observe. Their echolocation calls, which are strongest at around 39 kHz, are lower-pitched than those of Common or Soprano Pipistrelle. Therefore, for those with acoustic bat detectors and the ability to record and analyse calls, there is a significant opportunity to add to knowledge of the species by focusing any detecting and recording effort on open waterbodies in the region.

Image: East Sussex, © Hugh Clark/www.bats.org.uk
Author: James Davidson

DISTRIBUTION IN NORTH-EAST SCOTLAND AND THE CAIRNGORMS

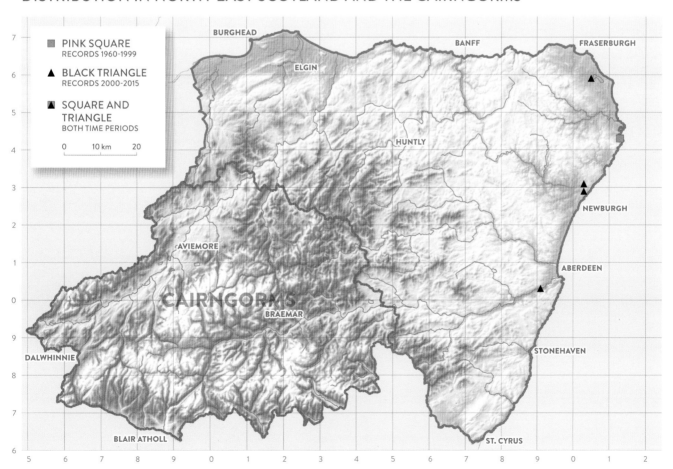

BROWN LONG-EARED BAT

(Plecotus auritus)

HABITAT AND ECOLOGY

Brown Long-eared Bats feed on insects, often gleaned off foliage during slow flight among trees and shrubs. Prey is detected using echolocation and their diet includes moths, beetles, flies, earwigs and spiders (Bat Conservation Trust, 2010a). Brown Long-eared Bats are found in wooded areas, preferring open deciduous woodland (Entwistle & Swift, 2008). Woodland edges are often used for foraging. Non-native conifer plantations are generally avoided, apart from their edges. In summer, they roost in buildings and trees, breeding in small colonies of about 20 females. These bats have a preference for large roost spaces that facilitate indoor flight before emerging to forage outdoors. Winter roosts tend to be located in underground structures such as caves, ice-houses, or north-facing, protected, thick stone walls of older buildings. These provide the stable environmental conditions that are necessary for hibernation.

MANAGEMENT AND CONSERVATION

All bats and their roosts are legally protected in Scotland by the Conservation (Natural Habitats, &c.) Regulations 1994 (as amended). Roosts are protected throughout the year even when bats are absent, i.e. a summer roost site is protected during winter months.

Threats to Brown Long-eared Bats include poisoning from timber treatment and loss and fragmentation of habitat through loss of deciduous woodland (Harris et al., 1995). Conversion of steadings and barns for residential use, as well as renovation of dwellings are also a potential risk to bat roosts. Works which could impact Brown Long-eared Bats or their roosts may require a licence from Scottish Natural Heritage.

RECORDS

Sources of records for this species include records from Scottish Natural Heritage (47%). These include data from visits to home owners with bat issues, as well as historic records. The Bat Conservation Trust's national monitoring programme accounts for 11% of records and the remainder come from a mix of commercial surveys, ranger services and individual reports. Typically, identification at species level for bats is made via survey methods including bat detector recordings and sound analysis, in-field observation of foraging bats, identification of bats in the roost or through identification and recording of droppings.

BRITISH ISLES DISTRIBUTION, POPULATION AND TRENDS

The Brown Long-eared Bat is the third most common bat species in Britain, after the Common and Soprano Pipistrelles. They occur throughout Britain and Ireland, except in mountainous and exposed regions of North-West Scotland and offshore islands (Harris et al., 1995). Out of a population estimate of 245,000 in the UK, the number in Scotland is estimated at 27,500 (Battersby et al., 2005). This was one of the most widely distributed bat species at the beginning of the 20th century and outnumbered all other bats in the north of mainland Scotland (Entwistle & Swift, 2008). While numbers have declined since then, the current trend is unclear. It is thought that the loss of roost sites in roof spaces, the use of organochloride pesticides in timber treatment and habitat loss may have caused a substantial decline (Harris et al., 1995). More recently, though, national data from the Bat Conservation Trust suggest that that there is no significant trend of decline or increase based on hibernation and roost count monitoring between 1998 and 2014 (BCT/JNCC 2014).

NORTH-EAST SCOTLAND AND CAIRNGORMS DISTRIBUTION AND TRENDS

The Brown Long-eared Bat's distribution in the atlas area reflects the wider pattern of avoidance of open mountainous areas. Although probably under-recorded in the atlas area, the map does show that the majority of records are associated with rivers and tributaries. This is due to roost selection for sites closer to deciduous woodland and foraging opportunities linked with watercourses (Entwhistle et al., 1997). Records for the coastal zones and the less wooded and exposed Buchan plateau are sparse, while Deeside and Speyside, both well-wooded river valleys, feature the most records.

OBSERVING BROWN LONG-EARED BATS

Brown Long-eared Bats are most easily observed close to their roosts either around sunset or just before dawn on warm summer nights. With their preference for larger roof spaces, this species can often be observed in the parkland grounds of mansions. The Brown Long-eared Bat is also known as the 'whispering bat' as its echolocation calls are very quiet compared to other species. A bat detector can, therefore, be useful to eliminate some noisier bat species though calls are nonetheless sometimes masked by those of other species. The long 'rams-horn' shaped ears that give the bat its name can often be seen in flight.

81

Image: Birkwood, Lanarkshire, John Haddow
Author: Steff Ferguson

DISTRIBUTION IN NORTH-EAST SCOTLAND AND THE CAIRNGORMS

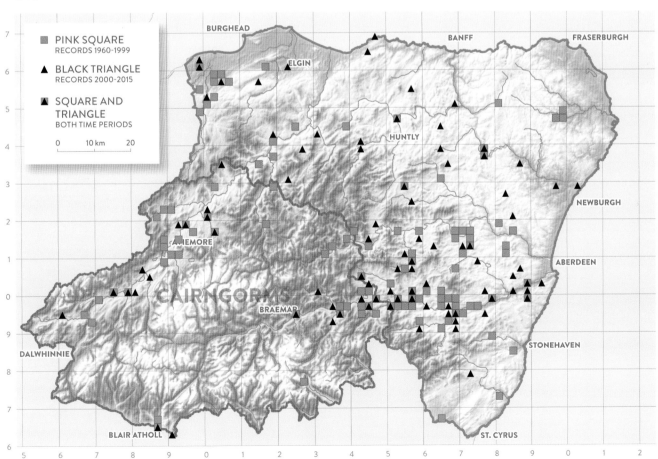

■ PINK SQUARE
RECORDS 1960-1999

▲ BLACK TRIANGLE
RECORDS 2000-2015

▲ SQUARE AND TRIANGLE
BOTH TIME PERIODS

0   10 km   20

SCOTTISH WILDCAT AND FERAL CAT

(Felis silvestris and *Felis catus)*

Wildcats and Feral Cats are closely related species. In line with Wilson & Reeder (2005), we refer to them here as separate species though they are sometimes regarded as part of the same species (e.g. Driscoll et al., 2007). Although having different histories in the British fauna, the management, conservation and status of these animals are closely interwoven and, hence, they are treated here in a single combined account.

HABITAT AND ECOLOGY

The atlas area has populations of Scottish Wildcats (hereafter referred to as Wildcat), feral domestic cats (Feral Cat) and cats which are hybrids of these two. Wildcats are generally larger than Feral Cats, on average by about 1 kg, with characteristic markings that are distinct from feral tabby cats. Wildcats and Feral Cats are rarely found at high altitudes, preferring lower-level straths and glens. Both species use habitat boundaries for foraging, such as forest edges, field margins and scrub habitats. Grassland is preferred over moorland though Wildcats may be less inclined to use open grassland habitats than Feral Cats. Feral Cats are also more common around human settlements, farm steadings and industrial sites.

The favoured prey of the Wildcat is Rabbit (Malo et al., 2004) but small rodents, such as voles, probably form the main component of their diet in areas of Scotland where Rabbits are scarce. Other items, such as hares and birds, are also taken. Feral Cats have similar prey preference to Wildcats, but their smaller size means that larger prey, such as adult Rabbits and hares, are likely to be less favoured.

Female Wildcat home ranges typically cover around 2 km² in the east of Scotland (Corbett, 1979; Daniels et al., 2001), though they are larger in the west (Scott et al., 1992). Male Wildcat home ranges may encompass several female ranges. Feral Cat home ranges vary widely according to food availability.

Wildcats breed in winter, giving birth to usually three to four kittens in the spring, after a gestation of about 68 days (Hartmann, 2005). Later births are common, though. Kittens are independent at four to five months and males are sexually mature at nine to ten months (Macdonald et al., 2004). Reproduction in Feral Cats is similar, though the gestation period may be slightly shorter (63 days) and the timing of breeding less seasonal (Daniels et al., 2002) with multiple litters per year possible.

Wildcats are usually solitary while Feral Cats can be either solitary or gregarious, depending on food availability. Group-living female Feral Cats may aid in the rearing of the kittens of related mothers. Wildcats make use of a wide variety of den sites, including rocky cairns, brash piles, burrows of other species, wind-blown conifer trees and uninhabited buildings.

MANAGEMENT AND CONSERVATION

The Wildcat has been legally protected in the UK since 1988 and is a European Protected Species. Feral Cats are classed as non-native. They can be legally controlled by land managers and a licence from Scottish Natural Heritage is required for their release into the wild. Due mainly to persecution, the range of the Wildcat contracted to a small area in the far north-west of Scotland by around 1915 (Langley & Yalden, 1977). Persecution reduced following World War I and the Wildcat range gradually expanded into areas solely occupied by domestic and Feral Cats. Range expansion may also have been aided by changes in forestry after the creation of the Forestry Commission in 1919. It is perhaps at this point that interbreeding between Wildcats and domestic cats began to occur commonly. Today, the frequency of hybridisation in the population is higher than recorded for any Wildcat population in mainland Europe (Macdonald et al., 2004).

Ongoing hybridisation is the chief threat facing the Wildcat. It is likely that most individual Wildcats now carry some domestic cat heritage (e.g. Littlewood et al., 2014) and ongoing conservation efforts are concentrating on ensuring that those individuals with the lowest proportion of domestic cat ancestry are able to survive and breed. Since hybrid cats are not legally protected and distinguishing between Wildcats and hybrids can be difficult (Kitchener et al., 2005), accidental persecution is also a threat to remaining Wildcats. Mortality may also be caused by collisions with road traffic and disease transfer from Feral Cats.

In addition to the threat that they cause to Wildcats, where artificially high densities of Feral Cats are maintained through supplementary feeding they are a serious threat as predators of native wildlife (Woods et al., 2003; Baker et al., 2005). Lethal control by land managers and Trap, Neuter and Release (TNR) programmes are the main methods for managing Feral Cat populations.

RECORDS

Most of the 488 Wildcat records used for compiling the map are known or presumed to be of sightings. The degree to which such records refer to Wildcats or hybrids is notoriously difficult to assess. An inclusive approach is taken to compiling the Wildcat map here with all animals reported as Wildcats or hybrids included, unless there were specific reasons to believe that the record was more likely to refer to a Feral Cat or a domestic cat. This inevitably means that the range of records shown for Wildcat may be significantly larger than the actual current distribution of animals that most closely match the conventional definition of a Wildcat.

The increased use of camera traps has greatly enabled the submission of verifiable records with 9% being of this type. Recent intensive camera trap surveys, specifically targeting Wildcats in Aberdeenshire, the Cairngorms National Park and elsewhere (Hetherington & Campbell, 2012; Littlewood et al., 2014; Kilshaw et al., 2016), have provided a clearer picture of the status and distribution of both Wildcats and Feral Cats in some localities. The other main source of information is from road casualties, providing 4% of records. Records from scats and tracks have not been included in the maps, due to the difficulty in distinguishing between Wildcat and Feral Cat, or distinguishing cat scats from those of other carnivores.

Relatively few records refer specifically to Feral Cats. It can be difficult to distinguish between a Feral Cat and a domestic cat, whilst many cats may live an intermediate existence. Most records mapped here as Feral Cat are from sightings or camera trap records.

BRITISH ISLES DISTRIBUTION, POPULATION AND TRENDS

Scotland hosts the most northerly wild population of any *Felis silvestris*. Wildcats are currently restricted to an area of Scotland north of the central belt (but including the Kintyre peninsula) and they are not known from any of the Scottish islands. Harris et al. (1995) reported an estimate of 3,500 adult Wildcats, though this undoubtedly included hybrid cats. Based on Daniels et al.'s (1998) finding that 12% of wild-living cats, in what was regarded as a Wildcat stronghold, possessed a traditional Wildcat pelage, Macdonald et al. (2004) updated this estimate to arrive at a total population of 400 individuals, suggesting that the population of hybrid cats numbered approximately 3,000. This estimate is further complicated by recent findings that the relationship between pelage and genetics is imperfect (i.e. some cats with traditional Wildcat pelage showed significant levels of domestic cat genetic ancestry and vice versa (Littlewood et al., 2014)).

Davis & Gray's (2010) survey, conducted in 2006-2008, found no evidence of a change in the distribution of the Wildcat since the previous survey in 1983-1987 (Balharry & Daniels, 1998). They suggested that the population in core areas had remained stable, but also stated that many questionnaire responses commented on a decline. Daniels et al.'s (1998) finding that 12% of wild-living cats in an area regarded as a Wildcat stronghold looked like traditional Wildcats closely matches Littlewood et al.'s (2014) figure of 13%, also suggesting stable Wildcat populations in core areas. These assessments should be treated cautiously, however, as they may conceal an underlying decline in the genetic status of remaining Wildcats.

Reliable population estimates of Feral Cats are difficult to obtain because they have quite a varied relationship with Humans. This ranges from wild-living Feral Cats that obtain all their food from hunting through colonies that rely on concentrated food sources (either human food waste or human food hand-outs) to free-living domestic cats that are associated with one or more households. Harris et al. (1995) estimated a British population of 813,000 Feral Cats. In Scotland, this estimate was 130,000 of which 125,000 were in rural areas. Data from the National Gamebag Census indicate no significant change in rural Feral Cat numbers in Scotland, though there has been a significant decline in the UK as a whole (Aebischer et al., 2011).

NORTH-EAST SCOTLAND AND CAIRNGORMS DISTRIBUTION AND TRENDS

North-East Scotland and the Cairngorms contained the highest proportion of survey squares containing Wildcats during the 2006-2008 survey (Davis & Gray, 2010). The atlas area was also considered to have good populations during the 1983-1987 survey (Balharry & Daniels, 1998). The best areas are on the lower ground within the Cairngorm National Park (Badenoch and Strathspey, Strathavon, Strathdon, Deeside, the Angus Glens and Blair Atholl) and in the foothills of the Grampian Mountains that run from Keith south to Banchory. Indeed three of the six zones across Scotland that are regarded as priorities for Wildcat conservation lie within these areas. There are few or no records in areas around Fraserbugh, Aberdeen and coastal Moray. No trends are known for the atlas area, though it is likely that, as elsewhere, the Wildcat population is experiencing increased hybridisation.

OBSERVING WILDCATS AND FERAL CATS

Wildcats, hybrids and feral tabby cats can be difficult to distinguish though a broad, blunt-tipped tail with well separated black hoops is a good starting point for a Wildcat identification.

All wild-living cats use habitat edges to hunt so forest margins, especially next to rank grassland or areas of clear-fell forestry, are an ideal place to observe them. Scrub areas, such as Gorse or Juniper thickets, are also commonly used by cats and areas with plenty of Rabbits and voles will be favoured. Plantation forestry with mixed ages of conifer stands, including clear-felled blocks, are especially favoured by Wildcats for hunting and shelter. Wildcats make use of quieter roads and forest tracks, particularly at night, though where forestry areas have low human disturbance, Wildcats can be active during daylight.

Image (page 82): NE Scotland, Alan Ross
Image (below): Wildcat caught on camera trap at Foudland, Yzanne Turbett
Authors: Roo Campbell & Emma Rawling

Bushnell Ⓜ Camera Name   30°F-1°C ◐   12-22-2013 12:23:39

SCOTTISH WILDCAT DISTRIBUTION IN NORTH-EAST SCOTLAND AND THE CAIRNGORMS

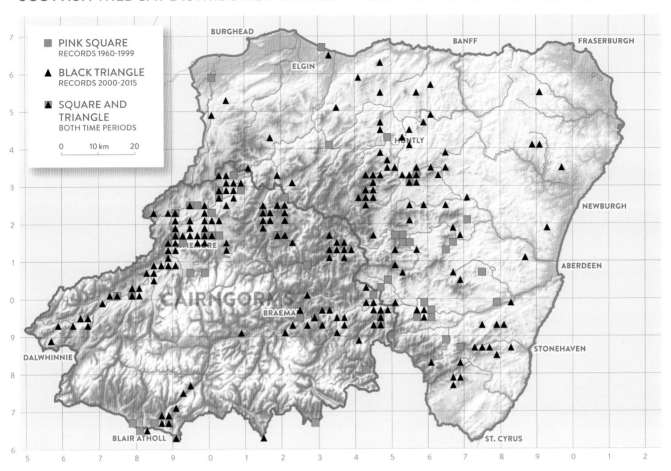

FERAL CAT DISTRIBUTION IN NORTH-EAST SCOTLAND AND THE CAIRNGORMS

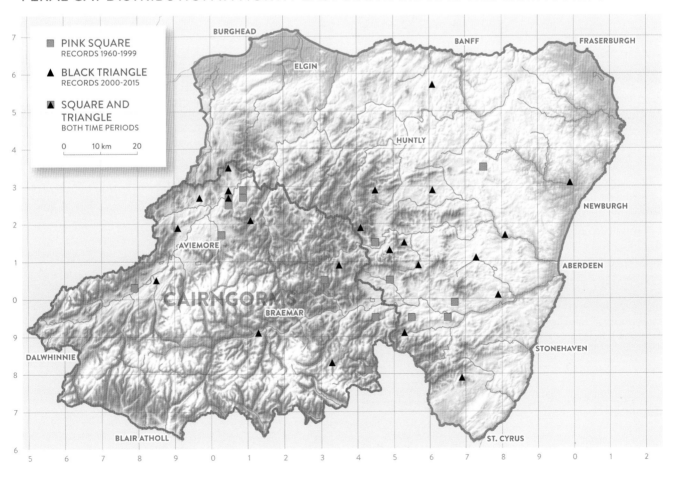

FOX

(Vulpes vulpes)

HABITAT AND ECOLOGY

The Fox is a native carnivorous mammal. It is mainly nocturnal and feeds predominantly on small mammals such as Rabbits, Wood Mice and Field Voles (Baker & Harris, 2008). However, it will scavenge for anything it can find including carrion, invertebrates, amphibians, fruit and, especially in urban areas, food discarded by people. Foxes utilise a diversity of habitats and will commonly use habitat edges to forage.

Female Foxes (vixens) can breed when 10 months old, usually giving birth to four or five cubs. Family groups can share a joint territory, usually moving between several dens, or "earths", dug out of the ground during the breeding season, but males (dog Foxes) will move into other territories in search of a mate in December to February. Old Rabbit burrows can be adapted and a sett may even be shared with Badgers (Baker & Harris, 2008). Foxes hold territories, the size of which varies depending on habitat and prey availability. These can be smaller than 0.1 km² in urban areas or up to 40 km² in hill country. Outside the breeding season, dense cover is preferred and a den will only be used in bad weather. The main causes of Fox deaths are roadkill, shooting and the mite induced disease known as sarcoptic mange (Baker & Harris, 2008).

MANAGEMENT AND CONSERVATION

Foxes are continually in conflict with Humans. They have long been perceived as a pest species by gamekeepers and farmers since they will prey opportunistically on poultry, game birds and birds' eggs. In confined situations where penned prey cannot escape and the stimulus to kill remains at close quarters, Foxes may kill multiple times. Foxes can also come into conflict with some conservation interests and have been linked to the decline in the Capercaillie population (e.g. Baines et al., 2011). The Protection of Wild Mammals (Scotland) Act 2002 made it illegal to use traditional hunting with dogs to kill Foxes, although they may still be flushed out by dogs for shooting under certain circumstances. Shooting of Foxes is permitted only with the appropriate firearms licence.

RECORDS

In recent years the use of camera traps has been useful for highlighting Fox activity and 9% of our records are a product of this method. Urban Foxes can frequently be seen scavenging in city streets at night and may visit the same gardens nightly. Foxes are quite often killed on roads and 9% of our records are described as roadkill.

BRITISH ISLES DISTRIBUTION, POPULATION AND TRENDS

Foxes are found throughout mainland Britain and Ireland though are thought to be absent from all of the Scottish islands apart from Skye (Harris & Lloyd, 1991). The rural population in Great Britain has been estimated at around 225,000 (Webbon et al., 2004) with an urban population estimated at 33,000 (Harris et al., 1995). The overall Scottish population is thought to be around 23,000 (Battersby et al., 2005). The UK Fox population increased through most of the 20th century (Battersby et al., 2005) though this trend appears to have reversed in more recent years with numbers falling significantly between 1995 and 2014 (Harris et al., 2015).

NORTH-EAST SCOTLAND AND CAIRNGORMS DISTRIBUTION AND TRENDS

Foxes occur widely across the atlas area. Although records from mountainous areas are rare, Foxes are recorded at all altitudes up to the highest parts of the Cairngorms (e.g. Watson, 2013). They can be found in just about any habitat such as upland heath, lowland farmland, dunes and beaches, remote forests and even busy urban areas. The greatest concentration of records is along the eastern side of the region from Aberdeen north to Fraserburgh. Although this may in part reflect observer activity, it is also likely that low-lying productive farmland in this area is capable of supporting a high density of Foxes. Records are sparser in some of the more intensively managed grouse moor areas where numbers are kept low by active gamekeeping.

Fox records in urban areas appear to have increased in recent years. This could be attributed to a rise in the number of active recorders in urban areas but is more likely to indicate a trend towards increased use of urban areas by Foxes, linked to food availability.

OBSERVING FOXES

In the countryside, Foxes are elusive creatures but identification is easy for observers since there is no similar species. As for field signs, Fox droppings are normally black when fresh, often with a distinctive twist at one end and are 5 to 20 cm long (Baker & Harris, 2008). There is often a strong musky smell where a Fox territory has been scent marked.

In urban locations, Foxes are less fearful of people and can be seen occasionally at night, touring the streets in search of discarded food.

Image: Girdle Ness, Paul Chapman
Authors: Glenn Roberts & Joe Malster

DISTRIBUTION IN NORTH-EAST SCOTLAND AND THE CAIRNGORMS

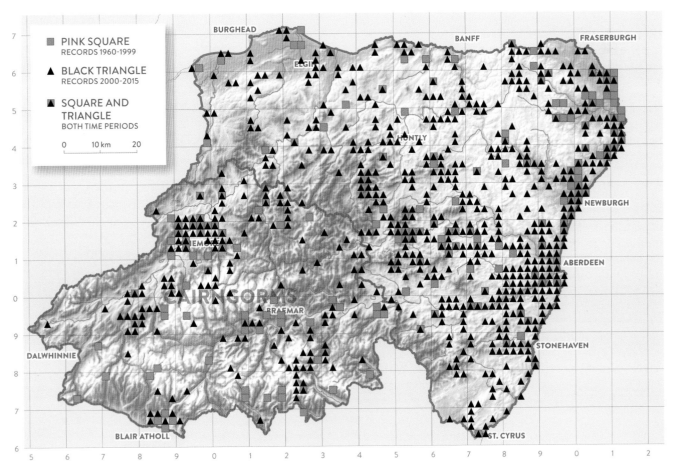

BADGER

(Meles meles)

HABITAT AND ECOLOGY

Badgers are highly social animals, with each 'clan' or social group normally associated with a single main sett (Kruuk, 1989). The setts are extensive earthworks, most often on slopes, with, typically, three to ten large entrances. In the atlas area, the setts are encountered in conifer, deciduous and mixed woods, scrub, Bracken, moorland and fields. Setts can also be found in man-made habitats including beneath buildings, on road or rail embankments and cuttings, cairns, sandpits, quarry spoil, and rubbish dumps.

Badgers are opportunistic omnivores, eating whatever happens to be available and edible in a particular locality at a given time. Their diet includes earthworms, slugs, snails, insects, Rabbits (especially kits), Moles, Hedgehogs, carrion, ground nesting birds' eggs and chicks, fruit, grain and Pignut tubers (Roper, 2010).

MANAGEMENT AND CONSERVATION

The Protection of Badgers Act, 1992 (as amended in Scotland) prohibits Badgers being wilfully killed, injured or taken, or disturbed whilst occupying a sett. Badger setts are protected from damage or destruction and their entrances from obstruction.

In the atlas area, Badgers are neither rare nor endangered. Road kills are frequent, some human persecution occurs and urban expansion, road building and other developments remain a threat. Under certain circumstances a licence may be obtained through Scottish Natural Heritage to close down a sett; for example, construction of the Aberdeen Western Peripheral Route, which commenced in 2015, has necessitated some sett closures and the establishment of artificial ones.

RECORDS

Known setts account for 53% of the records. Road kills make up 27%, whereas camera trapping and Badger signs each contribute 8% of records. Live sightings account for only 4% of records. A strong link with farmland is confirmed by the distribution map. However, Badgers are also recorded well into hill country and finding their prints in snow at fairly high altitude is not exceptional. Perhaps the most intriguing record is of a Badger reported "in a Fox's mouth".

BRITISH ISLES DISTRIBUTION, POPULATION AND TRENDS

Following centuries of being hunted for food, pelts and dug and baited for sport, then persecuted as vermin, Badger populations started to recover after World War I, perhaps linked to a decline in gamekeeper numbers. By the early 1930s, Badgers were reported to be fairly common in suitable areas all over England and Wales (Neal & Cheeseman, 1996). Neal (1948) considered

Badgers to be well distributed and locally numerous across Great Britain and Ireland, though adding the rider that there were parts of England and Scotland where Badgers were decidedly rare.

Surveys of Badger populations in Great Britain were undertaken in 1985-88 and 1994-97, with main setts increasing from an estimated 41,900 to 50,240 (Wilson et al., 1997). The mean adult social group size from British studies is approximately five (Byrne et al., 2012). A survey of main setts in Scotland in 2006-09 provided an estimated 7,300 to 11,200, depending upon the statistical assumptions made (Rainey et al., 2009). The same survey reported a moderately high density in Grampian (0.22 main setts/km²) though the densities in Tayside (0.04 main setts/km²) and Highland (0.03 main setts/km²) were much lower.

NORTH-EAST SCOTLAND AND CAIRNGORMS DISTRIBUTION AND TRENDS

Sim (1903) reported that Badgers in Aberdeenshire and Kincardine were fast approaching extinction. Clearly though, as elsewhere in Britain, Badger populations increased during the second half of the 20th century. Nethersole-Thompson & Watson (1974) reported that Badgers were scarce but widely distributed throughout Deeside, that their numbers had increased greatly in Morayshire and that they were widespread in the Spey Valley and in the lower glens of Atholl, Glen Shee and Angus. As the map shows, Badgers are now present in almost all lowland areas east of the Cairngorms as well as in Speyside and in lowland parts of Moray. There are very few records from higher ground within the Cairngorms which probably reflects genuine scarcity in these areas.

In 1989, the late Mike Harris initiated a comprehensive Badger survey in Banff/Buchan and Gordon districts. Whilst the unpublished sett records remain in private hands, they do indicate that official surveys greatly underestimate Badger density in North-East Scotland. Harris's survey indicated that main sett density increased in Moray, Aberdeenshire and Aberdeen City between 1988 and 2009. The Scottish Badger survey estimated that there were around 1,930 main setts in Grampian, with Badger density being greater in Moray than in Aberdeenshire (Rainey et al., 2009).

OBSERVING BADGERS

For Badger study, one should search for setts, which are often well hidden. Walk fence lines and other boundaries, seeking Badger signs, such as hair on barbed wire fencing, prints, snuffle holes and latrines. Follow tracks from fields into woodland, or other appropriate habitat, then investigate slopes and areas of dense cover. If watching for animals emerging from a sett, sit quietly, downwind of the entrance. Mid-summer is best as Badgers will often emerge then before dark.

Image: Mid-Deeside, Harry Scott
Author: Eric Jensen

DISTRIBUTION IN NORTH-EAST SCOTLAND AND THE CAIRNGORMS

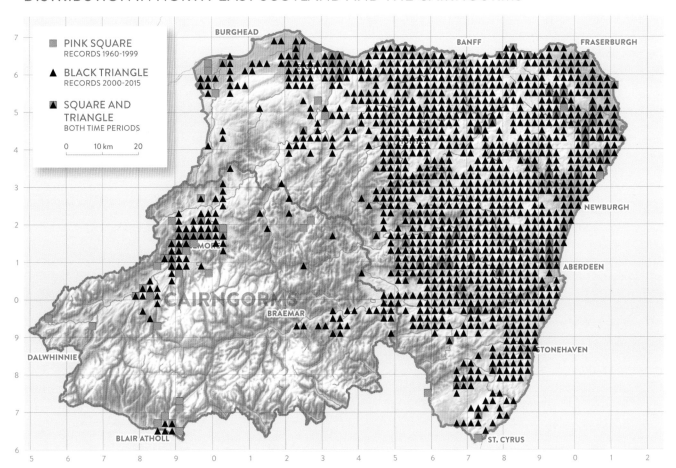

OTTER

(Lutra lutra)

HABITAT AND ECOLOGY

Optimal habitat for Otters includes lakes, rivers, streams, marshes, coasts and estuaries that hold good populations of uncontaminated prey. Fish dominate in the Otter's diet, but they will also take amphibians, birds, small mammals and invertebrates.

Riparian home ranges can extend over tens of kilometres and encompass a patchwork of habitats. Otters are largely nocturnal and hunting trips of 3-10 km are made each night. The use of different habitats appears to be dependent on prey abundance and may include both urban and agricultural areas. Otters use resting sites (holts or couches) which provide some degree of cover. These vary from bracken thickets and reed-beds to tree root dens, rock falls, peat burrows and tunnels, with individuals using many different sites within their home ranges (Chanin, 2003; Kruuk, 2006).

MANAGEMENT AND CONSERVATION

In the past, Otters have been hunted for sport and pelts and were considered a pest by food and sport fisheries (Jefferies & Woodroffe, 2008). Now, Otters are a European Protected Species and are fully protected under The Conservation (Natural Habitats, &c.) Regulations 1994. The species' present status globally is classed as 'near threatened' and decreasing (IUCN, 2015). Road mortality is one of the chief causes of Otter

deaths in many areas (Jefferies & Woodroffe, 2008) and Otters are also known to drown in creels, eel fyke nets and fish traps. Fish productivity affects the number of Otters that an area will support and the severe decline in European Eels, a favoured prey item, may be adversely affecting the Otter population in Scotland and elsewhere (Kruuk, 2014).

RECORDS

Otter records include spraints (faeces) (45% of records for which the circumstances are documented), footprints (22%), live sightings (15%), road casualties (5%), and animals captured on camera traps (4%). Spraints are a useful indication of the presence of Otters in an area, but not of the number of Otters present.

Camera traps are providing valuable new information on Otter ecology and behaviour, including on the presence of cubs. Additionally, advances in DNA technology permitting the identification of individual Otters from spraints may help to build accurate estimates of population size and structure in the future (O'Meara et al., 2012; O'Neill et al., 2013).

BRITISH ISLES DISTRIBUTION, POPULATION AND TRENDS

Otter numbers in some parts of the UK suffered a devastating decline between 1957 and the 1980s. This was linked with organochlorine insecticides that were used for cereal dressings and sheep dip and which are now banned (Chanin, 2003). Fortunately, many areas of Scotland, including the atlas area, were largely spared this decline such that in the mid-1980s, an estimated 6,600 animals from a British population of 7,350 were in Scotland (Harris et al., 1995). Water quality improvement and recovering fish stocks are thought to have assisted in the Otter's recolonisation of much of its former range in England and Wales. They are now distributed widely, although unevenly, throughout most of Britain and Ireland (Crawford, 2011).

In Scotland, the fourth national survey of Otters confirmed that the species had consolidated its range and was ubiquitous (Strachan, 2007). Now, Otters are even frequenting highly disturbed waterways, including those in urban centres, where they seem largely unaffected by human activity.

NORTH-EAST SCOTLAND AND CAIRNGORMS DISTRIBUTION AND TRENDS

The distribution of Otters largely reflects the species' use of freshwater habitats. However, Otter signs have also been found well away from waterways, left by animals moving between foraging locations. With the exception of the Cairngorms massif, large areas on the map that are lacking in records are more likely to reflect a relative absence of observers than of Otters.

Otters require a source of freshwater to maintain good coat condition when foraging on the coast, so stretches of coast without rivers, streams or adjacent lochs are unsuitable habitat. This applies to some stretches in the atlas area and most coastal records are concentrated at the mouths of rivers such as the Dee, Don, Ythan and Spey.

In the upland areas of the Cairngorms, most watercourses are small, low nutrient streams supporting few fish and lacking cover. Despite this, Otters have been shown to use these areas, albeit less intensively than in lowland habitats (Strachan, 2007).

OBSERVING OTTERS

Otters have a broad muzzle, a long slender body, short legs and a long tapering tail. From nose to tail tip, adults are about a metre long. The feet are webbed and Otters swim leaving a U-shaped wake.

Otters are secretive and largely nocturnal in inland areas so sightings are generally infrequent. However, there are some areas where they are more often seen, such as at Loch of Strathbeg and in Aberdeen along lower stretches of the rivers Dee and Don. They are quite near-sighted and walking quietly by rivers or sitting and observing lochs, especially when there is ice cover, will increase the likelihood of seeing them.

Image: Bridge of Don, Andy Coventry
Author: Elizabeth Bacon

DISTRIBUTION IN NORTH-EAST SCOTLAND AND THE CAIRNGORMS

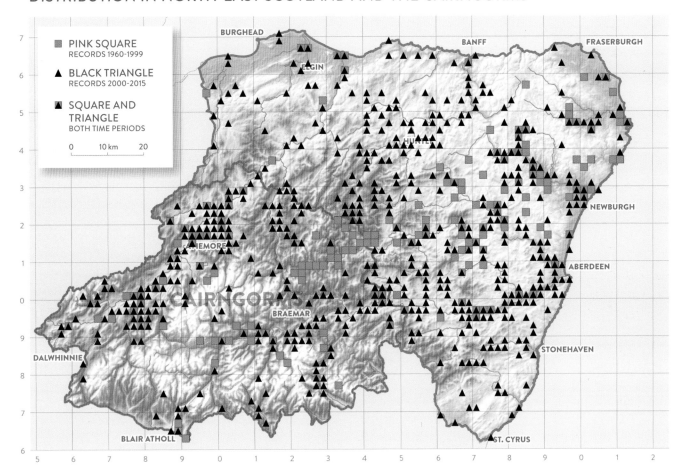

PINE MARTEN

(Martes martes)

HABITAT AND ECOLOGY

Pine Martens are adaptable omnivorous animals. Their diet consists mainly of small mammals, berries and small birds (Coope, 2007; Caryl et al., 2012). They are primarily found in wooded areas, though are not restricted to pinewoods, despite their common name. Areas of scattered woodland, including broadleaved stands, are used as are dense Sitka Spruce plantations and occasionally dispersing animals are recorded well away from woodland.

MANAGEMENT AND CONSERVATION

Pine Martens have been legally protected in the UK since 1988 under the Wildlife and Countryside Act 1981 (as amended). They may come into conflict with people by predating chickens or taking Pheasant poults. Recently, concern has been expressed that predation of eggs and chicks by Pine Martens may impact on Capercaillie populations. Although most research shows that such impact is likely to be minimal compared to other drivers of Capercaillie declines (e.g. Baines et al., 2011) there have been calls in some quarters for reducing the Pine Marten's legal protection.

Red Squirrels form a minor part of the Pine Marten's diet but there is emerging evidence of Pine Marten range expansion being linked to a decline in Grey Squirrel populations and subsequent Red Squirrel recolonisation (Sheehy et al., 2013; Sheehy & Lawton,

2014). This provides for the intriguing possibility that the reoccupation by Pine Martens of mid and lower Deeside may benefit Red Squirrel conservation in the long term.

RECORDS

For this species possibly more than any other, camera traps have revolutionised recording. Of records for which the circumstances are known, 49% were made by this method. Live sightings account for 23% of records with roadkill, tracks and hair sample records (primarily as a by-product of squirrel surveying) each providing 6%.

Historically, most records were of scats and these are still often the first signs of the presence of the species. DNA evidence, though, shows that Pine Marten scats are not as easy to identify as was previously supposed, with even experienced fieldworkers frequently recording scats of other species as Pine Marten (Davidson et al., 2002). Records based solely on scats have been excluded here, where possible, except when confirmed through DNA analysis, and these account for 10% of records for which the recording method is adequately documented.

BRITISH ISLES DISTRIBUTION, POPULATION AND TRENDS

The Pine Marten is native to mainland Britain, Wales

and Ireland (Balharry et al., 2008). Although formerly widespread, historical woodland loss and persecution during the nineteenth century, especially on sporting estates, caused a contraction of the main range within Britain to North-West Scotland. Isolated records from England and may derive solely from clandestine releases (Jordan et al., 2012) and an official Welsh reintroduction project is now underway (Macpherson et al., 2015).

From a low point in the early 1900s, the Scottish Pine Marten population recolonised much of mainland Highland, Grampian and Tayside and the species is now found south to the Kintyre Peninsula and the Central Belt (Croose et al., 2013). Pine Martens colonised Skye following construction of the road bridge in 1995 (Scott, 2011), a small population has persisted in Galloway following releases in the 1980s (Croose et al., 2013) and other populations are starting to become established following releases in the Scottish Borders (Croose et al., 2014).

The pre-breeding Scottish population was estimated at 3,500 animals by Harris et al. (1995). It seems very likely in light of the ongoing range expansion that the current figure will be considerably higher.

NORTH-EAST SCOTLAND AND CAIRNGORMS DISTRIBUTION AND TRENDS

The Pine Marten's distribution in the atlas area largely matches that of major forest tracts. Animals are found mainly in the valleys of the rivers Spey, Dee and Don and also in extensive forest plantations at Fetteresso

and Clashindarroch and in a scatter of sites through the centre and north of the region. Although doubtless present in more tetrads than mapped, Pine Martens probably are largely absent from mountainous areas and from lowland agricultural areas, especially across Buchan.

The distribution in the region is currently expanding. Velander (1983), based on fieldwork carried out in 1980-82, reported that Pine Martens had begun to recolonise Grampian although her survey was based largely on scats in pre-DNA analysis times. Subsequently, Balharry (1996) reported that Pine Martens had started to recolonise northern and western parts of our region by the 1990s. The spread has continued to central and southern Aberdeenshire (Croose et al., 2013) and, by 2012, animals were being recorded on the periphery of Aberdeen.

OBSERVING PINE MARTENS

Pine Martens are short-legged and long-bodied animals with a bushy tail, measuring up to 0.8 m in total length. They are mostly chocolate-brown in winter with a shorter, darker coat in summer and have a conspicuous creamy white bib. They are usually quite secretive and, combined with their preference for forest habitat, sightings are infrequent in most areas. However, feeding stations with viewing facilities are established in Speyside and provide excellent opportunities to see the species.

Image: Mid-Deeside, Harry Scott
Author: Nick Littlewood

DISTRIBUTION IN NORTH-EAST SCOTLAND AND THE CAIRNGORMS

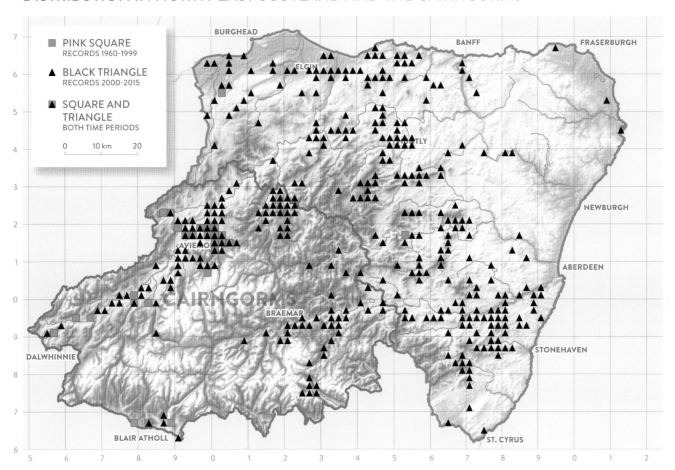

STOAT

(Mustela erminea)

HABITAT AND ECOLOGY

Stoats are almost exclusively carnivorous. They mainly eat small mammals but when prey is scarce they will diversify and may take advantage of autumn fruit such as Blackberries. Stoats are found in any habitat that provides cover and prey. The presence of drystane dykes and hedges may be important, especially in less wooded parts of the atlas area.

Rabbits are the most important prey species. In the atlas area, Stoats are rarely seen in areas where Rabbits are not recorded. Water Voles were probably the staple prey before the introduction of Rabbits, which is often still the case in mainland Europe (Sleeman, 1989).

In the past, most Stoats in the atlas area turned white during their autumn moult. In North-East Scotland, Hewson & Watson (1979) found that, in January, over 90% of Stoats were at least partly white and most of those had totally white fur, apart from the black tail tip (termed as being in full ermine). Autumn temperature is an important determinant of the extent to which a Stoat whitens (McDonald & Harris, 1997) so climate change could drive changes in the proportion of animals that are in ermine over the winter months.

MANAGEMENT AND CONSERVATION

Stoats come into conflict with people by predating poultry and eggs and chicks of gamebirds. As a result, they are legally killed by gamekeepers and some farmers. The vilification of Stoats as vermin might seem a little unjust given that this native species is a major predator of the introduced Rabbit and, to a lesser extent, the introduced Brown Rat.

Trapping and shooting can cause a localised reduction in Stoat numbers but usually the population is maintained by immigration (McDonald & Harris, 2002). Widespread issues such as the use of rodenticides, which may lead to secondary poisoning, and habitat loss are more serious long-term threats to the Stoat population (McDonald & Harris, 1997).

RECORDS

Live sightings make up the largest proportion (77%) of records for which the method of recording is known. Road casualties account for 13%, camera trapping has generated 3% of records and identification of prints and scats (both difficult to correctly separate from other mustelids) also 3%.

BRITISH ISLES DISTRIBUTION, POPULATION AND TRENDS

Stoats are rather under-recorded, perhaps in part because inexperienced observers may confuse them with Weasels (Arnold, 1993). However, they are known to be present throughout mainland Britain and Ireland and on some islands, including Orkney where they first appeared, probably introduced accidentally, in 2010 (Fraser et al., 2015a). Within Scotland, the majority of records are from the south and east of the country.

The British Stoat population has been estimated at 462,000, including 180,000 in Scotland (Harris, et al., 1995). The population was much higher prior to the arrival of myxomatosis in the Rabbit population in the 1950s, after which it crashed to very low numbers. As the Rabbit population recovered, so the Stoats followed, reaching another peak in the 1970s. Subsequently, some data suggest that there was a further decline with numbers then being stable since 1995. These trends, though, are based on analysis of game bags and, with a reduction in trapping activity, may not be reliable (Battersby et al., 2005; McDonald & King, 2008a).

NORTH-EAST SCOTLAND AND CAIRNGORMS DISTRIBUTION AND TRENDS

Stoats in the atlas area are most frequently recorded from valleys and other areas that are well wooded, such as Deeside, Donside and Speyside. The east coast, north of Aberdeen, is another area with a high number of records. This distribution does, to some extent, reflect areas where mammal recorders have been most active and, although populations might be lower in arable areas of inland Banff and Buchan, they are unlikely to be as sparsely distributed as the map suggests. There are very few records in the higher areas of the Cairngorms, which may reflect lower population levels, though animals have been seen up to an altitude of at least 850 m (Watson, 2013).

Changes in the status of the Rabbit population are a major factor in how Stoats are faring. In the atlas area, Rabbit numbers appear to be in decline and this may also drive a decline in the Stoat population.

OBSERVING STOATS

Stoats are larger than Weasels and have a black tip to the longer tail. The border between the brown back and white belly is straight as opposed to wavy on a Weasel. The most frequent Stoat sighting is of one dashing across a road. Roads with verges that have some form of cover may give the greatest chance of a sighting. Observers can get a closer view by standing very still, since the Stoat's eyesight is much more attuned to movement than shape. Sometimes an individual can be enticed out of cover by sucking on the back of one's hand in imitation of the call of a distressed Rabbit.

Image: Drumoak, Nick Littlewood
Author: John Malster

DISTRIBUTION IN NORTH-EAST SCOTLAND AND THE CAIRNGORMS

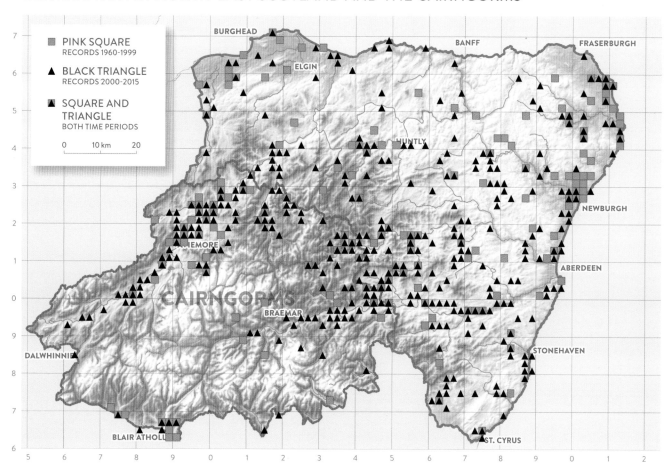

WEASEL

(Mustela nivalis)

HABITAT AND ECOLOGY

Weasels are supreme predators; the old name, mouse-hunter, seems very appropriate. They live in tunnels and small spaces and are rarely seen far from cover. For this reason, Weasels are found where there is long vegetation such as lightly grazed and ungrazed land and in young plantations. Mole tunnels are often used. They are unlikely to be found in older plantations with little understorey vegetation and may be less common in areas dominated by arable farming, especially where drystane dykes and hedges are scarce.

Weasels are relatively short-lived animals, usually surviving for no more than two years, and undergo population changes that synchronise with those of their prey. Indeed, predation by Weasels may be one important factor in driving Field Vole population cycles (e.g. Graham & Lambin, 2002). These rises and falls in population are more pronounced than in other predators in the British Isles, with the ability of young to breed in the year of their birth facilitating rapid population growth when prey is plentiful.

MANAGEMENT AND CONSERVATION

Weasels have no legal protection in the UK and may be killed at any time. Although they are less important predators of gamebirds than are Stoats, trapping by gamekeepers occurs in some areas. This, though, is generally thought to have just a temporary local effect on population sizes (McDonald & King, 2008b).

Most larger predators will catch Weasels. Domestic cats are often reported to have presented their owner with a Weasel, sometimes alive! A Stoat eating a Weasel has not been recorded, but Weasels do avoid their larger relatives. In 1,300 hours of radio-tracking, Pounds (1981) never recorded the two species coming together.

The removal of boundary features, such as hedges and drystane dykes, has reduced suitable habitat. However, incentives for farmers to leave unploughed field margins may provide additional habitat.

RECORDS

There were 401 records of Weasel used to compile the map. This is fewer than half the number of Stoat records, which is most likely to be because Weasels spend more of their time hidden, rather than being a reflection of relative population sizes.

From the records for which the recording method is known, 64% were sightings of live animals, 14% were made using camera traps, 10% were of roadkill animals and 9% were of Weasels found dead in other situations.

BRITISH ISLES DISTRIBUTION, POPULATION AND TRENDS

Weasels are found throughout mainland Britain but are absent from most islands and from Ireland. Harris et al. (1995) estimated the British population in spring, before the birth of young, to be about 450,000 animals, of which 106,000 were in Scotland. The population increased following the establishment of myxomatosis in the Rabbit population in the 1950s, as the lack of Rabbit grazing allowed an increase in vole numbers. National game bag data suggest a subsequent gradual decline since the 1960s, especially in southern England, though it is unclear if this is a genuine reduction or if it reflects a reduction in trapping effort by gamekeepers (Battersby et al., 2005; McDonald & King, 2008b).

NORTH-EAST SCOTLAND AND CAIRNGORMS DISTRIBUTION AND TRENDS

Weasels are mainly recorded from our river valleys, in coastal areas and on some lower altitude moorland areas. Records are scattered, though, and Weasels are likely to be under-recorded in at least some areas, which may account for some apparent gaps in the distribution in the lowlands of Banff and Buchan. There are also fewer records from the hillier parts of the atlas region. Whilst perhaps less common in such areas, the scarcity of observers could be a major factor as Watson (2013) lists a number of observations of Weasels in the Cairngorms at altitudes of 500 to 600 m. Despite their avoidance of Stoats on the ground, distribution maps for the two species show a broadly similar pattern.

Little is known about population trends in the atlas area though analysis of game bag data from sporting estates in Eastern Scotland over the 1961 to 2002 period did not reveal any significant changes (Battersby, et al., 2005).

OBSERVING WEASELS

Weasels are generally smaller than Stoats though overall lengths can overlap. Weasels lack the black tail tip shown by Stoats and have a wavy border between the brown back and white belly, unlike the straight border on a Stoat.

It is very difficult to plan to see Weasels and most sightings will be limited to chance encounters lasting only a few seconds. The best areas to look are close to rivers in the lowlands and where there is plenty of ground cover. Weasels are sometimes attracted to tunnels that are baited for rodents and can be camera trapped in this way.

Image: Coignafearn, Highland, John Dixon
Author: John Malster

DISTRIBUTION IN NORTH-EAST SCOTLAND AND THE CAIRNGORMS

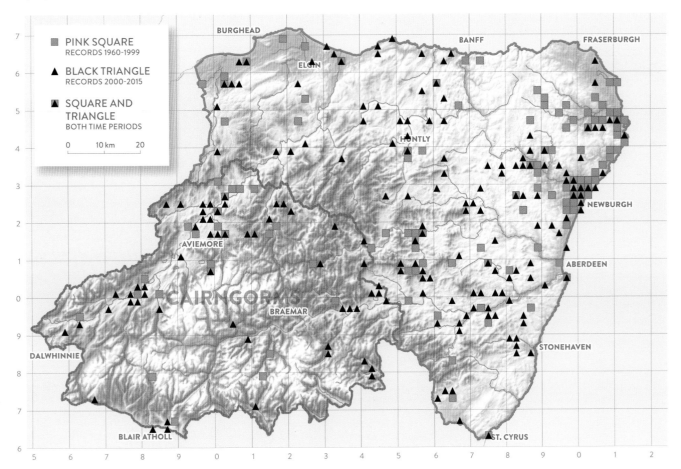

FERAL FERRET, POLECAT-FERRET AND POLECAT

(Mustela furo, Mustelo furo x *putorius* and *Mustela putorius)*

HABITAT AND ECOLOGY

This account combines these two closely related species and their hybrids due to the absence of recent unambiguous records of Polecat in North-East Scotland and the Cairngorms, and the challenges involved in separating them. In fact, the Ferret derives from the domestication of the wild Polecat over millennia, and is extremely similar genetically (Kitchener & Birks, 2014; Birks, 2015); they could even be regarded as two forms of the same species (Birks & Kitchener, 1999). Therefore Ferrets can be very difficult to tell apart from Polecats and, with intergrading and hybridisation being frequent, they can produce fully fertile offspring (Kitchener & Birks, 2014). Some guidelines for separation are given by the Vincent Wildlife Trust (2002). Ferrets range from an almost white albino form to so-called 'Polecat-Ferrets' which have much darker pelage and can resemble wild Polecats.

Most Ferrets are kept for pets or as working animals used to bolt Rabbits. When escaped into the wild, many do not survive. Self-sustaining populations are, therefore, not common, though they occur on some offshore Scottish islands, where Rabbit prey is abundant and other competitors and predators are rare (Vincent Wildlife Trust, 1998). As in Highland (Scott, 2011), nothing is known about the ecology or home range size of Feral Ferrets in North-East Scotland or the Cairngorms. However, Polecats elsewhere are mainly solitary, nocturnal predators which can take a range of prey, with Rabbits being the most important. They often frequent hedgerows and woodland edges, breed once per year, with up to six young born in early summer, and disperse in September (Vincent Wildlife Trust, 1998).

MANAGEMENT AND CONSERVATION

The Polecat is protected under Schedule 4 of the Conservation (Natural Habitats &c.) Regulations 1994 & 2010, and Schedule 6 of the Wildlife & Countryside Act 1981. However, Feral Ferrets are not protected (they are protected from cruelty only by the Wild Mammals (Protection) Act 1996), so can legally be killed, for example by gamekeepers. According to the Game & Wildlife Conservation Trust's National Gamebag Census, which asks for information on Polecats, but not Feral Ferrets, from 2010/11 to 2014/15, no Polecats were submitted in 157 returns in the 'Grampian' region (N. Aebischer, pers. comm.). During 2005/06 to 2009/10, returns from 151 estates contained five Polecat records from three sites, totalling 25 animals (Aebischer et al., 2011). It is not possible to say whether these records were of pure Polecats or Ferret hybrids, but the latter seems more likely.

There are few reported management or conservation issues connected with escaped Feral Ferrets in our area, though on some islands elsewhere they can predate ground nesting birds (e.g. Kitchener & Birks, 2008; Bodey et al., 2010). Ferrets may be considered as alien non-native species, but Polecats are certainly native. The main threats to Polecats in the UK are considered to be road deaths, persecution (which is still occurring despite their protected status) and hybridisation with Feral Ferrets (Morris, 1993). There may also be mortality caused by secondary rodenticide poisoning (Vincent Wildlife Trust, 1998). However, these factors appear insufficient to have prevented a substantial range expansion in Wales and England since the mid-1900s (Vincent Wildlife Trust 1998). The genetic status of many animals in Britain (in relation to Ferrets) is, though, difficult to determine (Kitchener & Birks, 2014).

RECORDS

We have followed the approach in the Highland Atlas (Scott, 2011) and assumed all records were of Ferrets unless positively determined as Polecats by specimens or photographs. However, there were no such records in our atlas period. Eleven records were submitted as 'Polecat' in the post 1960 period, with five from 1996-1999 and six post-2000. All were live sightings except for two dead specimens, from Mar Lodge in 1997 and St Cyrus in 2013. None was verified by national specialists and two have supporting information which casts doubt on whether they were definitely the pure species. Given the difficulty of separating them from dark Polecat-Ferret hybrids, we cannot be certain that any was definitely a Polecat, especially given the likely distance to other animals elsewhere in Scotland.

Twenty-two records of Feral Ferrets, and seven 'Polecat-Ferrets' were noted, post-1960. The earliest was in 1966, with 11 records up to 1999 and 18 from 2000-2010. For records of all types including 'Polecat', all except four came from the March to October period. At least nine were road casualties but for other reports the circumstances were not noted. In Highland, most records came from this source (Scott, 2011).

The map displays together all records of animals reported as Feral Ferret, Polecat-Ferret or Polecat.

BRITISH ISLES DISTRIBUTION, POPULATION AND TRENDS

Around 2,500 Feral Ferrets may be present in the UK, with most in Scotland (Birks & Kitchener, 1999). They have been introduced, sometimes intended for Rabbit control, on Harris, Islay, Mull, Shetland and the Uists, with a population also present in the 1980s in Strathearn, Perthshire. Elsewhere, reported populations in several places may not have persisted; there is one reported population in Ireland (Harris et al., 1995; Kitchener & Birks, 2008).

The Polecat is native to Britain and was formerly widespread, including over much of Scotland (but it is absent from Ireland). Its population is thought to be currently around 47,000 individuals, with fewer than 500 in Scotland (Birks, 2008) and densities can reach one animal per 1 km^2 in core areas (Vincent Wildlife Trust, 1998). Over centuries, large numbers were killed as 'vermin'. They may have still been widespread in Scotland in the early 19th century but they are thought to have become extinct in various parts of our atlas area between 1870 and 1915 (Langley & Yalden, 1977). During the 20th century, in common with many predatory species, the Polecat's population and range began to expand again as persecution reduced, though it remains primarily confined to Wales and England. Its status in many places is often confused due to the presence of Feral Ferrets. It is possible that 'unofficial' reintroductions may still take place, including in Scotland, where, since the 1970s, populations have become established in Argyll and the west Highlands. These may still persist, though recent evidence is slight (Vincent Wildlife Trust, 1998; Battersby, 2005; Croose, 2016). As with Feral Ferret, there appears to be an extant reintroduced population in southern Perthshire and Angus (Birks & Kitchener, 2008; Croose, 2016). Specimens confirmed as Polecats have been found in Caithness and Sutherland, with evidence here also suggesting reintroduced individuals, rather than a remnant population (Scott, 2011), and the numbers here may now be very small (Croose, 2016). In Britain as a whole, the Polecat population appears to be secure and expanding, but there is much former range still to be regained.

NORTH-EAST SCOTLAND AND CAIRNGORMS - DISTRIBUTION AND TRENDS

Nothing is known about the history of Ferret-keeping in our atlas area. Records have been episodic and no clear trend over time is apparent. Most 'Ferret' or 'Polecat-Ferret' records have come from Badenoch and Strathspey and central or eastern Aberdeenshire with one outlier at Atholl. It seems likely that most relate to temporarily escaped animals, rather than persisting populations. The eleven 'Polecat' records came from widely separated areas from Atholl through to Mar Lodge, east to the coast near Stonehaven and north to Forres and Buckie. They were recorded in months spread throughout the year, with no clear temporal trend. If any of the records in our atlas area were genuinely of pure Polecats, then local releases may have been involved.

OBSERVING FERRETS AND POLECATS

Feral Ferrets/Polecat-Ferrets are very rare in our area, unpredictable in their occurrence and probably not truly 'wild'. They leave few signs and are mostly nocturnal. Thus the chances of observing them are very low indeed. It is very likely that some are still trapped on shooting estates. Road casualties offer the best chance of detection, and any dead mustelid specimen should be examined closely to check for Polecat-Ferret features and retained for further examination (Kitchener & Birks, 2014). It is possible that true Polecats may, in time, recolonise the area; the nearest reintroduced animals may still be extant some 40 km away in southern Perthshire and Angus, though introgression with Ferrets is known from this population (Birks, 2008; Croose, 2016).

Image (page 98): Speyside, Ruari Law
Image (below): Montrose Basin, Andy Wakelin
Author: Ian Francis

FERAL FERRET AND POLECAT-FERRET DISTRIBUTION IN NORTH-EAST SCOTLAND AND THE CAIRNGORMS

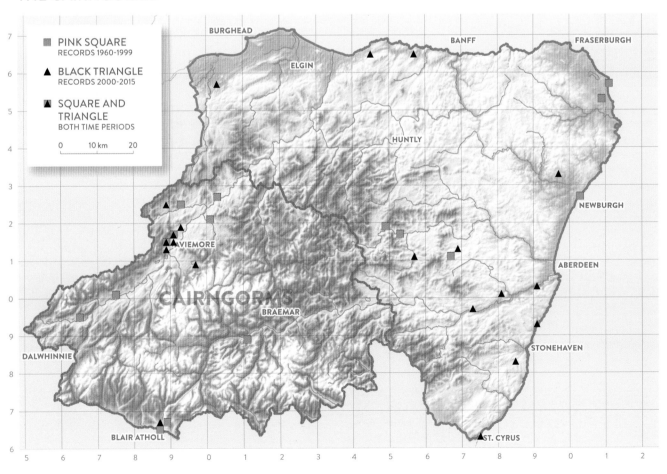

AMERICAN MINK

(Neovison vison)

HABITAT AND ECOLOGY

American Mink are adaptable predators with a broad diet that includes amphibians, small mammals, fish and birds. They are a semi-aquatic, solitary, territorial species occupying linear territories along rivers, lochs and coastlines (Dunstone, 1993). Mating occurs in February to March, when rutting males, but not females, abandon their territories, travelling tens of km in search of mating opportunities (Melero & Palazón, 2011; Melero et al., 2015). Most juveniles leave the natal range when approximately five months old, seeking a vacant territory and, in North-East Scotland, travel 30 to 40 km on average (Oliver et al., 2016). Territories are shortest (around 1 km of waterside habitat) in the most productive areas (Bonesi et al., 2000; Melero et al., 2014).

MANAGEMENT AND CONSERVATION

American Mink is one of the most widespread, invasive, non-native mammals worldwide and, given their carnivorous nature, they can have a large impact on local fauna. They have an invasive range spanning three continents and cause severe conservation damage (Macdonald & Harrington, 2003). The species is controlled in many areas with varying success (Bryce et al., 2011; Santulli et al., 2014). In North-East Scotland and the Cairngorms, a large-scale mink control programme started in 2006, aimed at reducing impacts on native riparian fauna, especially Water Voles. Initially centred around the Cairngorms National Park, the programme gradually expanded over time to include the whole of North-East Scotland, covering 20,000 km² by 2012 (Bryce et al., 2011; Melero et al., 2015). The project operates over multiple river catchments and is largely carried out by volunteers, who operate mink detection rafts and trap and remove mink as they appear.

RECORDS

Around 12% of records for which the circumstances are recorded are of live sightings. Most of the remainder are records collected during American Mink survey and control work and are primarily of footprints or captures on mink detection rafts. A small number of records (<1%) come from animals killed on roads and from camera traps. Because mink rafts are very widely distributed in the atlas area, the aggregated records should give a faithful reflection of American Mink distribution prior to and during the removal process (but see below). Records based on scats or unspecified signs should be treated with caution since, as with Pine Marten, there is much scope for misidentifying mink scats.

BRITISH ISLES DISTRIBUTION, POPULATION AND TRENDS

Since 1962, American Mink have colonised all of the British Isles bar the north-western corner of mainland Scotland, north of Ullapool (Fraser et al., 2015b). Population trends are ambiguous and uncertain. Despite repeated claims that mink numbers were declining as the Otter recovered in England (Bonesi et al., 2004; Bonesi et al., 2006), there is little convincing evidence of either a decline or any causal link with Otter abundance. Indeed, both species co-exist at all scales and can share the same stretch of waterways with their behavioural interactions not leading to either species being excluded (Harrington et al., 2009). The colonisation of the atlas area was largely due to escaped mink from fur farms in both the east and south-west of Scotland and range expansion northward in Scotland is ongoing (Fraser et al., 2015b).

NORTH-EAST SCOTLAND AND CAIRNGORMS DISTRIBUTION AND TRENDS

The distribution map confirms that American Mink were, until recently, ubiquitous in all but moorland and montane habitats. The lowlands of Aberdeenshire were particularly favoured, with a high density of records. American Mink were found in valley bottoms deep into the Cairngorms National Park. Trapping records, though, revealed that mink caught above 250 m altitude were mostly young males, with only a few recent records of breeding females, suggesting that it was ubiquitous except for at high altitudes (Bryce et al., 2011). Systematic mink control efforts have resulted in a sharp contraction in distribution and abundance, with most recent sightings originating from the catchments of the Rivers Tay and Deveron. American Mink are now sparsely distributed in the atlas area.

OBSERVING AMERICAN MINK

American Mink are streamlined animals with short legs. They are very dark brown, appearing almost black, with a small white mark under the chin. They are occasionally confused with Otters but are only around half the length and have a narrower head and muzzle. Any mink observation should be reported to the Scottish Mink Initiative for swift action as most of the atlas area is now devoid of mink, but the species' high dispersal ability makes recolonisation a constant possibility. Mink are bold and anglers often report hooked fish or packed lunches taken by them. Where a mink is present, multiple sightings typically ensue.

Image: Sandhaven, Ed Duthie
Author: Xavier Lambin

DISTRIBUTION IN NORTH-EAST SCOTLAND AND THE CAIRNGORMS

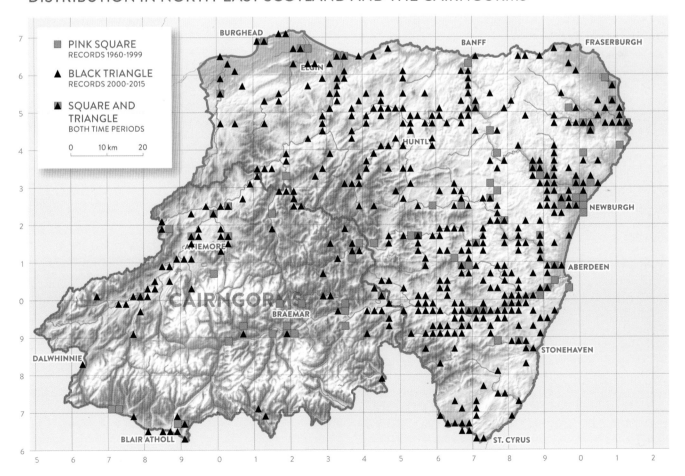

COMMON SEAL

(Phoca vitulina)

HABITAT AND ECOLOGY

The Common (or Harbour) Seal is the smaller of the two seal species that occur frequently on our coasts. They do not range far out to sea and are generally faithful to the same portion of coast through the year. Their diet consists mainly of fish, with some invertebrates, including squid. No dietary studies have been carried out in our region, but in the inner Moray Firth in the 1980-90s, Clupeids (Herring and Sprat) dominated in some years, with sandeels and Gadids (Cod-like fish) dominating in other years, linked to the relative local abundance of these species (Thompson et al., 1996; Tollit et al., 1997). Common Seals can range up rivers, although this is not frequent in the atlas area.

MANAGEMENT AND CONSERVATION

Common Seals are protected under the UK's Conservation of Seals Act 1970, now replaced in Scotland by the Marine (Scotland) Act 2010, and are also listed on Annexes II and V of the European Habitats Directive (92/43/EEC). The Act prohibits the taking of seals except under licence. Licences can be granted for the protection of fisheries, for scientific and welfare reasons and for the protection of aquaculture activities. In addition, in Scotland it is now an offence to disturb seals at designated haul-out sites though there are no designated haul-outs in the atlas area and, at present, no licenses have been issued. The directive requires that Special Areas of Conservation be established for the species and that management ensures that the species maintains a favourable conservation status.

Common Seals have been hunted by Humans for food and pelts in the past (Sim, 1903). At present, Common Seals in North-East Scotland are fully protected but, prior to this protection, some were killed due to interaction with coastal net fisheries. There is a seal management plan in place for the Moray Firth (Butler et al., 2008).

RECORDS

All records within the database were of sightings of live animals, but dead stranded animals have also been reported from the region (e.g. Brownlow et al., 2015).

BRITISH ISLES DISTRIBUTION, POPULATION AND TRENDS

Common Seals are widespread around the shores of the British Isles, but are generally concentrated in a number of places, including the Wash, Orkney, the Inner Hebrides and Strangford Lough. Very few occur on British coasts from the Thames Estuary clockwise to the southern Firth of Clyde. The majority of haul-outs are found on the coasts of Scotland.

The UK held around 37,300 Common Seals in 2014 (SCOS, 2014). This is scaled up from counts made at coastal haul-outs during the moulting period in August. Scotland holds approximately 79% of the UK population, with 16% in England and 5% in Northern Ireland.

Numbers of Common Seals in England (mainly in the Wash) have been considerably affected by phocine distemper virus epidemics in 1988 and 2002 (SCOS, 2014). However, populations have since increased dramatically such that they are now considered to have fully recovered.

NORTH-EAST SCOTLAND AND CAIRNGORMS DISTRIBUTION AND TRENDS

Common Seals are distributed at low density on all parts of the coast of North-East Scotland. More are recorded between Aberdeen and Fraserburgh than elsewhere though this may, at least in part, reflect the concentration of recording activity in this area. There are records from the estuaries of the Dee, Don, Ythan, Deveron and Spey, with the species apparently being present year-round in the Ythan. There are, though, no documented records of Common Seals breeding in the atlas area.

There have been significant declines in the numbers of Common Seals around the east and north coasts of Scotland since 2000. Whilst there is no knowledge of trends in North-East Scotland, the number of Common Seals in the Tay Estuary has declined by around 85%, in Orkney by approximately 75% and in Shetland by approximately 30%. Numbers in the Moray Firth have fluctuated but show no real trend. The potential causes of the declines appear to vary by region. They may include interactions with Grey Seals through competition for resources and habitat, as well as predation (SCOS, 2014) though there have been no records of such predation in North-East Scotland (Brownlow et al., 2015). In other regions, exposure to toxins from harmful algae may contribute to the declines (SCOS, 2014).

OBSERVING COMMON SEALS

Common Seals are smaller than Grey Seals with a more dog-like face as opposed to the straighter profile of a Grey Seal's head. Their fur colour varies but they typically show a finer pattern of spots than do Grey Seals. They may be sighted along most coasts. Although very significantly out-numbered there by Grey Seals, the haul-out at the northern side of the entrance to the Ythan estuary, where up to a dozen animals have been recorded, is one of the more reliable sites in winter. The tidal section of the River Don in Aberdeen is another good place to look.

Image: Sandhaven, Ian Francis
Authors: Mark Tasker & Eunice Pinn

DISTRIBUTION IN NORTH-EAST SCOTLAND AND THE CAIRNGORMS

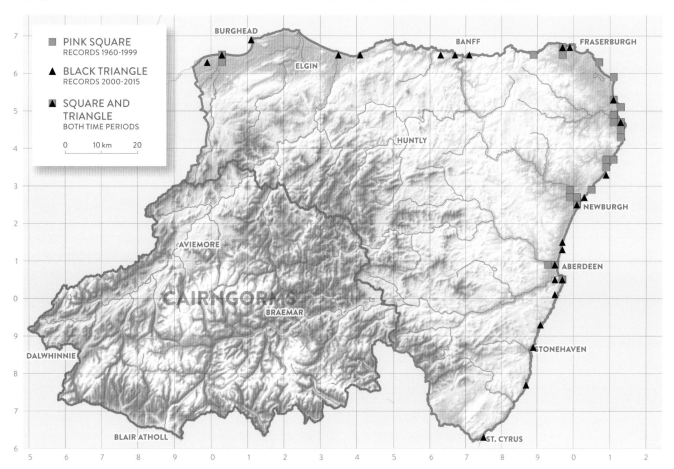

PINK SQUARE
RECORDS 1960-1999

BLACK TRIANGLE
RECORDS 2000-2015

SQUARE AND TRIANGLE
BOTH TIME PERIODS

0   10 km   20

GREY SEAL

(Halichoerus grypus)

HABITAT AND ECOLOGY

The Grey Seal is the larger of the two seal species that regularly occur on our coasts. Within this environment, they have no particular habitat preference. The species can range far and studies of tagged seals have shown that those seen in the atlas area may originate both locally and from further away, such as the Firth of Forth or Orkney (McConnell et al., 1999). Their diet consists mainly of fish with some invertebrates, including squid. No dietary studies have been carried out in our region but sandeels were the dominant fish in the diet in the wider North Sea in the early 2000s with Gadids (Cod-like fish) and flatfish being important also in the Moray Firth (Hammond et al., 1994). Grey Seals can range up rivers, but usually only visit estuaries.

MANAGEMENT AND CONSERVATION

The Grey Seals Protection Act of 1914 made it unlawful to kill the species between 1 October and 15 December each year. This was the first piece of legal protection ever introduced for a wild mammal species in the UK. The species was further protected under the UK's Conservation of Seals Act 1970, now replaced in Scotland by the Marine (Scotland) Act 2010, and it is also listed on Annex II and V of the European Habitats Directive (92/43/EEC).

Grey Seals can take fish out of nets, take Salmon at river mouths and even break open fishing creels to remove both the bait and any catch (Harwood & Greenwood, 1985). This conflict is managed under legislation. The Marine (Scotland) Act prohibits the taking of seals except under licence. Licences can be granted for the protection of fisheries, for scientific and welfare reasons and for the protection of aquaculture activities. However, this system is largely self-policed and there have been allegations of illegal shooting.

In addition, in Scotland it is now an offence to disturb seals at designated haul-out sites though there are no designated haul-outs in the atlas area. The Habitats Directive requires that Special Areas of Conservation be established for the species and that management ensures that the species maintains a favourable conservation status. There is a seal management plan in place for the Moray Firth (Butler et al., 2008).

RECORDS

All records used to compile the map were of sightings, but dead stranded animals have also been reported from the region (e.g. Brownlow et al., 2015).

BRITISH ISLES DISTRIBUTION, POPULATION AND TRENDS

Grey Seals occur on all coasts of the British Isles with the largest part (88%) of the breeding population being in Scotland, including particular concentrations in the Orkney Isles and Outer Hebrides. Censuses of Grey Seals are undertaken in autumn by counting pups during their 17-23 day suckling period on land, prior to going to sea. The counts are then converted to an estimated number of breeding animals, based on several assumptions. In 2012, there were an estimated 111,600 UK Grey Seals (SCOS, 2014). In contrast to Common Seals, their numbers have been increasing continuously since the 1960s, though with recent signs of levelling off in some colonies. Approximately 44% of global pup production occurs in the UK. This growing Grey Seal population may be one of the drivers behind the decline of Common Seals, due to competition for both food and habitat.

NORTH-EAST SCOTLAND AND CAIRNGORMS DISTRIBUTION AND TRENDS

Grey Seals occur on all coasts of North-East Scotland, mostly at low density but they are perhaps more frequently recorded from Aberdeen to Banff, especially at the Ythan estuary, with a smaller number seen in Stonehaven Bay and scattered along the southern Moray Firth coast. Regular observations would show that they are likely to be present at least daily off all coasts of the region.

No comprehensive census of Grey Seals in North-East Scotland has occurred but regular counts at the Ythan estuary show numbers to be increasing, with a peak count of 1,855 made in 2013. Numbers at this site are at their highest in April and May. Numbers in both the areas to the north and south of the region have also increased. Whilst it is not impossible that the occasional Grey Seal might give birth to a pup on one of our rocky shores, such an event has not been documented and the closest regular breeding site is the Isle of May in the Firth of Forth.

OBSERVING GREY SEALS

Grey Seals are larger than Common Seals and have a straighter face and nose profile. They are often more two-toned, being darker with blotchy spots above and paler below. They may be observed in open seas or estuaries with many hundreds sometimes hauling out at the mouth of the Ythan estuary. They may also be seen closely and watched feeding by looking from the road on the south side of Aberdeen harbour on the way to Girdle Ness.

Image: Ythan estuary, Martyn Gorman
Authors: Mark Tasker & Eunice Pinn

DISTRIBUTION IN NORTH-EAST SCOTLAND AND THE CAIRNGORMS

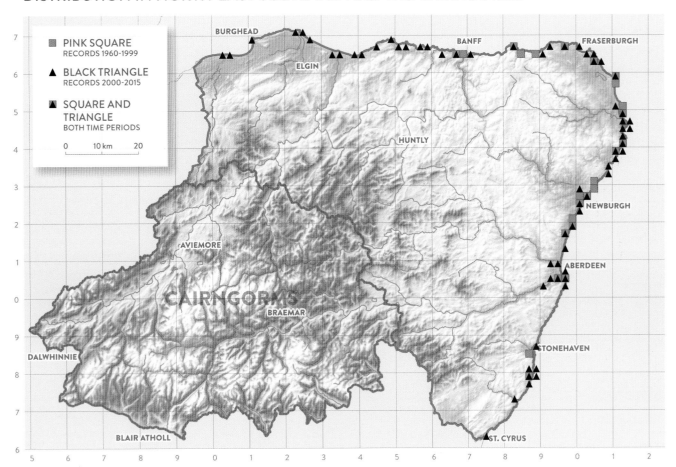

PINK SQUARE
RECORDS 1960-1999

BLACK TRIANGLE
RECORDS 2000-2015

SQUARE AND TRIANGLE
BOTH TIME PERIODS

0   10 km   20

BEARDED SEAL

(Erignathus barbatus)

HABITAT AND ECOLOGY

As an inhabitant of shifting sea ice, the Bearded Seal is truly an Arctic animal. Breeding takes place on pack ice from late March to early May (Shirihai, 2006) where, as a protection against Polar Bear predation, Bearded Seal pups are able to take to water soon after birth (Hall, 2008). Although not generally regarded as a migratory animal, some do live a pelagic existence and wander far from their natal area (Dunn et al., 2012) with records in Europe extending south to the Iberian Peninsula (Aulagnier et al., 2009).

MANAGEMENT AND CONSERVATION

Beaded Seals are protected in Scotland under the Habitat Regulations 1994 (as amended in Scotland) Schedule 3, which prohibits certain ways of taking the species.

No direct management is undertaken in the British Isles for this vagrant species, though one animal in England that was found to be unwell was taken into a wildlife rehabilitation centre and later released in Shetland (Hall, 2008).

RECORDS

Records in the British Isles typically concern sightings of single live animals, often hauled out onto land. One record, from Skye in 1999, was of two Bearded Seals together, hauled out with Grey Seals (Hall, 2008). Some animals have remained in one site or area for long periods. Indeed one of the two animals recorded in North-East Scotland, whilst being seen in the region on just one date, was seen nearby in eastern Scotland over a four month period.

BRITISH ISLES DISTRIBUTION, POPULATION AND TRENDS

Twenty-five Bearded Seals were recorded in Britain up to 2012. There is evidence of an increase in occurrences with just one recorded prior to 1950 and ten since 2000 (Hall, 2008; Dunn et al., 2012). Ireland also had its first in 2002 (Moores, 2007). The majority (16) of the British records have been from Shetland or Orkney with most of the remainder from northern Britain. Aside from the two animals recorded in the atlas area, the only other record on the east side of the Scottish mainland was of one seen several times in November 2007 in the Inverness Firth (Scott, 2011).

NORTH-EAST SCOTLAND DISTRIBUTION AND TRENDS

Just one Bearded Seal has been seen alive in the atlas area, an animal that was hauled out at St Cyrus on 14 October 2011. Eight days earlier, it had been seen at Lunan Bay, around 15 km to the south, in Angus. What was probably the same animal was then seen at Tayport, on the south side of the Firth of Tay, on 27 December 2011 and at Monifieth, on the north side of the Firth of Tay, on 19 February 2012 (British Marine Life Study Society, 2016). One further record in the atlas area is of an animal that was found dead on the beach at St Fergus, on 27 February 2012. From the photographs available, this appears to be a different animal to that seen at St Cyrus.

OBSERVING BEARDED SEALS

Finding another Bearded Seal in North-East Scotland will require considerable luck. However, some previous Bearded Seals in Scotland have remained faithful to their haul-out sites for some time so, should one appear, it may prove to be popular with observers.

Image: Tayport, Sam Gibson
Author: Nick Littlewood

DISTRIBUTION IN NORTH-EAST SCOTLAND AND THE CAIRNGORMS

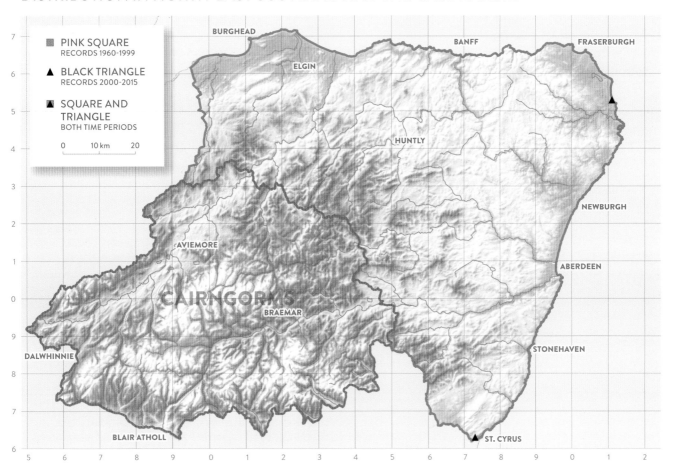

PINK SQUARE
RECORDS 1960-1999

BLACK TRIANGLE
RECORDS 2000-2015

SQUARE AND TRIANGLE
BOTH TIME PERIODS

0   10 km   20

WILD BOAR

(Sus scrofa)

HABITAT AND ECOLOGY

The Wild Boar is a woodland animal although it also frequents wetlands and agricultural land if sufficient cover is present. It is largely nocturnal, sleeping in dense cover during the day and feeding at night. Boars are omnivorous, taking a wide range of foods including roots, grubs, fruit, nuts, seeds, crops, carrion and birds' eggs. Most of their diet is plant material and they often leave obvious foraging signs where they have rooted up the ground. The females and young tend to live in groups while adult males are solitary. Mating can occur from October through to June, peaking in mid-winter. Litters of around four to six young can be born from February to October, with a peak in April (Goulding et al., 2008).

MANAGEMENT AND CONSERVATION

The restoration of Wild Boars to woodland ecosystems is welcomed by some conservationists as their foraging can break up dense areas of Bracken and create an ideal seedbed for tree regeneration. Captive herds have been used for this purpose in the Glen Affric area (Trees for Life, 2013). However, Wild Boars are not universally welcomed and the damage they can cause to agricultural land and commercial forestry means that many land managers operate a zero tolerance policy when they appear in new areas. There is no legal protection for the species, which can be hunted at any time of year.

RECORDS

Half of the records of Wild Boar came from camera traps that were deployed to search for Wildcats. The remaining records were live sightings, including of two animals that were subsequently shot.

BRITISH ISLES DISTRIBUTION, POPULATION AND TRENDS

The Wild Boar is a former native species. It became extinct in Ireland by the Neolithic era (Goulding et al., 2008) whilst the indigenous British population is thought to have been hunted to extinction in the 13th century, although subsequent reintroductions led to free-living populations that persisted until the 16th century (Yalden, 1999). Following an increase in Wild Boar farming in the 1980s, the species became re-established as a result of escapes and deliberate releases, although in some cases these may have involved hybrids with domestic pigs (e.g. Frantz et al., 2012).

Escaped individuals and transient populations have appeared in many locations since the 1990s, though have only persisted in a small number of areas. Well established populations are found in Kent/ Sussex, Dorset, Devon, Somerset and the Forest of Dean in Gloucestershire, with a total population of several hundred animals (Wilson, 2014). In Scotland, populations may have become established in Dumfries and Galloway since the early 2000s and west Lochaber since 2007 (Campbell & Hartley, 2010).

NORTH-EAST SCOTLAND AND CAIRNGORMS DISTRIBUTION AND TRENDS

The Gaelic name for Wild Boar, torc, appears in the hill names Carn an Tuirc and An Torc (the Boar of Badenoch), which are likely to refer to the shape of the hills. Lynturk, near Alford, and Bogturk, in the Forest of Birse, are place names that are more likely to relate to historical occurrences of the species in the region prior to extinction.

There was a failed attempt by the Earl of Fife to reintroduce Wild Boar at Mar Lodge in 1790 (Murray & Watson, 2015). In 2002, there was an isolated sighting of a boar between Newtonmore and Laggan (Hetherington, 2013) but sightings have become more frequent since 2010. Between June 2010 and September 2011, adult male and female boars and a group of at least seven piglets were recorded on camera traps at several locations in Glenlivet. These were close to a farm that keeps Wild Boar and it is not clear whether the piglets were born in the wild or escaped as a family group. In October 2011, a single male was seen on a roadside near Rothes.

Between November 2013 and January 2015, there was a series of records from the forests of mid-Deeside between Glen Tanar and Glen Dye, including at least two males that were subsequently shot. In 2015, there were also anecdotal reports of the species in Glen Muick (not shown on the map). The origin of the Deeside animals is not clear as there are no known boar farms in the area.

In the two main areas where the species has been recorded, it is thought that local landowners have culled animals to prevent them becoming established and it is uncertain whether the species is becoming re-established in the atlas area.

OBSERVING WILD BOAR

Adult Wild Boar have dark bristly fur whilst boar piglets have horizontal brown and cream stripes. Live sightings of Wild Boar in the region are very rare. Given the current uncertain status of the species, there are no reliable sites for observing Wild Boar in the atlas area. The use of camera traps may be the best way of finding out if there are Wild Boar in any given site, especially since they are mostly nocturnal when foraging.

Image: Glenlivet, Roo Campbell/RZSS
Author: Paul Chapman

DISTRIBUTION IN NORTH-EAST SCOTLAND AND THE CAIRNGORMS

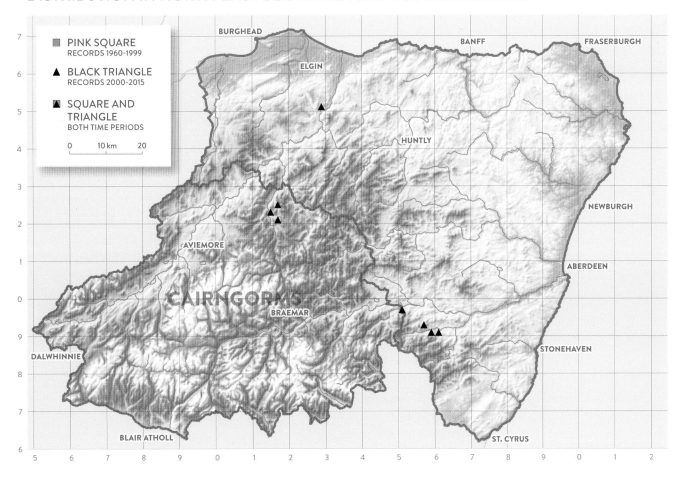

RED DEER

(Cervus elaphus)

HABITAT AND ECOLOGY

The Red Deer is the largest land mammal in the British Isles. Named after their rusty-red summer coats, they are concentrated in Scotland, ranging on upland moors and mountains, as well as in native woodland and commercial forestry. In the atlas area, Red Deer are particularly numerous in the Cairngorms National Park, where many landowners maintain herds for stalking.

Red Deer are primarily grazers, selecting a diet of grasses and herbs in summer (Staines & Crisp, 1978), but they also browse new Heather growth, and other woody plants, including young trees, especially in winter (Latham et al., 1982). Females (hinds) select diets that are higher in quality than males (stags), which tend to select for quantity. These sex differences in diet are attributed to differences in body size and the demands of reproduction, particularly lactation (Clutton-Brock et al., 1982). Except during autumn breeding (rut), these diet differences lead to the sexes segregating into predominantly hind herds with juveniles, and stag herds.

MANAGEMENT AND CONSERVATION

All species of deer in Scotland are protected by the Deer (Scotland) Act 1996. Alive, deer do not belong to anybody. However, landowners have the reserved right to take or kill them within limited seasons. For Red Deer, the closed season for stags is 21 October to 30 June, and for hinds it is 16 February to 20 October. Landowners and tenants can only shoot deer during the closed season if they are causing serious damage to livelihoods.

During the last 50 years, Red Deer populations have doubled (Clutton-Brock et al., 2004), prompting concerns about their impact on the natural heritage, including heather moors (Albon et al., 2007) and Caledonian pine forests (Palmer & Truscott, 2003). Also, there is a potential loss of revenue associated with browsing damage in commercial forestry and the risk of more road traffic accidents (Putman, 2012). The main threat to Red Deer is hybridisation with Sika that are expanding eastward.

RECORDS

The majority of records of Red Deer are of live sightings. There are systematic count data for Red Deer in most of the upland parts of the atlas area, where neighbouring estates are organised into Deer Management Groups (see below). In commercial forestry managed by Forest Enterprise Scotland there may be estimates of Red Deer numbers from a variety of methods, including vantage point counts, dung counts, or numbers shot in relation to effort. More generally in woodland, presence is confirmed by cull returns or sightings. See also Figure 5-2 (p.151).

BRITISH ISLES DISTRIBUTION, POPULATION AND TRENDS

The last survey conducted by the British Deer Society, in 2011, shows that compared to similar surveys in 2007, Red Deer continue to expand their range, particularly in South-West England and East Anglia (Hailstone, 2012). Also, there has been an expansion in North-East Scotland out from the main mountain massif onto lower hills and woodlands.

Estimating the total UK Red Deer population size is difficult because in many places Red Deer inhabit woodland, where they are difficult to census, and only in Scotland have open-hill populations been systematically counted (see above). Changes in sheep numbers grazing the same hills in summer explained much of variation in Red Deer numbers in Scotland, which doubled between 1961 and 2000 (Clutton-Brock et al., 2004). More recent reductions in sheep numbers, following the Foot and Mouth epidemic in 2001, combined with milder winters, may have led to further increases in Scottish Red Deer numbers. Currently the UK free-ranging population is thought to exceed 400,000, with more than 95% of these in Scotland (Staines et al., 2008).

NORTH-EAST SCOTLAND AND CAIRNGORMS DISTRIBUTION AND TRENDS

Red Deer in the atlas area have expanded from the Cairngorms and Cabrach, colonising some hills and woodland out into the agricultural lowlands that extend to the North Sea coast. Cull returns to Scottish Natural Heritage suggest that in the lowlands of Aberdeenshire (including Banff & Buchan and Kincardine) and Moray numbers have increased by 10% per year since 2000. Also, there have been sightings within 10 km of the towns of Banff, Elgin and Stonehaven, and as close as 15 km to Peterhead.

Counts of Red Deer on open hill ground in the three Deer Management Groups areas (Cairngorm/Speyside, West Grampian and East Grampian) which account for nearly 3,000 km² of the atlas area, suggest that numbers peaked around 2005-6. Five years later, heavy culling in Cairngorm/Speyside and East Grampian had reduced numbers by more than 45% and 20%, respectively, to estimated densities of 3.9 and 8.1 per km². Over the same period, numbers in West Grampian rose, though, by 6%, to a density of 23.4 per km².

OBSERVING RED DEER

For much of the year, one of the best places to observe Red Deer stags is just south of the Glen Muick Visitor Centre. During the October rut stags can be heard roaring and seen at higher elevations to the east of Glen Muick as they maintain their harems.

Image: Glen Muick, Ian Francis
Author: Steve Albon

113

DISTRIBUTION IN NORTH-EAST SCOTLAND AND THE CAIRNGORMS

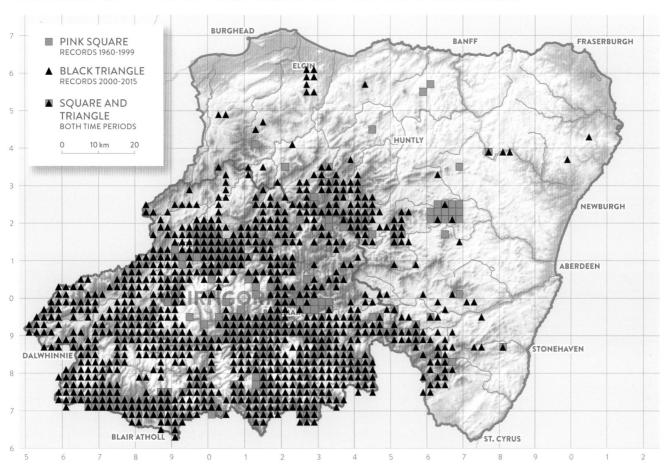

PINK SQUARE RECORDS 1960-1999

BLACK TRIANGLE RECORDS 2000-2015

SQUARE AND TRIANGLE BOTH TIME PERIODS

0   10 km   20

SIKA

(Cervus nippon)

HABITAT AND ECOLOGY

Sika were introduced to UK deer parks from Japan from 1860 onwards (Ratcliffe, 1987). Over the years, escaped individuals have established populations in several places. In Scotland, Sika have spread rapidly in the last few decades through commercial forestry plantations in Argyll, Highland Region, and the Southern Uplands (Perez-Espona et al., 2009). Most recently they have expanded eastward, including into forestry in the atlas area.

In most locations, Sika overlap with native Red Deer. Although each species tends to mate with its own kind, hybridisation has undoubtedly occurred, producing fertile offspring (Abernethy, 1994). There is little information about the feeding ecology of Sika, outside of their native Japan, where they feed on Dwarf Bamboo, particularly in winter, and grasses (Campos-Arceiz & Takatsuki, 2005). Thus, like the similarly sized Red Deer, Sika are likely to be primarily grazers, selecting a diet of grasses and herbs in summer but also browsing new Heather growth and other woody plants, including young trees, in winter.

MANAGEMENT AND CONSERVATION

All species of deer in Scotland are protected by the Deer (Scotland) Act 1996. Alive, deer do not belong to anybody. However, landowners have the reserved right to take or kill them within limited seasons. For Sika, the closed season for males is 21 October to 30 June, and for females it is 16 February to 20 October. It is only permissible to kill deer by shooting, using ammunition of a specified size. Landowners and tenants can only shoot deer during the closed season if they are causing serious damage to livelihoods.

Although mating between Sika and Red Deer may be as rare as one occurrence in 1,000, frequent back crosses over time can lead to a high introgression of Sika genes and, in some localities, hybrid 'swarms' (Pérez-Espona et al., 2009). Hybridisation is considered the biggest threat to the genetic integrity of Red Deer. The consequences are Sika-like deer getting bigger, while Red-like females are getting smaller (Senn et al., 2010b).

RECORDS

The majority of records of Sika are from animals culled by deer stalkers but they are, nonetheless, probably under-reported. There are relatively few sightings because Sika tend to stay within forested areas. Although they may venture onto moors and agricultural land, they rarely stray far from cover, compared to bolder Red Deer (Chadwick et al., 1996).

BRITISH ISLES DISTRIBUTION, POPULATION AND TRENDS

The British Deer Society gathers distribution data on all six species of deer that are resident in the UK. The last survey, in 2011, shows that, compared to a similar survey in 2007, Sika continue to expand their range in southern England and eastwards in Scotland (Hailstone, 2012). Populations are also present in three areas in Ireland (Putman, 2008). Estimating the total UK Sika population size is difficult because they prefer to stay in woodland, which is difficult to census, and appropriate survey methods are not systematically used. Vantage point counts to estimate densities in Argyll and the Southern Uplands, Scotland, suggest that densities of Sika are similar to those of Red Deer in most forest growth stages, reaching as high as 35 per km² in thicket stage (Chadwick et al., 1996). Cohort reconstruction of culled animals suggested that, in 1990, the Southern Uplands Sika population was 600. However, line-transect methods applied to dung counts in 1995/96 in the same forests produced an estimate of around 1,100 Sika (Marques et al., 2001). This rate of increase is plausible because of very high fertility rates, including a proportion of calves becoming pregnant. Since around 6,500 Sika have been culled each year in Scotland recently, and it is reckoned that populations can support a 25% cull, there may be more than 25,000 Sika in Scotland alone. Putman (2008) comments that there may have been a doubling in Sika numbers from an estimated 11,500 in Britain in the early 1900s, when more than 85% were thought to reside in Scotland.

NORTH-EAST SCOTLAND AND CAIRNGORMS DISTRIBUTION AND TRENDS

In the atlas area, 41 Sika were reported in the cull returns submitted to Scottish Natural Heritage in 2014/15. Most (33) were shot in Strathspey. To the east of the Cairngorms National Park, single stags were shot at both Ballogie and Clashindarroch. Unfortunately, most of these records were not available for inclusion in the map, which largely shows the locations of reported sightings. Numbers reported culled vary between consecutive years by as much an order of magnitude and there is little evidence of a trend.

OBSERVING SIKA

Sika are the most elusive of the deer species resident in the atlas area. With luck, they might be seen in woodland in Speyside or around Laggan in Badenoch, or at least heard there as males have a distinctive, high-pitched, screeching call during the autumn rut.

Image: Findhorn Valley, Highland, John Dixon
Author: Steve Albon

DISTRIBUTION IN NORTH-EAST SCOTLAND AND THE CAIRNGORMS

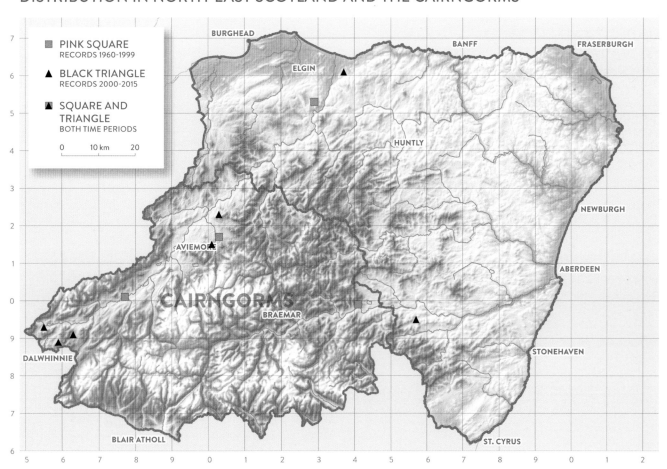

FALLOW DEER

(Dama dama)

HABITAT AND ECOLOGY

Fallow Deer frequent broadleaf or mixed woodland and farmland, though coniferous plantations with patches of open ground are also used (Harris et al., 1995). Their diet varies with season and habitat. Whilst grasses are preferred, root crops are taken in arable fields. In woodland, Fallow Deer eat ground vegetation, dwarf shrubs and trees (De Nahlik, 1959) supplemented in autumn by nuts, seeds and fruits (Langbein et al., 2008).

Female Fallow Deer (does) give birth to a single fawn in June or July. They can live for up to 16 years though males (bucks) in the wild usually only live for up to eight to ten years.

MANAGEMENT AND CONSERVATION

In Scotland, Fallow Deer are legally protected during the close season, which runs from 1 May to 31 July for bucks and 16 February to 20 October for does. The only permitted exceptions are when they pose a reasonable threat to crops, enclosed woodland, natural heritage or human safety. Low genetic diversity and road collisions are key threats to populations of Fallow Deer in the British Isles (Harris et al., 1995).

At high densities, Fallow Deer can alter vegetation structure and species composition (Battersby et al., 2005). As with other Cervids, they can carry bovine tuberculosis, a disease of economic and health importance (Rhyan & Saari, 1995). Habitat availability, culling and sport shooting all strongly influence the Fallow Deer's distribution and abundance (Harris et al., 1995).

RECORDS

Although there have been several reports of Fallow Deer in the atlas area, there is just a single record that is adequately documented to be mapped here. The sparsity of records appears to be due to very low abundances combined with the fact that Fallow Deer are primarily active around dawn and dusk (Langbein et al., 2008). The single mapped report is of a series of sightings of live individuals at one location. Some further poorly documented records were not mapped where the possibility of confusion with other species could not be reasonably eliminated.

BRITISH ISLES DISTRIBUTION, POPULATION AND TRENDS

Fallow Deer existed in Britain before the last Ice Age though the current population is derived from Mediterranean stock, introduced to estates and hunting forests from around 900 years ago (Harris et al., 1995). The species now occurs widely through England, Wales and Ireland though is patchily distributed in mainland Scotland (Langbein et al., 2008). Populations often originated as deer park escapes and remain clustered around these locations, reaching high densities in suitable habitat. The number of English deer parks holding Fallow Deer declined from 700 in the mid-17th century to 120 in 1988 (Harris et al., 1995) so escapes are now probably less frequent. Britain's wild Fallow Deer population has been estimated at 95,000 in England, under 1,000 in Wales and under 4,000 in Scotland (Harris et al., 1995). In the 1990s, an estimated 17,000 Fallow Deer lived in deer parks in Britain. Additionally, 10,000 were in deer farms including an estimated 3,250 in Scotland (Harris et al., 1995).

NORTH-EAST SCOTLAND AND CAIRNGORMS DISTRIBUTION AND TRENDS

Fallow Deer are well-established south of the atlas area, near Dunkeld. Individuals from this population may be expected to enter the southern parts of the Cairngorms National Park though no such records were available for this atlas. However, the presence of individuals observed with young in Strath Avon, close to a site known to hold captive animals, suggests that the species may breed at large within the atlas area. Fallow Deer were also reported around Braemar and at Mulben Forest in the 1960s, whilst cull returns submitted to Scottish Natural Heritage for 2014/15 show that three animals were reported as being culled in Aberdeenshire. In both cases, though, the records are not shown on the map as precise location data were not available. In Glen Muick, a small herd has been established since at least 2013 though as these are kept within a large enclosure, they too are not mapped here.

OBSERVING FALLOW DEER

Fallow Deer are intermediate in size between Roe and Red Deer. They typically have a brown coat with white spots but the background colour can vary between white and almost black. Male Fallow Deer have distinctive broad flattened antlers. The species is most active whilst foraging at dawn and dusk. There are no reliable sites for observing Fallow Deer at large in the atlas area though close by they may be observed at the Loch of the Lowes Scottish Wildlife Trust reserve or by the Field Studies Council's centre at Kindrogan.

Image: West Sussex, Ian Francis
Author: Alistair Allan

DISTRIBUTION IN NORTH-EAST SCOTLAND AND THE CAIRNGORMS

ROE DEER

(Capreolus capreolus)

HABITAT AND ECOLOGY

The Roe Deer is the most numerous (Hewison & Staines, 2008) and widely distributed of the six deer species resident in Britain (Hailstone, 2012). Although considered a woodland deer, the ubiquity of Roe Deer reflects the wide range of habitats that they now occupy, including agricultural land, coniferous plantations, native woodlands, upland moors and urban greenspaces. In the atlas area, Roe Deer occur everywhere, except on the mountain plateaux of the Cairngorms National Park.

Roe Deer are selective feeders. In Scottish plantation forests they eat predominantly forbs (herbaceous plants other than grasses) in summer, and a mixture of forbs, heaths, shrub and tree browse in winter (Latham et al., 1982). Studies of Roe Deer feeding in agricultural landscapes in Hampshire, England, found that woodland remained an important source of forage throughout the year but that they used cereal crops in spring/early summer and root crops in autumn/early winter (Putman, 1986). Studies in France found that Roe Deer use cultivated fields when their native food resources are depleted or decline in quality (Abbas et al., 2011).

MANAGEMENT AND CONSERVATION

All species of deer in Scotland are protected by the Deer (Scotland) Act 1996. Alive, deer do not belong to anybody. However, landowners have the reserved right to take or kill them within limited seasons. For Roe Deer, the closed season for males (bucks) is 21 October to 31 March, and for females (does) is 1 April to 20 October. It is only permissible to kill deer by shooting, using ammunition of a specified size. Landowners and tenants can only shoot deer during the closed season if they are causing serious damage to livelihoods.

There are concerns about the impact of locally high densities of deer on their habitats, particularly in woodland. In native woodlands, Roe Deer may reduce diversity among understorey plants and retard natural regeneration (Putman & Moore, 1998). In commercial forests, they may impact on the growth form of trees and hence the value of the timber (Ward et al., 2004). As Roe Deer have expanded into urban areas, there is the risk of more road traffic accidents (Putman, 2012).

RECORDS

The majority of records of Roe Deer are of live sightings. There are few estimates of population sizes in any habitat, except in woodlands. In some commercial forestry managed by Forest Enterprise Scotland there may be estimates of Roe Deer numbers from a variety of methods, including vantage point counts, dung counts, or numbers shot in relation to effort. Additional information on distribution may come from road traffic accidents.

BRITISH ISLES DISTRIBUTION, POPULATION AND TRENDS

Roe Deer are widely distributed in Britain though absent from Ireland, The British Deer Society gathers distribution data on all six species of deer that are resident in the UK. The last survey, in 2011, showed that, compared to a similar survey in 2007, Roe Deer continue to expand their range, in particular in the Midlands, South-East England and Wales (Hailstone, 2012). On the Scottish mainland, they occur everywhere except a few isolated parts of the north-western coast. The expansion of Roe Deer may reflect improved recruitment and survival in the generally mild winters in recent years and the reduction in domestic livestock in much of the Britain since the Foot & Mouth disease outbreak in 2001.

Estimating the total British Roe Deer population size is difficult because most animals seek refuge in cover and there is no systematic monitoring across habitats. In some woodland habitats information on relative densities or trends within sites is available from dung counts or numbers culled per unit effort. Nonetheless there are estimates that the British population is around 500,000, with about 70% being in Scotland (Hewison & Staines, 2008).

NORTH-EAST SCOTLAND AND CAIRNGORMS DISTRIBUTION AND TRENDS

Roe Deer occur in all parts of the atlas area except on the high mountain plateaux. Records of sightings tend to be aggregated where there are more people, particularly along the east coast margins and along the major river valleys. Concentrations in the forest/moor and forest/agricultural mosaics may reflect particularly active local recorders, since apparent absences elsewhere would not be expected given that the Great British Deer Distribution Survey 2011 claims that Roe Deer are ubiquitous across the North-East (Hailstone, 2012). Cull returns to Scottish Natural Heritage show a steady increase in the numbers shot over five year periods from 2000/01 on the agricultural/forest lowlands of Aberdeenshire, Buchan, Kincardine and Moray, as well as in Strathspey/West Grampian. However, numbers shot in the Cabrach/Glenbuchat area have declined and culls peaked in the East Grampian and Morven areas between 2005/6 and 2010/11.

OBSERVING ROE DEER

Small groups (typically two to eight) of Roe Deer may best be seen feeding or resting in agricultural land close to the edges of woodland. Otherwise fleeting glimpses of one or two are not uncommon when one is walking within woodlands, or as deer run across roads.

Image: Near Stonehaven, Genevieve Leaper
Author: Steve Albon

119

DISTRIBUTION IN NORTH-EAST SCOTLAND AND THE CAIRNGORMS

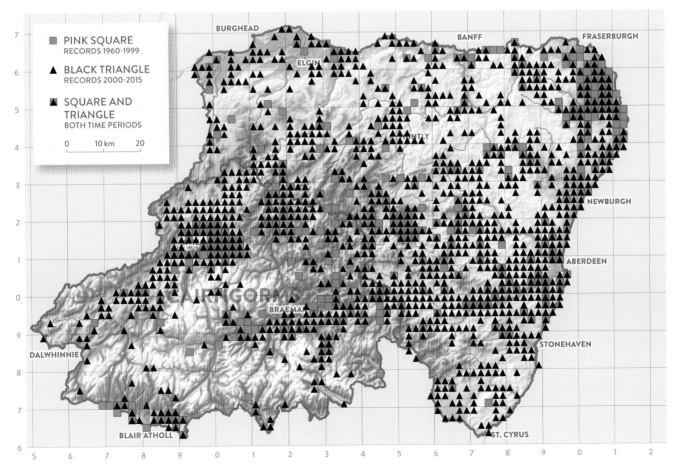

FERAL GOAT

(Capra hircus)

HABITAT AND ECOLOGY

Feral Goats live in steep and rocky upland habitats where their long, shaggy coats protect them from the harsh weather conditions and their agility allows them to reach seemingly inaccessible ledges. They are primarily browsers rather than grazers, preferring to eat coarse vegetation such as trees and shrubs rather than grass. Males and females live in separate herds for most of the year, only coming together for the rut in the autumn. The young can be born as early as January and consequently the species is vulnerable to severe winters (Hart-Davis, 2002).

MANAGEMENT AND CONSERVATION

Feral Goats are the descendants of domestic goats that have been released or escaped into the wild and have established free-ranging breeding populations. They are sometimes referred to as Wild Goats, but that name more correctly refers to the indigenous populations of south-west Asia that were the wild ancestor of the domestic goat.

Feral Goat herds may represent the last surviving remnants of the British primitive goat breed, which traces its origins back to the very first domestic livestock that were introduced to Britain by Neolithic farmers, but which fell out of favour once more

productive goat bloodlines started to be imported from overseas during the 19th century. Conservation interest in the Feral Goat therefore focuses on its ancient origins and potential status as a landrace and rare breed, although its genetic history is not yet fully understood (Werner, 1998; Werner, 2010).

The Feral Goat has no special legal protection and is hunted for sport in some areas, in a similar way to Red Deer stalking. Due to its browsing habits, the species poses a risk to woodland and montane scrub and culling is often carried out to maintain populations at a low level in areas where these habitats are being managed.

RECORDS

All records for the atlas related to live sightings, which is the usual way in which the species is recorded (Arnold, 1993).

BRITISH ISLES DISTRIBUTION, POPULATION AND TRENDS

The Feral Goat has a fragmented distribution within the upland areas of the British Isles. The main British strongholds are in Snowdonia, Northumberland's Cheviot Hills, Galloway, up the west coast of Scotland from Kintyre to Wester Ross (including several of the inner Hebrides) and extending east to include populations around Loch Lomond and Loch Ness and in Highland Perthshire and the Monadhliath (Arnold, 1993; Bullock, 2008).

Harris et al. (1995) estimated the British population to be over 3,565 individuals, with over 2,650 of these in Scotland. At that time, it was thought that the Scottish population had been stable since the 1960s. More recently, concerns have been expressed by Feral Goat enthusiasts and animal welfare groups about local population reductions in some areas where culls have been carried out to protect woodland.

NORTH-EAST SCOTLAND AND THE CAIRNGORMS DISTRIBUTION AND TRENDS

Since the mid-20th century, Feral Goats appear to have been restricted to the western edge of the atlas area. A herd frequented the area around the Slochd by the A9 north of Carrbridge until at least 1999, but they are reported to have since been eradicated from this area (Collier, 2013). A herd is present at Creag Dhubh, near Newtonmore, where the population is said to have been established about 50 years ago, peaking at around 100 animals, but it is currently managed to maintain a population of 25 to 30 animals (Scottish Natural Heritage, 2010). Between these two locations, but just outside the atlas area, Feral Goats are also present at Coignafearn in Strathdearn.

Feral Goats appear to have been more widely scattered throughout the area historically with records from Bennachie in 1932, Craig Maskeldie in Glen Esk in 1945, Kinveachy, north of Aviemore in 1951, Glen Callater until the 1950s and Dalnacardoch, Atholl in 1972 (Arnold, 1993). The Glen Callater herd numbered at least 85 animals and ranged into the surrounding hills, but was badly affected by the severe winter of 1947 and eventually wiped out by another severe winter in 1958 (Watson, 2013). The Gaelic word for goat, gobhar, appears in the names of the hills Creag nan Gabhar (between Glen Callater and Glen Clunie) and Carn nan Gabhar (the highest peak of Beinn a' Ghlo in Atholl), providing a further indication of the species' former occurrence in these areas.

OBSERVING FERAL GOATS

Despite their non-native and domestic origins, Feral Goats are popular animals with many tourists and wildlife enthusiasts. Creag Dhubh, near Newtonmore, appears to be the only site in the atlas area where Feral Goats are currently likely to be seen.

Image: Creag Dhubh, Newtonmore, Adam Francis
Author: Paul Chapman

DISTRIBUTION IN NORTH-EAST SCOTLAND AND THE CAIRNGORMS

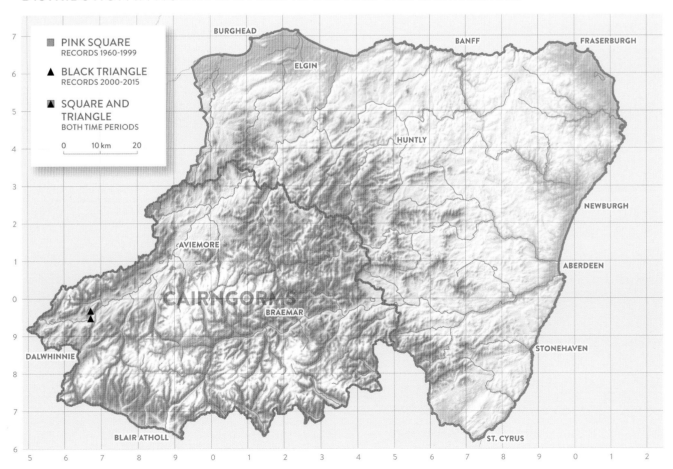

PINK SQUARE
RECORDS 1960-1999

BLACK TRIANGLE
RECORDS 2000-2015

SQUARE AND TRIANGLE
BOTH TIME PERIODS

0   10 km   20

HUMAN

(Homo sapiens)

HABITAT AND ECOLOGY

Humans sit indisputably within the scope of this atlas yet also completely outside the frame of reference for the other species covered. Few, if any, mammal atlases have included our species, yet our influence in shaping the area vastly exceeds any other, and our signs are everywhere. Nationally we are amongst the most abundant wild mammals, probably outnumbered only by the Field Vole, and without doubt that with the largest biomass (Yalden, 1999). The rural nature of our atlas area means that here, among our domestic livestock, sheep outnumber us and cattle outweigh us, but this is reversed nationally. Over half a million people live in North-East Scotland and the Cairngorms, concentrated into a few large settlements but also spread thinly over much of the land. There are enormous contrasts between ourselves and our fellow mammals (for example we have no predators) yet there are also some similarities - principally, that our distribution is also influenced by climatic and environmental factors and our mortality can also be influenced by extremes of weather, especially cold winters.

MANAGEMENT AND CONSERVATION

Humans present completely different issues to those faced by other mammals, where 'conservation' is effectively the management of our impact on other species. For us, conservation management can be viewed as conscious attempts to change our own activities as we create an enormous number of management challenges, including to ourselves. However, the conservation status of our own species is favourable and secure by any biological standard; complex societies and technology have largely over-ridden potentially controlling 'natural' factors.

RECORDS

There is a comparative wealth of available information for Humans, with minimal recording effort bias. There are many data sources, including the national population census, the latest of which took place in 2011. The map used here for Humans is different to that used for other mammals, since the same mapping criteria for distribution applied to our species would produce a map with presence or signs in every tetrad!

BRITISH ISLES DISTRIBUTION, POPULATION AND TRENDS

People in the UK are principally concentrated in the London area and in several other large conurbations, such as the main Scottish central belt cities and towns. Our area has a comparatively low population density. In 2011, the UK population stood at 63.2 million, with 5.3 million in Scotland. The Republic of Ireland's population was 6.4 million in 2011. Numbers in the UK increased by 4.1 million (nearly 7%) between 2001 and

2011; this trend continued and in 2014 the population was approximately 64.6 million (Office for National Statistics, 2012; 2015). Around the start of our mammal atlas period (1961), the UK population was 52.8 million; it is now 26% higher.

NORTH-EAST SCOTLAND AND CAIRNGORMS DISTRIBUTION AND TRENDS

Human population density is concentrated towards Aberdeen and some other larger towns in the northern and eastern coastal zones. Humans are resident and dispersed over most parts of the area, though virtually none live higher than 600 m. In fact, parts of the Cairngorms are amongst the least populated parts of the country, in some cases holding no resident people over many hundreds of square kilometres. Despite this, there are almost no areas unvisited, and none untouched, by Human management influence, ranging from agriculture and heather moor burning to buildings, lights, litter and pollution. In 2011, c.580,000 people lived in the whole atlas area (Local Authority website statistics), with an unknown number of temporary visitors; for example, an estimated 1.5 million visits are made to the Cairngorms National Park annually, where the resident population is around 17,000 (Cairngorms National Park Authority, 2015a). Population increases are taking place in most parts of the area. Taking Aberdeenshire as an example, the population grew by c.30,000 between 2001 and 2013

and is projected to grow further from 237,000 in 2013 to almost 300,000 by 2037 (Aberdeenshire Council - National Records of Scotland projection). In part this is fuelled by immigration to the area. As another example, in Aberdeen City, there was a net inflow of 1,665 people each year between 2012 and 2014 (National Records of Scotland, 2015). The annual general fertility rate in Aberdeen is around 48 children per 1,000 women aged from 15 to 44, slightly below the Scottish figure of 54.7. The annual death rate in Aberdeen is 9.4 per 1,000 people (National Records of Scotland, 2015).

HUMANS IN A LOCAL CONTEXT

We are by far the most conspicuous mammal and contrast with all others in this atlas in being detectable and visible almost everywhere all the time. Not only that, but our livestock are also amongst the most abundant and conspicuous mammals in the landscape. The challenge for the conservation of nature (including the other wild mammals) is to ensure that our impact is moderated and reduced where possible, at least enough to allow space for other parts of the natural environment to be maintained amidst ever-growing Human influence.

Image: Aberdeen City Centre, Paul Chapman
Author: Ian Francis

123

ESTIMATED POPULATION DENSITY IN NORTH-EAST SCOTLAND AND THE CAIRNGORMS*

*Derived from the number of postcodes per tetrad and the average population per postcode in each postcode district in the 2011 census © Crown copyright, 2014. Contains OS data © Crown copyright and database right 2016. Contains Royal Mail data © Royal Mail copyright and Database right 2016. Contains National Statistics data © Crown copyright and database right 2016.

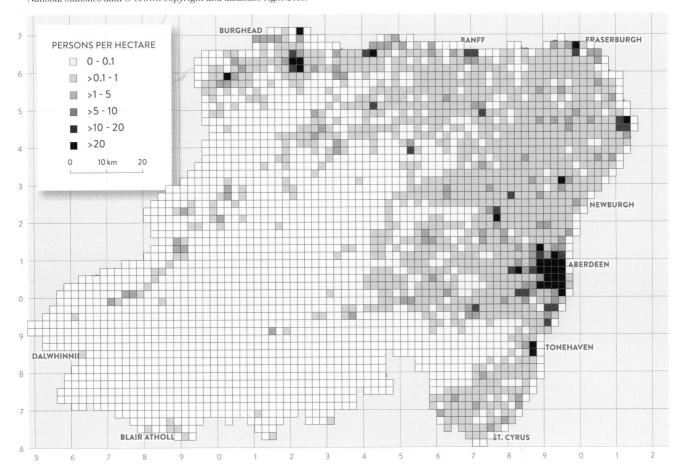

ADDITIONAL MAMMAL SPECIES

The main species accounts cover terrestrial mammals (including seals) that have occurred in a wild state in the region during the period 1960 to 2015, along with naturalised mammals breeding at large in the region. This section includes brief details on a selection of further species that do not merit a full account. It includes vagrant and introduced species reported before the start of the atlas period (but not since 1960) along with other species recorded in the region but in situations where their wild or feral status is more questionable. Also included is Black Rat, which was recorded within the main atlas time period though could not be mapped as no record was available at greater than hectad resolution. This section (as with the atlas as a whole) does not include long-extinct species such as Eurasian Lynx, Wolf, Brown Bear and Eurasian Beaver or mammals that may have been present in prehistoric times.

MUSKRAT (Ondatra zibethicus)

Muskrats that escaped from fur farms in the early decades of the 20th century established feral populations in a number of areas including Stirlingshire/Perthshire. These were wiped out following extensive control programs in the 1930s (Yalden, 1999). The only record in the atlas area is from Glenbervie in 1929 (Arnold, 1993).

HARVEST MOUSE (Micromys minutus)

A single hectad is mapped for the atlas area by Arnold (1993), this referring to a record from Kemnay in 1899. Sim (1903) refers to this and two further records in the region. Harvest Mice are widespread in southern and central England but much scarcer further north and the authenticity of these records may be doubtful (Trout & Harris, 2008).

BLACK RAT (Rattus rattus)

The Black Rat is thought to have arrived in the British Isles from India in the 3rd century or earlier (Arnold, 1993). After the introduction of the Brown Rat, the Black Rat population declined dramatically and by the mid-20th Century the remaining populations were largely restricted to ports and surrounding areas. These gradually died out or were eradicated. A population persisted on the Shiant Islands, in the Minch, though an eradication program is now being implemented. There are sporadic occurrences elsewhere and small populations may persist in some places (Toms et al., 1999; Bruce, 2010). In the atlas area, the Black Rat was noted in 1961 to be a long-established species in Aberdeen, though numbers were said to have reduced over the preceding five years (Bentley, 1964). Although it undoubtedly survived for several more years, a population has certainly not been present since at least 1983 (Twigg et al., 2008).

COYPU (Myocastor coypus)

There are records in the atlas area of this large South American rodent from two sites south of Elgin and from Cabrach, all dated as 1934 (Arnold, 1993). Coypu that escaped from fur farms established feral populations, most notably in East Anglia, which were finally eliminated in 1987 following several decades of control (Yalden, 1999).

NOCTULE (Nyctalus noctula)

A fresh dead male bat was found on 27 June 2012 at Cullen House (Isobel Davidson pers. comm.). The northern part of the British range of Noctule extends into southern Scotland. It is not known if this individual arrived in the region naturally.

KUHL'S PIPISTRELLE (Pipistrellus kuhlii)

An adult male bat was found alive at Dyce, in a shipping container from Romania, on 20 October 2015 (Isobel Davidson pers. comm.).

RINGED SEAL (Pusa hispida)

There are two records, both killed having been caught in salmon nets. The first was at Collieston in August 1897 and the second was in Aberdeen Bay in 1901 (Sim, 1903; JNCC, 2007).

HARP SEAL (Pagophilus groenlandicus)

Sim (1903) reported a specimen sent to him from Cruden Bay in August 1887, a female caught in salmon nets at Stonehaven on 7 March 1903 and a male, also caught in salmon nets, at Donmouth, Aberdeen, on 31 March 1903. These records, though, are not listed by JNCC (2007).

HOODED SEAL (Cystophora cristata)

One was recorded at the mouth of River Lossie, near Elgin, in 1903 (JNCC, 2007).

WALRUS (Odobenus rosmarus)

A Walrus, thought to be an immature female, was seen and photographed at Collieston on 24 February 1954 (Forman, 1954).

REINDEER (Rangifer tarandus)

Between 1952 and 1954, 29 Swedish Reindeer were introduced as an experiment to the Cairngorms and after 18 years the herd had increased to around 100 (The Reindeer Company Ltd, 1993). Animals were then sold off and the development of the Cairngorm Reindeer Centre in Glenmore led to the perpetuation of a small herd of around 25 to 50. These range freely in summer over a wide area, though are focused on a leased 'hefted' area on the north-facing slopes of Cairn Gorm, extending onto the plateau. They have been recorded from 30 tetrads in this area and north-eastwards from here. Although strictly speaking they are 'captive' and ear-tagged, they are unconstrained while grazing, resemble a wild herd and form a unique and surprising feature of our mammal atlas area. A backup herd of around 100 is kept on a farm in Glenlivet (Shaw & Thompson, 2006). In the 18th century, 14 were released on Atholl Estate and around 1820 some were introduced on Mar by the Duke of Fife, but none of these previously introduced populations survived (Nethersole-Thompson & Watson, 1981).

Image: Glenmore, Caingorm Reindeer Herd
Author: Nick Littlewood

CETACEANS IN NORTH-EAST SCOTLAND

The North-East of Scotland is a relatively rich area for cetaceans and close to half of the 29 species recorded in UK waters have been sighted alive in the region. Of the 14 species recorded (dead or alive), four are frequent, five are less frequent and the remaining five have been recorded at least once. Data have been reported through land or sea based systematic watches, casual sightings, and strandings. Almost any point along the coast is suitable for seeing cetaceans, but protruding cliff top headlands offer the best chance of sightings, both because additional height aids observations and because currents that pass around them provide opportunities for feeding.

RECORDS

Sightings over the last 25 years are revealing apparent changes in status and distribution for several cetacean species. Reviews of their status and distribution in the region have been made by Evans (1996), Weir & Stockin (2001), Weir et al. (2007), Canning (2007), Robinson et al. (2007) and Anderwald et al. (2010).

FREQUENT SPECIES

HARBOUR PORPOISE (*Phocoena phocoena*)

The Harbour Porpoise is the commonest and most widely distributed cetacean in the region although there has been a general southwards shift in abundance in the western North Sea since the 1990s (Reid et al., 2003; Anderwald et al., 2010; Hammond et al., 2013). It occurs here year-round but with greatest abundance between July and October (Anderwald et al., 2010). Peak births occur in June (Evans et al., 2003).

COMMON BOTTLENOSE DOLPHIN
(*Tursiops truncatus*)

A population of around 195 animals inhabits the coastal waters of East Scotland (Cheney et al., 2013). The number using the Moray Firth Special Area of Conservation in summer has remained more or less stable since 1989 but the total east coast population appears to be increasing and extending further south, first appearing on a frequent basis around Aberdeen in the mid-1990s (Anderwald et al., 2010; Cheney et al., 2014). Although occurring year-round, peak numbers are seen in late summer (July-September) (Anderwald et al., 2010). Births occur mainly between May and September (Evans et al., 2003).

WHITE-BEAKED DOLPHIN
(*Lagenorhynchus albirostris*)

A frequent inhabitant of the central and northern North Sea, this species ranges over wide areas offshore, entering coastal waters of the region mainly between July and August, possibly in response to inshore movements of shoaling fish (Canning et al., 2008; Anderwald et al., 2010). Births occur mainly between May and August (Evans et al., 2003).

MINKE WHALE
(*Balaenoptera acutorostrata*)

The Minke Whale is the most common baleen whale in the North Sea and elsewhere in UK waters (Hammond et al., 2002; Evans et al., 2003; Reid et al., 2003; Hammond et al., 2013). It has been recorded year-round in the region, but sightings show a marked peak between July and September, probably representing an inshore movement during late summer (Anderwald et al., 2010). Numbers of sightings can vary greatly between years, probably reflecting prey availability (Tetley et al., 2008; Robinson et al., 2009; Anderwald et al., 2010). Although mostly seen solitarily, or in small groups of up to three, larger feeding aggregations have been observed, including five off Girdle Ness, Aberdeen in July 2006 (Anderwald et al., 2010). A solitary Minke Whale followed a fishing vessel into Fraserburgh Harbour in July 2007, remaining there for several days before leaving.

LESS FREQUENT SPECIES

HUMPBACK WHALE
(*Megaptera novaeangliae*)

Records in the North Sea have increased markedly since the 1990s with the species now occurring annually in North-East Scotland (Evans et al., 2003; Anderwald et al., 2010). Most sightings are of single individuals and occur between June and August, although there have been a number of winter sightings between November and March (Anderwald et al., 2010). Records are widely distributed and some individuals appear to remain in the region for extended periods (e.g. three humpbacks during November 2011 in the area between Collieston and Balmedie). On one occasion, in June 2011, an animal was even observed feeding in Aberdeen Harbour entrance.

RISSO'S DOLPHIN (*Grampus griseus*)

Risso's Dolphins typically frequent scattered localities along the Atlantic seaboard of Britain (Evans et al., 2003; Reid et al., 2003). However, since the 1990s there has been a significant increase in sightings in the northern North Sea (Evans et al., 2003; Anderwald et al., 2010). Although recorded year round, most sightings in the region have been between July and September, and mostly between Stonehaven and Fraserburgh.

KILLER WHALE (*Orcinus orca*)

Killer Whales are seen in small numbers annually in the region, mostly during the summer months (May to August) (Anderwald et al., 2010). In August 2013, three animals in Aberdeen Bay were later filmed off Peterhead and positively identified as part of what was previously thought to be an exclusively West coast population.

SHORT-BEAKED COMMON DOLPHIN
(*Delphinus delphis*)

Sightings have increased substantially in the northern North Sea since 2000, mostly occurring between June and August (Anderwald et al., 2010). Group sizes are usually fewer than twenty individuals, but a large school of 300+ was observed off the north-east of the atlas area in July 2007 (Anderwald et al., 2010).

ATLANTIC WHITE-SIDED DOLPHIN
(*Lagenorhynchus acutus*)

This species occurs mainly beyond the shelf edge in northern British waters but, nevertheless, was recorded fairly frequently (mainly in small groups) in the region prior to 2003 (Evans et al., 2003; Reid et al., 2003). They have only been reported once since, in August 2005 in the Outer Moray Firth (Anderwald et al., 2010; Sea Watch Foundation, unpublished data).

OTHER SPECIES

In North-East Scotland, five other species have been recorded alive and one species from strandings:

LONG-FINNED PILOT WHALE
(Globicephala melas)

There are up to a dozen records from scattered locations in the region, with no particular seasonal pattern (Anderwald et al., 2010). Usually recorded in coastal waters, singly or in small groups, although larger pods of up to 150 have been seen offshore and in adjacent waters (including a pod of 26 that live-stranded near St Andrews, Fife, in September 2012).

FIN WHALE *(Balaenoptera physalus)*

The Fin Whale has been recorded ten times in the region since the 1970s, although multiple sightings in August 1984 were probably of the same individual; two individuals were reported offshore south-east of Stonehaven in August 1997 (Anderwald et al., 2010).

SPERM WHALE *(Physeter macrocephalus)*

This species occasionally strays into the North Sea from deep Atlantic waters (Evans et al., 2003; Reid et al., 2003). It has only been recorded live in the region twice, with two animals off Peterhead in October 1998 and six live stranding in Cruden Bay in January 1996 (Anderwald et al., 2010; Sea Watch Foundation, unpublished data).

NORTHERN BOTTLENOSE WHALE
(Hyperoodon ampullatus)

This species has been reported twice in the region: a single animal offshore east of Peterhead in January 1997 and two close to Aberdeen in January 2006 (Anderwald et al., 2010). The latter was just five days after a much publicised stranding of an animal on the River Thames in London, suggesting a small influx to the North Sea.

SOWERBY'S BEAKED WHALE
(Mesoplodon bidens)

This species has been recorded in the region only from a few strandings, and it is not known whether the animals involved were alive upon entering the inshore waters of North-East Scotland.

Image (page 126): Common Bottlenose Dolphin, Aberdeen, Harry Scott
Image (below): Minke Whale, near Stonehaven, Kevin Hepworth
Author: Kevin Hepworth

DOMESTIC LIVESTOCK

This atlas is primarily concerned with the wild mammals of the region, but it is important not to overlook domesticated mammals that live outdoors. Cattle, sheep, goats, pigs and horses have been present in Scotland since Neolithic times and have had an enormous impact on the landscape and habitats of the region. Over 20% of the area of North-East Scotland is occupied by agriculturally improved grassland for cattle and sheep grazing while a further 25% is classified as rough grazing (Scottish Government, 2015b), where semi-natural habitats are grazed by livestock, often alongside wild herbivores such as deer.

Recent population data in this section are derived from the agricultural censuses (Scottish Executive, 2001; Scottish Government, 2015b). Data for North-East Scotland region (Aberdeenshire, Moray and Aberdeen City) have been combined with estimates for other parts of the atlas area based on census data for Highland and Tayside to provide an estimate for the whole area.

DOMESTIC CATTLE (*Bos taurus*)

Cattle undoubtedly have the highest overall biomass of any mammal within the atlas area. The population is around 375,000 (c.20% of the Scottish total), with about 100,000 breeding cows and the remainder comprising calves and fattening cattle. The majority of the cattle herd is used for beef production, with breeding herds on upland farms producing calves that are sold on at 6-12 months to farms in the more productive lowland areas, where they are fattened for slaughter, typically at 18-30 months of age. However some farms, particularly in the lowlands, undertake the whole process, breeding and fattening their own calves.

The traditional black cattle of the region were developed into the modern Aberdeen-Angus breed during the 19th century through the efforts of livestock breeders such as William McCombie of Tillyfour, near Alford. These animals formed the mainstay of beef production in the region until the latter half of the 20th century, when a greater variety of breeds was introduced. These included continental breeds, such as Charolais, Limousin and Simmental, which have been cross-bred with native stock to produce larger and faster-growing animals.

Most cattle graze grass fields from May to October and are kept in sheds or out-wintered on areas of less productive land from November to April, when there is insufficient grass growth for grazing. Grass that is cut during the summer and made into silage or hay is the main winter feed, although forage crops, such as swedes or kale, are sometimes grown for grazing over the winter.

The size of the beef cattle herd has remained fairly stable in recent years, but the relatively small dairy herd has declined by more than 50% since the turn of the millennium, due to economic pressures. Dairy cattle in the atlas area now number around 12,000 animals (less than 5% of the Scottish total, which is largely concentrated in South-West Scotland).

DOMESTIC SHEEP (*Ovis aries*)

The sheep is the most abundant species of domestic livestock in the atlas area, with a population of around 700,000 animals (c.10% of the Scottish total), including around 260,000 breeding ewes, although there has been a decline of about 12% since the year 2000. In the hills, hardy breeds, such as the Scottish Blackface, predominate feeding on rough grassland and heather moorland. They produce mostly single lambs which are used as flock replacements or moved to farms at lower altitudes for fattening. At these lowland farms, there is a wider range of more productive breeds that produce mostly twin lambs. These include crossbreeds, known as Mules, which are produced by crossing ewes of hill breeds with longwool breeds such as the Blue-faced and Border Leicester. These are often then crossed with a ram from a specialist meat breed, such as a Suffolk or Texel, to produce fast-growing and high quality lambs for slaughter.

DOMESTIC PIG (*Sus scrofa domesticus*)

The Aberdeenshire and Moray area is the most important part of Scotland for pig farming, although this may not be obvious to the casual observer as most pigs spend their lives indoors. Despite a 50% decline in numbers since the turn of the millennium, the population of just over 180,000 pigs represents well over half of the Scottish total and is particularly concentrated in the lower Deveron and Ythan catchments (Volkova et al., 2008). The population of breeding sows is around 18,000 animals, which includes the animals that can be seen outdoors on some farms. Commercial pig farming is a high-input, high-output farming system, with each sow capable of producing 24-29 piglets per year and piglets being fattened to slaughter in six months (SAC Consulting, 2015). At the other end of the scale, small numbers of traditional pig breeds and Wild Boars are kept on smallholdings and rare breeds farms. Escapes from these are likely to be the source of free-living Wild Boar sightings.

DOMESTICATED HORSE
(*Equus caballus ferus*)

Prior to the introduction of tractors, horses were a vital part of the farming industry, with over 8,000 used for agricultural work in Aberdeenshire 200 years ago (Keith, 1811). Today, though, fewer than 200 horses are kept for agricultural purposes within the atlas area. Highland ponies were also traditionally used to remove deer carcases from the hill on stalking estates, but this role has largely been replaced by all-terrain vehicles. Despite the decline in working horses, the total horse population has increased by 35% since the year 2000 and is now around 8,000 animals, most of which are kept for leisure purposes.

DOMESTIC GOATS (*Capra hircus*)

About 1,000 Domestic Goats are kept in the atlas area for meat and milk production, involving a variety of modern breeds and crossbreeds. Two hundred years ago there were estimated to be around 1,000 goats in Aberdeenshire alone, but these were concentrated in the upland parts of Marr (Keith, 1811) and may have been connected to the Feral Goat populations that were found in these areas up until the mid-20th century.

OTHER SPECIES

About 1,700 Red Deer are farmed in the atlas area for venison production. These are kept in fields with high fences, but escapes may be the source of some records of the species in the wild in lowland areas. About 400 Alpacas (*Vicugna pacos*) and Llamas (*Lama glama*) are kept in the region for wool production and as companion animals. A herd of around 50 American Bison (*Bison bison*) was established for meat production at Muchalls, south of Aberdeen, in 2005, later moving to Ballogie in Deeside, but was slaughtered in 2014 following a bovine tuberculosis outbreak (Aberdeen Press & Journal, 2014).

Image: Domestic Cattle, Tarland, Ian Francis
Image: Domestic Sheep, Near Alford, Ian Francis
Author: Paul Chapman

131

4 | Distribution patterns and species richness

This atlas is based on 77,496 individual mammal records collected in North-East Scotland and the Cairngorms between 1960 and 2015. The number of records generated has risen steadily through this period. There was a particular increase around the time of the formation of NESBReC in 2000 and the rate of recording has continued to increase through the main recording period for this mammal atlas project from 2013 to 2015 (Figure 4-1). The rates of recording for most species follow this same general pattern with records in a greater number of tetrads between 2000 and 2015 than between 1960 and 1999. A notable exception is Brown Long-eared Bat, perhaps reflecting an increased reliance on bat detectors, with which this species is hard to reliably record, as opposed to roost visits which are now subject to more formal licensing requirements than was previously the case.

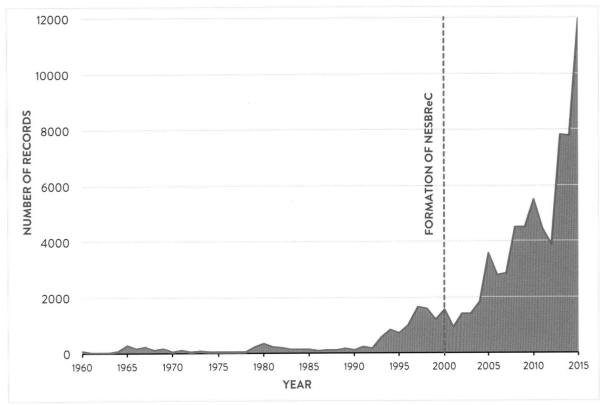

Figure 4-1: *Number of mammal records for each year covered by this mammal atlas.*

The breakdown of records by species reflects a range of factors, including how easy it is to observe and identify a species (or its signs) as well as its actual abundance. Thus Fox, Brown Hare and Badger, for example, are far better recorded than are any vole or shrew species, most of which are undoubtedly considerably more numerically abundant (Table 4-1). High-profile conservation programmes also raise awareness of particular species, including Red and Grey Squirrels, for which recording has been actively promoted for several years. This has led to Red Squirrel being the most frequently recorded species within this atlas project and also Grey Squirrel being the fourth most frequently recorded species, despite its rather restricted distribution in the region. The most widespread species, in terms of the number of tetrads in which it was recorded, is Roe Deer, reflecting both its ubiquity in most lowland areas as well as its relatively conspicuous nature. Roe Deer is closely followed by Mole which, though rarely observed in the flesh, is very easily detected due to the molehills that it creates.

Table 4-1: Number of tetrads in which each species was recorded and overall number of records. The figures for Scottish Wildcat here includes animals reported as wildcat hybrids whilst Feral Ferret also includes records of animals reported as Polecat and as Polecat-Ferret.

Species	No. of tetrads 1960-2015	No. of tetrads 1960-1999	No. of tetrads 2000-2015	No. of records 1960-2015
ROE DEER	1353	351	1253	11345
MOLE	1329	337	1222	4618
BADGER	1253	101	1224	2868
RED SQUIRREL	1109	356	1059	13473
RABBIT	986	328	855	5380
RED DEER	982	215	930	8292
FOX	799	185	702	2381
OTTER	684	177	586	2162
BROWN HARE	683	123	625	2202
MOUNTAIN HARE	574	236	450	3111
HEDGEHOG	487	223	359	1067
AMERICAN MINK	483	81	437	1475
STOAT	463	163	373	943
WATER VOLE	417	172	316	1784
PINE MARTEN	383	27	371	1316
WOOD MOUSE	321	84	261	916
FIELD VOLE	310	103	233	583
COMMON PIPISTRELLE	294	22	353	1213
SOPRANO PIPISTRELLE	288	12	284	872
WEASEL	283	119	188	401
COMMON SHREW	263	117	170	421
GREY SQUIRREL	237	58	224	7301
SCOTTISH WILDCAT	236	57	198	488
BROWN RAT	199	66	146	305
BROWN LONG-EARED BAT	174	112	88	366
BANK VOLE	163	61	112	292
DAUBENTON'S BAT	137	61	91	350
PYGMY SHREW	114	52	66	165
GREY SEAL	75	25	65	748
WATER SHREW	64	20	45	70
COMMON SEAL	43	25	25	294
FERAL CAT	37	15	23	72
HOUSE MOUSE	34	15	20	41
FERAL FERRET	34	16	20	40
NATTERER'S BAT	19	6	14	45
SIKA	11	4	7	4
WILD BOAR	8	0	8	9
NATHUSIUS' PIPISTRELLE	4	1	5	22
FALLOW DEER	4	1	3	5
FERAL GOAT	3	1	2	49
LEISLER'S BAT	2	0	2	5
BEARDED SEAL	2	0	2	2

NUMBER OF MAMMAL RECORDS BY TETRAD

Legend:
- ☐ 0
- ☐ 1 - 9
- ▨ 10 - 49
- ▨ 50 - 199
- ■ 200 - 499
- ■ > 500

0   10 km   20

The pattern of the number of records received for each tetrad reveals a number of particularly well-recorded areas (Figure 4-2). These include, especially, Aberdeen and lower Deeside and mid-Speyside. The former area includes by far the largest concentration of the Human population of the atlas region whilst mid-Speyside is one of the foremost areas for naturalists to visit, as well as containing a number of large nature reserves on which systematic wildlife recording takes place. There are some gaps in which no mammal records were available for this atlas, including some remote parts of the Cairngorms and, especially, central areas of Moray where the Human population density is relatively low and formalised countryside access is not as well developed as elsewhere.

Figure 4-2: Number of mammal records by tetrad, 1960-2015.

MAMMALS SPECIES RICHNESS BY TETRAD

Figure 4-3: Number of mammal species recorded in each tetrad, 1960-2015.

The species richness map (Figure 4-3) reveals a similar, though more dispersed, pattern of hotspots across the atlas area. Aberdeen itself stands out less well from surrounding areas with the whole of the Dee valley and also Donside and coastal areas from Stonehaven north to Peterhead showing areas of high species richness. Mid Speyside again shows a concentration of high mammal diversity. Whilst these areas are likely to be among those most visited by the region's naturalists, they also contain some of our more diverse lowland habitat mixes that might be expected to host the largest range of species. The single tetrad with the highest species count (27) is NO79I, centred on Crathes Castle, near Banchory (see Annex 6). This hosts a diversity of habitats including broadleaved and coniferous woodland, mixed farming and the River Dee whilst old buildings at Crathes Castle provide roost sites for a range of bat species. There is also ample formalised countryside access to facilitate recorder visits.

As with any distribution atlas, this book is only as good as the records that are submitted and analyses of these records will reveal patterns in true distributions as well as in where observers are most active. Nonetheless, these maps provide the first assessment made of where the region's most important areas are for mammals and provide a benchmark upon which future mammal recording can develop and improve.

Image: Fox, Girdle Ness. Paul Chapman

5 | Mammal conservation

This atlas summarises our knowledge of the distributions of mammals in North-East Scotland and the Cairngorms, but we have generally poor understanding of their numbers. This makes it difficult to assess the conservation status of most species. Nevertheless, here we consider briefly some of the main issues, as far as we understand them, related to mammal conservation in our atlas area.

THE GENERAL STATE OF THE MAMMALS OF NORTH-EAST SCOTLAND AND THE CAIRNGORMS

Local population estimates are not available for most mammals present, but the accounts identify some species found in the atlas area whose numbers appear to be notable at a national scale, particularly Red Squirrel, Mountain Hare, Scottish Wildcat, Pine Marten and Red Deer (Table 5-1).

Unlike some other fauna, such as birds, where there have been many obvious changes, the constituent elements of our mammal fauna seem to have remained relatively stable over recent decades, though this conclusion is based on often limited information. Three species were recorded in the atlas area during the twentieth century but have not been recorded since the start of the atlas recording period in 1960: Muskrat, Harvest Mouse and Coypu - though it is not certain that any were ever truly established in the region. Black Rat, which certainly was established, was lost sometime after 1961. On the other hand, we appear to have gained, or newly recognised, the presence of seven species in the decades since 1960: Grey Squirrel, Natterer's Bat, Leisler's Bat, Soprano Pipistrelle (due to separation of the species from Common Pipistrelle in 1993), Nathusius' Pipistrelle, Bearded Seal and Sika. Wild Boar has also been recently recorded after a long absence.

Despite the paucity of trend information, some mammal population levels and distributions have certainly changed since the start of the atlas period, though we can only be sure of this for a proportion of species. Indeed, for 25 land mammal species no trends can be identified, due either to lack of systematically collected data, population fluctuations or because there is only a very small number of records. The evidence in the species accounts suggests, though, that 11 species may have increased in number and expanded their ranges in our area since 1960 (Red Squirrel, Daubenton's Bat, Fox, Badger, Otter, Pine Marten, Grey Seal, Wild Boar, Red Deer, Roe Deer and Human). On the other hand, there is at least some evidence of declines for six species (Rabbit, Brown Hare, Mountain Hare, Hedgehog, Scottish Wildcat and Stoat) whilst Grey Squirrel and American Mink have also declined markedly over recent years in response to culling efforts. In addition, most cetaceans appear to have stable or increasing populations in recent decades.

These changes have been driven by a wide range of factors, which we consider below and in the species accounts. Reference should also be made to the habitat portraits in Chapter 2 for further context.

TABLE 5-1

	Likely local population trend (atlas period)	British population	Atlas area population notable in wider context?
RED SQUIRREL	Increasing	160,000	Yes
GREY SQUIRREL	Decreasing	2,500,000	No
BANK VOLE	Unknown	23,000,000	Unknown
FIELD VOLE	Unknown	75,000,000	Unknown
WATER VOLE	Unknown	1,169,000	Yes
WOOD MOUSE	Unknown	38,000,000	No
HOUSE MOUSE	Unknown	5,000,000	No
BROWN RAT	Unknown	7,000,000	No
RABBIT	Decreasing	37,500,000	No
BROWN HARE	Decreasing	817,500	No
MOUNTAIN HARE	Decreasing	360,000	Yes
HEDGEHOG	Decreasing	310,000	Unknown
MOLE	Unknown	31,000,000	Unknown
COMMON SHREW	Unknown	41,700,000	Unknown
PYGMY SHREW	Unknown	8,600,000	Unknown
WATER SHREW	Unknown	1,900,000	No
DAUBENTON'S BAT	Increasing	150,000	No
NATTERER'S BAT	Unknown	100,000	No
LEISLER'S BAT	Unknown	10,000	No
COMMON PIPISTRELLE	Unknown	2,430,000	Unknown
SOPRANO PIPISTRELLE	Unknown	1,300,000	Unknown
NATHUSIUS' PIPISTRELLE	Unknown	16,000	No
BROWN LONG-EARED BAT	Unknown	245,000	Unknown
SCOTTISH WILDCAT	Decreasing	400	Yes
FERAL CAT	Unknown	813,000	Unknown
FOX	Increasing	258,000	No
BADGER	Increasing	250,000	Unknown
OTTER	Increasing	7,350	Unknown
PINE MARTEN	Increasing	3,500	Yes
STOAT	Decreasing	462,000	Unknown
WEASEL	Unknown	450,000	Unknown
POLECAT	Unknown	47,000	No
FERAL FERRET	Unknown	2,500	No
AMERICAN MINK	Decreasing	110,000	No
COMMON SEAL	Unknown	37,300	No
GREY SEAL	Increasing	116,000	No
BEARDED SEAL	Unknown	0	No
WILD BOAR	Increasing	several hundred	No
RED DEER	Increasing	400,000	Yes
SIKA	Unknown	25,000	No
FALLOW DEER	Unknown	100,000	No
ROE DEER	Increasing	500,000	Unknown
FERAL GOAT	Unknown	3,565	No
HUMAN	Increasing	63,200,000	No

(From previous page) **Table 5-1:** Relative importance of mammal populations in the atlas area within a wider Scottish or British context. The likely local population trend stated is, in most cases, for the whole atlas period but for Grey Squirrel and American Mink the trend is shown as declining to reflect the results of recent culling programs. Figures for British populations are from Harris et al. (1995) except where more recent estimates are referred to in the respective species texts. For Common Seal, Grey Seal and Red Deer, these updated estimates are for the UK. The assessment of whether or not the atlas area population is notable in a wider context should be regarded as provisional and, in some cases, is based on limited or circumstantial evidence. It shows whether or not the population is considered to be markedly higher than the mean population for areas of similar landmass elsewhere in Britain or, in some cases, Scotland.

CONSERVATION ISSUES FOR MAMMALS IN NORTH-EAST SCOTLAND AND THE CAIRNGORMS

AGRICULTURAL CHANGE

Local agriculture has changed greatly in recent decades, including the crops grown, the timing and nature of farm operations and the kinds of habitat features present on farms. In turn, these changes are likely to have affected mammals. The lowland parts of North-East Scotland and the Cairngorms remain a classic area of mixed agriculture, with large areas of cereals grown for feeding livestock and for malting, forming a mosaic with grass fields grazed by livestock or cut for winter feed, mainly as silage. This mixed farmland landscape, which provides a greater variety of food and shelter, has probably helped to slow the declines of some mammals compared with some other parts of the British Isles, where agriculture has become more specialised. Nevertheless, open and intensively managed farmland does not offer good habitat for the majority of our mammals compared with other land cover types, and often they live in the 'non-farmed' habitat niches present.

Field margins and boundaries on farms can provide cover for many mammals, such as this Brown Hare near Alford
Ian Francis, 2009

This dry stone dyke and adjacent vegetation on a farm in Donside provides habitat for voles, mice and their predators, such as Stoats and Weasels
Ian Francis, 2009

WOODLAND MANAGEMENT AND NEW PLANTING

Around 18% of the atlas area is covered by woodland, mostly coniferous plantations, though there are some large areas of Caledonian pinewood and birch woodland. The threefold increase in the area of conifer plantation between the 1940s and the 1980s continued into the 1990s but planting rates have declined to much lower figures recently. The majority of newer planting has been of broad-leaved trees, often in small blocks or strips. Many conifer plantations have been restructured in the last 25 years as they have matured, and all have become more diverse, with greater structural diversity, variation in tree species and age, increased open space and edge habitat, and improvement of water quality in watercourses within plantations. Species that may have benefited from woodland management and expansion of all kinds include Red Squirrel, Fox, Badger, Pine Marten, Roe Deer and perhaps Scottish Wildcat, plus some bats; there is equally conflict between woodland expansion and the grazing and browsing effects of some mammals, especially voles, Rabbits, Mountain Hares and all species of deer.

SEMI-NATURAL HABITAT CHANGE

Chapter 2 summarises the considerable changes in land cover and mammal habitats between the 1940s and the 1980s, some of which have continued to the present day. For 'semi-natural' habitats of higher nature conservation value, there have been large losses of heather moorland, peatlands, scrub, hedgerows and broad-leaved woodland. It appears that few semi-natural habitats have increased to any large degree, though there have been some shifts in their nature. For example, birch woodland and scrub have invaded numerous wetlands or areas of unmanaged moorland; this can be seen well at the Muir of Dinnet, where a formerly open moorland landscape has become naturally established native woodland. Change over time, through vegetation succession, grazing or nutrient enrichment, has affected many semi-natural habitats and these trends remain. In the last ten years or so though, intentional damage to, or destruction of, semi-natural habitats has slowed, with most local development plan policies and agricultural or forestry regulations now designed to prevent such actions. Much of our mammal fauna is arguably best adapted to exploit woodland habitats, and successional shift in that direction may benefit more species than it affects negatively.

WETLANDS, WATER, ENVIRONMENTAL QUALITY AND POLLUTION

Although the Cairngorms experience high precipitation, the remainder of North-East Scotland is a relatively dry part of the country, and most major wetlands were drained long ago. Remaining wetlands are few, small and scattered, but even these are vulnerable, with many losses during the past 20 years. Some wetlands have been created as part of agri-environment schemes, but their nature has changed; for example, moist, soft-edged corners or flood areas have become scarcer and new wetlands often now tend to be steep, hard-edged ponds. Natural lowland wetlands such as raised bogs are now rarely grazed, burned or cut and fens have tended to become unmanaged, leading to vegetation succession, rank herb growth and, on some, colonisation by scrub and trees. The important network of raised bog remnants is still present in Buchan, but elsewhere most have been lost to conifer planting or woodland succession. There are many scattered fens but little is known about their current condition. Nevertheless, all these wetlands probably act as valuable refuges for some mammals, often because they offer non-cultivated rank habitat with cover.

Precipitation and runoff in watercourses are both subject to the influence of various pollutants, though current impacts on mammals are either indirect or unclear. The acidity of rainfall appears to be declining (e.g. see Morecroft et al., 2009) but deposited nitrous oxides are still causing the nutrient enrichment of some habitats, including grasslands which themselves are subject to fertiliser application. Much of the eastern and northern area of North-East Scotland is designated as a 'Nitrate Vulnerable Zone' with restrictions on farming practice designed to reduce nutrient inputs and nitrate and phosphate runoff. The water quality of some watercourses in intensively farmed areas is poor; for example, the Ythan is one of the most enriched of our rivers. Measures are being developed to deal with such issues, including through the EU Water Framework Directive, though other initiatives are a lso underway such as the Dee catchment management plan (see http://www. theriverdee.org). Evidence suggests that organochlorine pollutants in the aquatic environment have reduced following bans, with beneficial impacts on Otters.

INCREASED DEVELOPMENT PRESSURE

Chapter 2 showed that the urban area in North-East Scotland and the Cairngorms increased by 43% between the 1940s and the 1980s. This has continued and, depending on sources and definition, probably up to 5% of the land surface is now covered by urban and related developments. Although some mammals can thrive in urban areas (and Aberdeen is the stronghold for Grey Squirrels in North-East Scotland), in general, densities and diversities of most species are lower (Wembridge & Langton, 2016). The total area under urban land use is still relatively small compared to the UK as a whole.

INCREASED RECREATIONAL PRESSURE

Levels of recreational pressure in the atlas area are probably lower than in many other parts of the country, due to the relatively low Human population. Nevertheless, they are increasing and there may be potential conflicts in some places in terms of possible disturbance to mammals, such as in the high mountains, some woodlands and on water bodies, particularly lochs. Statutory rights introduced by the Land Reform Acts 2003 gave the legal right of access to most land and water bodies, but so far there is little evidence of adverse effects on mammals generally, since many mammals are nocturnal and may co-exist alongside many Human activities (though, as they are hard to monitor, this remains conjectural). Indeed, better access may have encouraged more mammal recording. However, on the coast, there have been some localised disturbance incidents related to seal haul outs, especially at the Ythan estuary, where a statutory protected area was consulted upon in 2015. At sea, some disturbance incidents affecting dolphins and porpoises have occurred, involving boats and jet skis. A code of conduct to prevent this has been developed - the Scottish Marine Wildlife Watching Code (Scottish Natural Heritage, 2006).

CHANGES IN THE MARINE ENVIRONMENT

Our seals and cetaceans are directly affected by the many changes taking place in the marine environment. Other mammals (such as Otter or American Mink) appear to utilise the sea in our area less than in some other parts of Scotland and so may be less likely to be affected. There have been some notable changes in patterns of occurrence of cetaceans off the coast of North-East Scotland. In common with seals, some have recovered in numbers, in part as a result of less direct persecution or hunting. At the same time, the marine environment has changed markedly. Factors include, for example, changes in sea temperatures, plankton populations, numbers of sandeels and many other fish (linked to the impacts of fishing exploitation), levels of oil pollution, plastics and other toxins (some of which are omnipresent in the tissues of marine mammals), along with marine noise and boat disturbance. Detailed consideration of these is not possible here, but there seems little doubt that numbers and usage patterns by marine mammals of the seas around North-East Scotland have changed markedly over time, and will change in future.

SITE PROTECTION, CONSERVATION ACTION AND NATURE RESERVE MANAGEMENT

One key contribution to the conservation of semi-natural mammal habitats in North-East Scotland and the Cairngorms is the network of protected sites, and how they are managed. This is summarised in Table 5-2. Most SSSIs or SACs are not designated directly for mammals but as the habitat is protected it is likely in many cases to benefit them, especially if the area protected is large. Designation is only one step towards conservation, and ensuring that appropriate management occurs is also critical. The extent to which this is happening is still unclear because of insufficient knowledge for many species. However, Table 5-2 shows that almost 7% of North-East Scotland is protected by SSSI designation. Within the Cairngorms National

Park, 49% is designated as Natura 2000 sites (both SACs and SPAs) and therefore of European importance (Cairngorms National Park Authority, 2015b).

TABLE 5-2

Geographic area	No. of SSSI	Area of SSSI (ha)	% of land SSSI	No. of SAC	Area of SAC (ha)	% of land SAC
Cairngorms National Park (total land area = 452,800 ha)	59	108,600	24.0	23	108,300	23.9
North-East Scotland (total land area = 868,699 ha)	124	59,291	6.82	28	50,608	5.82

Table 5-2. Sites protected under nature conservation designations in North-East Scotland and the Cairngorms. Data are from Scottish Natural Heritage (www.snh.org.uk/snhi/default.asp) and Cairngorms National Park Authority. Note that these two geographic areas overlap so the figures here cannot be combined.

SSSI: Site of Special Scientific Interest (under Wildlife & Countryside Act 1981 as modified) SAC: Special Area of Conservation (for wildlife and habitats - under EU 'Habitats' Directive 1992; together with Special Protection Areas (SPAs) under the Birds Directive, they make up Natura 2000 sites)

SPECIES AND HABITAT ACTION PLANS

Originating from the 1992 United Nations Biodiversity Convention, a set of species and habitat action plans was developed as part of the UK Biodiversity Action Plan and Scottish Biodiversity Strategy. This began in North-East Scotland in 1996 and in the precursor of the Cairngorms National Park in 1999. Local Biodiversity Action Plan (LBAP) partnerships formed in each area, lists of qualifying species and habitats were developed, biodiversity 'audits' were undertaken (Alexander et al., 1998; Leaper, 1999) and local action plans produced (North East Scotland Biodiversity Steering Group Partnership, 2000; Cosgrove, 2002). These audits and plans cover many species in a general sense, but there are only a few action plans dealing specifically with mammals in our area (Red Squirrel is one example). In the Cairngorms National Park, the strategy shifted to a comprehensive general plan under 'Cairngorms Nature' in 2013. All plans depend heavily on other mechanisms for delivery of management (such as agri-environment programmes) and their existence has led to the insertion of protection policies in Local Authority plans and other strategies, covering species and biodiversity issues. The partnerships involved in this process have also led to a wider public awareness of the idea of the conservation of biodiversity. This has continued under the Scottish Biodiversity Strategy (Scottish Executive, 2004) and the recent '2020 Route Map' (Scottish Government, 2015a). Such conservation plans, strategies and designations are strongly limited by finance. With sufficient funding and scientific underpinning, benefits could be delivered for some mammals and their status improved. However, funding is rarely sufficient to achieve this, though projects aimed at Red Squirrel and Water Vole conservation have shown some signs of success, and a recent initiative on Scottish Wildcat conservation is very active.

NATURE RESERVES

Within the atlas area, the National Trust for Scotland (NTS) owns the greatest proportion of nature reserves, followed by RSPB Scotland, then other bodies, including Scottish Wildlife Trust (SWT), Scottish Natural Heritage (SNH) and the Woodland Trust. The Local Nature Reserve (LNR) network is dominated in area by Findhorn Bay, though here there has been little active nature conservation work; all other LNRs are small. Most of the highest mountains are owned at least in part by NTS or RSPB Scotland whilst SNH owns the important sand dune, heath and coastal habitats at Sands of Forvie and St Cyrus. The most important sites managed by SWT are Spey Bay, Gight Woods and Red Moss of Netherley. In addition to this, large areas on some estates, such as Glenfeshie and Glen Tanar, are managed with natural processes and nature conservation as important objectives, as are parts of the Forestry Commission Scotland's National Forest Estate. Such land holdings constitute a substantial area of rich habitat for mammals.

LEGISLATION AND SPECIES PROTECTION

The legislative situation for mammals is complex and varies greatly between species. Only a brief summary can be given here: a very thorough account is provided in Harris & Yalden (2008). The legislative provisions in Great Britain for the protection of wild animals are contained primarily in the Wildlife and Countryside Act, 1981, Sections 9-12. The wild animals which are protected are listed in Schedules 5-7 of the Act and the provisions for the granting of licenses and enforcement are set out in Sections 16-27. In Scotland, enforcement provisions were extended and some amendments for protection made by Section 50 and Schedule 6 of the Nature Conservation (Scotland) Act 2004. Specific legislation for protecting Badgers is provided by the Badgers Act, 1992 (amended, for Scotland, by the Nature Conservation (Scotland) Act 2004), for wild deer in the Deer Act, 1963 (amended by the Deer Act, 1991), and for seals in the Conservation of Seals Act 1970. The closed season for seals in (some areas of) Scotland was extended by the Conservation of Seals (Scotland) Order 2002. A non-exhaustive list of other items of important legislation relevant to mammals is given below:

Wildlife & Countryside Act 1981, Schedule 6
Bern Convention, Appendix III
EU Habitats Directive, Annex V
The Conservation (Natural Habitats, &c.) Regulations 1994, Schedule 3
Wild Mammals (Protection) Act 1996
Protection of Wild Mammals (Scotland) Act 2002
Hunting Act 2004
Animal Welfare Act 2006
Conservation of Habitats and Species Regulations 2010, Schedule 4
Wildlife and Natural Environment (Scotland) Act 2011

Of our native terrestrial and marine mammals, many of the more common species do not receive specific legal protection, but there are still laws that protect them against cruelty or exploitation. However, some species of mammal found in Scotland receive specific protection because they are rare, vulnerable to disturbance or have a history of persecution. These are Red Squirrel, Water Vole, hares, bats, Scottish Wildcat, Badger, Otter, Pine Marten, seals, deer and cetaceans whilst shrews receive protection insofar as live trapping requires a license (Scottish Natural Heritage, 2015).

Certain methods of killing or taking wild animals are prohibited. In Great Britain, it is an offence to use any self-locking snare, bow, crossbow, explosives or decoys for the purpose of causing bodily harm, killing or taking any wild animal. Snares must be inspected at least once every 24 hours and in Scotland, it is an offence to sell a self-locking snare, or to possess one without reasonable excuse. Generally, prohibited or restricted methods (depending on the species) include any trap, snare, net, electrical device, poison or stupefying substance, automatic or semi-automatic weapons, smoke, gas, artificial lights, mirrors, sound recordings or decoys and any mechanically propelled vehicles in immediate pursuit of a protected wild animal for the purpose of driving, killing or taking the animal. Foxes cannot be hunted by pursuit dogs. The law requires trappers to exclude non-target species from traps set, for example in tunnels or cages, but in practice it is often still possible for protected species to enter them; for example, a trap set for a Stoat may well not exclude a Water Vole.

In the United Kingdom, acts which are prohibited under legislation can be authorised by a licence issued by the appropriate authority for the purpose of science, education, conservation and photography, or to preserve public health or safety, to prevent the spread of disease or to prevent serious damage to livestock, crops, growing timber, property or fisheries.

MAMMALS, NATURE CONSERVATION AND CONFLICTS WITH HUMAN ACTIVITIES

The numbers of some of our mammals are very directly influenced by people - they are killed deliberately to reduce numbers, for food or sport, or controlled or persecuted because of actual or perceived impacts on human health and property, crops, trees or other animals (usually game birds or livestock). The species most affected by direct killing are Grey Squirrel, mice, Brown Rat, Rabbit, Brown and Mountain Hare, Mole, Fox, Stoat, Weasel, American Mink, deer and also at times Grey Seal (legally under licence and possibly also illegally) and probably Badger and Pine Marten (illegally). There are no local estimates as to the numbers killed for most of these species. The few estimates that are available include for deer shot on estates (Scottish Natural Heritage data), mammalian predators also killed on estates (Game & Wildlife Conservation Trust's National Gamebag Census (Aebischer et al., 2011)) and rodents killed by Local Authority Environmental Health departments. In recent years, some Red Grouse shooting estates have intensified their trapping of mammals and many now hold high densities of 'bridge' and other such traps.

Inadvertent killing is also widespread, including road collision deaths, entrapment with litter or in discarded bottles. In particular there may be a large impact of domestic pets, especially cats, on several small mammals. Some illegal killing of protected species takes place in our area - principally Brown Hare coursing and some killing of Badgers in snares and perhaps through Badger baiting, though this seems to be rare here.

Brown Rat discarded from bridge trap, Deeside. These traps are positioned at artificially created crossing points and should be set such that only target species which can be legally killed can enter
Ian Francis, 2015

For almost all of these, we have no information as to whether mammal population levels are affected. Clearly, there should be local impacts, at least over short time periods (this is the primary purpose of rat and mouse killing, deer shooting and 'vermin' control on shooting estates). But many small mammals can breed quickly and longer term population impacts may be hard to discern, especially when considered along with habitat changes

Circular disturbed ground round a tree where a Badger had been trapped for some time in a snare on a Donside estate
Ian Francis, 2005

and weather impacts. It is highly likely that long-term relaxation in killing was one reason why Pine Martens have been able to establish themselves once more and why Foxes have become more abundant. Conversely, a concerted attempt to eradicate American Mink has led to major reductions in their numbers in some parts of our atlas area and consequent recovery in Water Vole numbers; Grey Squirrel has also been subject to range reduction in this way (Figure 5-1). This, systematic, landscape-scale killing clearly can have a major impact on the numbers of some mammals.

Figure 5-1. Range contraction of Grey Squirrel. For each recorded tetrad, the colour indicates the date class of the more recent record up to the end of 2016. Targeted Grey Squirrel control has reduced the range of the species and, at the end of the atlas period, records were concentrated in a few small areas in and close to Aberdeen.

Moles killed and displayed on fence, North Yorkshire. Such displays can also sometimes be seen in North-East Scotland.
Martyn Gorman, 2005

FIGURE 5-1. RANGE CONTRACTION OF GREY SQUIRREL

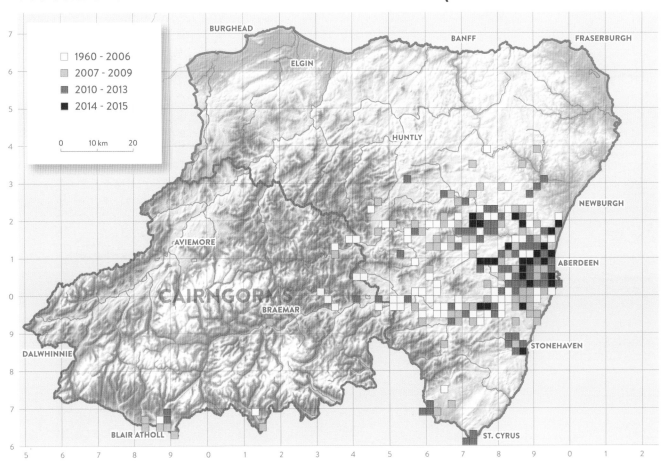

REINTRODUCTIONS AND INTRODUCTIONS

Some human activities boost the numbers of certain mammals, directly or indirectly. For example, earlier in the 20th century, American Mink were kept for fur production at several places in the atlas area and escapees resulted in the establishment of wild populations. Grey Squirrels were introduced to the area, leading to the current population centred on Aberdeen. Deer are farmed, and escapes may occur, and this is also true of Wild Boar. Although Eurasian Beavers have not yet been recorded in our area, they are present only a few kilometres from the Cairngorms National Park in the Garry catchment near Pitlochry. It seems plausible that they will reach our atlas area soon. These emanated from escapes or releases in Tayside over the previous two decades and, in November 2016, received legal protection as a reintroduced population of a native species. There is also a free-ranging herd of domestic Reindeer in the Cairngorms, with a unique and long-established history.

MAMMALS AND IMPACTS ON LAND

Mammals can cause obvious impacts at local or landscape levels. Locally, these include Rabbits and Moles, each of which can create substantial areas clearly affected by their activities. Often these impacts are seen as undesirable (such as Rabbits eating crops) but they can also be viewed more positively, such as when Rabbit grazing helps maintain flower-rich short swards. But probably the best example of large scale impact is that of Red Deer, where in parts of the atlas area, densities are high and there is a clear negative effect on tree regeneration and the condition of vegetation communities. Figure 5-2 shows the variation in Red Deer numbers across our area, and demonstrates where they are at their highest density - principally in upper Deeside and parts of highland Perthshire. The effects of high deer numbers are well known, and lead to the need for fencing around woodland and resultant large differences in vegetation within and outwith exclosures. In other parts though, Red Deer are barely present, so their impacts are negligible. However, despite these impacts, most wild mammals have little effect on landscapes compared to domestic livestock.

A large scale Rabbit warren near Towie, Donside
Ian Francis, 2016

150

*Moles also create landscape
impacts, Strathdon
Ian Francis, 2016*

FIGURE 5-2. RED DEER PEAK COUNTS

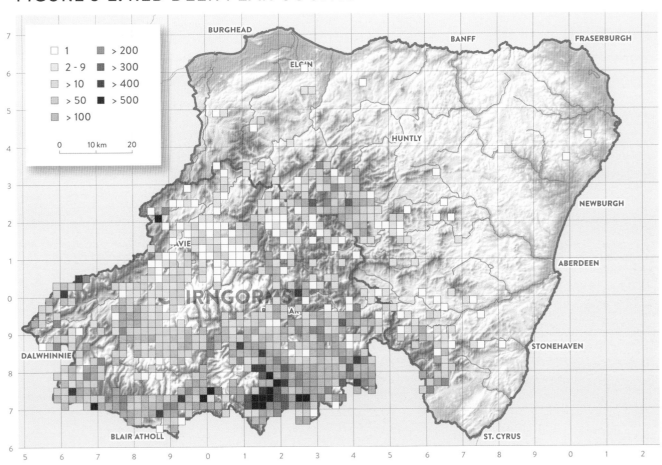

*Figure 5-2: Red Deer peak counts. The colour in each tetrad represents the highest single count reported from that tetrad
between 2006 and 2015, using data used to compile the distribution map on page 113, which includes counts from Deer
Commission of Scotland (2006 to 2010) and Scottish Natural Heritage (2010 to 2015) in addition to records submitted
directly to NESBReC.*

*Fence effect - excluding high
numbers of Red Deer from a
woodland near Braemar creates
short vegetation outside and a
dense understory within*
Ian Francis, 2009

*Mineral licks within pine woodland
near Blair Atholl cause locally
intense deer browsing and
trampling*
Ian Francis, 2015

MAMMALS AS PREDATORS AND PREY

In rural areas, especially where gamebirds are reared for shooting, where sheep are widespread or where there are populations of declining ground-nesting birds (such as Capercaillie or Curlew), the impacts of predation by mammals are widely talked about and are controversial. The balance of predators (mammal and bird) has changed over time as habitats and the impacts of direct killing have also changed. Some mammal species are widely considered to be significant predators and are thus controlled on sporting estates, farms and sometimes nature reserves. Foxes are probably the most widespread predator and many thousands are thought to be killed in our area. Studies from elsewhere have shown they can indeed be influential on prey populations, and their removal has been demonstrated to improve the prospects of the species to be conserved (e.g. Fletcher et al., 2010).

The impacts of most other mammalian predators are less certain. There is a long list of other species which do take a wide range of native and domestic prey; all bat species (solely eating insects), seals, Scottish Wildcat and Feral Cat, and all eight mustelid species. Many Weasels and Stoats are killed on shooting estates, but there are few studies which show what impact they have on prey and to what degree killing them affects this. Recently, there has been controversy about the potential impacts of Pine Martens on Capercaillie breeding success in the Cairngorms and Deeside. While they certainly do take Capercaillie eggs and probably chicks, it is still not clear to what extent this is a major controlling factor on the bird's population. Finally, the most important predators of all are Humans - we influence all other mammals directly and indirectly - and of course suffer no direct predators of our own! In fact, Humans and other mammals have grown accustomed to a 'predator scarce' environment, with Wolf, Brown Bear and Lynx lost first of all, then smaller predators all reduced substantially from late 1800s, and we are now adjusting towards a new status quo as some protected mammalian (and avian) predators are allowed to recover. As prey populations try to adapt, we may have to adjust our perceptions of what is 'normal'.

Part of a herd of over 600 Red Deer in Garbh-choire, Braemar. This species has impacts at a landscape scale
Ian Francis, 2013

153

Mammals also function as extremely important prey species. The majority of our smaller species are eaten by other mammals and many birds of prey. In some cases, mammals, especially rodents, shrews and Rabbits, strongly influence the numbers of their predators, whose populations fluctuate according to prey abundance. This is as true of Foxes and Pine Martens as it is of Barn Owls and Buzzards. This subject is too complex to be covered here, but there are many and subtle interactions between habitats, human influence and mammal population levels such that all can change constantly over time and between different places.

THE IMPACTS OF INTRODUCED MAMMALS ON NATIVE SPECIES

Among the 43 species for which distribution maps are included in this atlas, 11 are introduced to the region by man and a further three have, to a greater or lesser extent, been reintroduced. Some of these introductions happened so long ago that the species are now regarded as a natural part of our fauna and even in some cases, notably Brown Hare, benefit from conservation actions. Other introduced species, such as Brown Rat and Rabbit, are locally controlled where they cause nuisance or economic loss. The term "invasive" is applied to introduced species that cause an observable detrimental impact to the local ecosystem and native species. However, no introduction is without some impact, albeit often unmeasurable, such as on the plants or animals eaten by the introduced animal and/or competition that this introduces with those species already present. Among the mammals, there are a number of cases of significant direct impact of introduced species on native species. Some are well documented and have prompted conservation projects to reduce the impact while others are less well known or have occurred far enough into the past that the current species interactions are seen now as the norm. The most clearly observed such impacts in the atlas area fall, broadly, into four main types as detailed below.

PREDATION

The best established introduced carnivore in the region is the American Mink. Although the Mink's diet is broad, and includes amphibians, small mammals, fish and birds, it is their impact on Water Vole populations that has received most attention. Water Voles in Britain have declined by 98.7% over the period 1939 to 1998. Habitat loss may have played a role in this but the impact of predation by American Mink is thought to be the principal driver (Strachan et al., 2000).

COMPETITION

The mechanics behind how the introduced Grey Squirrel interacts with the largely reintroduced population of the native Red Squirrel are still not fully understood. Direct antagonism is rarely observed but it appears that Grey Squirrels are better able to exploit resources, at least in broadleaved woodland, leading to reduced fitness and, ultimately, population decline of Red Squirrels (e.g. Gurnell et al., 2004). Grey Squirrels have now replaced Red Squirrels across most of Britain and Ireland though a substantial proportion of the remaining Red Squirrels are in the atlas area. Across most of Britain, Grey Squirrels also pass Squirrelpox virus to the Reds. This is generally harmless to the Greys but has a devastating impact on Red Squirrels, causing death in most cases. The virus is not yet, however, present in the atlas area.

A more historical and less documented likely example of competition is that of Mountain Hares and Brown Hares. Mountain Hares were once more widespread in Britain and Ireland than they currently are. Both woodland expansion and the spread of the Brown Hare, since its introduction, probably in the Iron Age, have been suggested as drivers of the Mountain Hare's current British range, which is now mostly confined to the Scottish uplands (Iason et al., 2008). In Ireland, where Brown Hare is only represented by a small 19th century introduction, Mountain Hares remain widely distributed at all altitudes. As the two species met in Britain so long ago, their interactions have not been much studied, though research elsewhere in Europe suggests that Brown Hares are able to replace Mountain Hares through competitive exclusion (summarised by Thulin, 2003) - in effect, Brown Hares are more efficient at exploiting resources. Going forward, in a warming climate, it is possible that the Brown Hare's range may further expand uphill, to the detriment of Mountain Hares.

Milder winters may increase competition between Mountain Hares and Brown Hares, Morven
Nick Littlewood, 2013

HYBRIDISATION

When a native species is so closely related to an introduced species that they are able to produce fertile hybrid offspring, there is a risk of dilution of the native gene pool. One such example is the Scottish Wildcat. Most of its historic range contraction was due to land use change and persecution, but Feral Cats are now the major threat to its continued survival. Whilst Feral Cats may negatively impact on Scottish Wildcats, through disease transmission and competition for resources, it is hybridisation that most threatens the integrity of remaining wildcats in Scotland (e.g. Daniels & Corbett, 2003). Domestic cats have been present in Britain for around 2,000 to 3,000 years, so the risk of hybridisation has existed for a very long time. However, the currently tiny Scottish Wildcat population is especially vulnerable, given that Feral Cats and Feral Cat/wildcat hybrids now outnumber Scottish Wildcats across most of the species' range (e.g. Littlewood et al., 2014; Kilshaw et al., 2015).

A comparable potential scenario exists between Sika, introduced from Japan, and the native Red Deer, albeit at an earlier stage in interactions between the species. Sika were brought to British deer parks in the 19th century from where they established into the wild. Hybridisation between these animals appears not to be frequent though a small number of instances can lead to a substantial proportion of animals having mixed heritage. For example, at a site in Argyll where the two species have been in contact since around 1970, by 1996 some 44% were determined to be hybrids with the proportion of pure Red Deer declining in the population (Senn et al., 2010a). A study based on samples collected from four sites in the western part of the Cairngorms National Park in 2008 and 2009, though, did not reveal significant genetic evidence of hybridisation at that time (Senn & Pemberton, 2009).

FOOD RESOURCES

Not all interactions between introduced and native mammals are negative ones for the native species. Introduced mammals can bring a new potential food resource for predators, none more so than the Rabbit. Stoats may specialise on feeding on Rabbits during times when the Rabbit population is high (McDonald et al., 2000) and fluctuations in Stoat populations may track large changes in Rabbit availability (McDonald & Harris, 1997). Scottish Wildcat distribution can also closely match the availability of Rabbits, which can make up a substantial proportion of their diet (Silva et al., 2013). Clearly the diets of both predator species have adapted to take advantage of a prey item that was not available to them prior to the Rabbit's introduction in Norman times.

This summary is not exhaustive and describes just some of the most direct causal interactions between introduced and native mammal species. Many, more subtle, interactions will shape species distributions on a fine scale but may be masked by impacts of habitat change. It is notable, though, that the three highest profile mammal conservation projects in the region are each aimed at improving the status of a single mammal species (Red Squirrel, Water Vole and Scottish Wildcat) and each are examples where an introduced mammal is the greatest threat. The long-term viability of maintaining programmes aimed at conserving native mammals through control of non-natives or, indeed, eliminating the introduced species that are now causing such issues, is, though, yet to be established.

Stoat with Rabbit prey, Dinnet
Nick Littlewood, 2015

CLIMATE CHANGE

The climate of the area is projected to change in the coming decades, in line with global trends. There is some evidence of gradually increasing temperatures, particularly in summer, changes to the phenology of spring warming, fewer and less severe snowy periods particularly at mid-altitudes (Harrison et al., 2001; Barnett et al., 2006) and increasingly erratic rainfall events (including severe floods). Despite projections of likely climate change, to date there is little direct evidence of mammal numbers or distribution in North-East Scotland or the Cairngorms having responded clearly to trends in climate. This may be due largely to the complexity of such factors and the difficulty of carrying out the necessary studies, together with absence of monitoring. There are numerous potential impacts on mammals that could be predicted resulting from, for example, a higher incidence of warmer winters, wetter and stormy weather, potentially reduced snow cover and longer growing seasons. There could also be significant impacts on bats - both on survival in winter and also the arrival of southern species into the area. But until our knowledge of our local mammals improves, the potential impacts of climate change must remain speculative.

CONCLUSIONS

North-East Scotland and the Cairngorms is an important part of the British Isles for many mammals. A range of species offers some great spectacles, with the chance to see some of our most renowned mammals. This atlas has summarised the knowledge we have, and set a baseline for further survey, recording, study and conservation action. Our mammal populations are changing, and we understand them better than ever, but the essentially cryptic and often nocturnal behaviour of many species leads to there being many gaps in our knowledge. We invite all those who care about our local mammals to take up the challenge and build on this atlas; we look forward to its successor and hope that it will take mammal study and conservation to levels well beyond those achievable in this atlas.

Image: *Daubenton's Bat, Mosset Burn. Mark Shewry*

R | References

Image: Badgers, Glen Affric, Highland. Harry Scott

REFERENCES

Aars, J., Lambin, X., Denny, R. & Griffin, A.C. (2001) Water vole in the Scottish uplands: distribution patterns of disturbed and pristine populations ahead and behind the American mink invasion front. *Animal Conservation*, 4: 187-194.

Abbas, F., Morellet, N., Hewison, A.J.M., Merlet, J., Cargnelutti, B., Lourtet, B., Angibault, J-M., Daufresne, T., Aulagnier, S. & Verheyden, H. (2011) Landscape fragmentation generates spatial variation of diet composition and quality in a generalist herbivore. *Oecologia*, 167: 401-411.

Aberdeen City Council (2015) Briefing Paper 2015/02. Population Report, Aberdeen City and Shire.

Aberdeen Press & Journal (2014) Story from website, https://www.pressandjournal.co.uk/fp/news/aberdeenshire/8694/scotlands-only-bison-heard-slaughtered/ (accessed 08-02-16).

Abernethy, K. (1994) The establishment of a hybrid zone between red and sika deer (genus *Cervus*). *Molecular Ecology*, 3: 551-562.

Aebischer, N.J., Davey, P.D. & Kingdon, N.G. (2011) *National Gamebag Census: Mammal Trends to 2009*. Game & Wildlife Conservation Trust, Fordingbridge.

Agrell, J. (1995) A shift in female social organisation independent of relatedness: an experimental study on the field vole (*Microtus agrestis*). *Behavioural Ecology*, 6: 182-191.

Albon, S.D., Brewer, M.J., O'Brien, S., Nolan, A.J. & Cope, D. (2007) Quantifying the grazing impacts associated with different herbivores on rangelands. *Journal of Applied Ecology*, 44: 1176-1187.

Alderton, D. (1999) *Rodents of the World*. Blandford, London.

Alexander, G., Leaper, G., Francis, I. & Tulloch, M. (1998) *Biodiversity in North-East Scotland: An Audit of Priority Species and Habitats*. NE Scotland Local Biodiversity Action Plan Steering Group, Aberdeen.

Altringham, J.D. (2003) *British Bats*. Collins New Naturalist Library, Harper Collins, Glasgow.

Anderwald, P., Evans, P.G.H., Canning, C., Hepworth, K., Innes, M., Macdonald, P., Sim, I., Stockin, K. & Weir, C. (2010) *Cetaceans of the East Grampian Region*. Sea Watch Foundation, Aberdeen.

Anon (2013) *Searching for 'Ratty'*. Friday 6th September 2013. Wildlife Trust, http://www.wildlifetrusts.org/news/2013/09/05/searching-%E2%80%98ratty%E2%80%99 (accessed 02-01-16).

Arnold, H.R. (1993) Atlas of Mammals in Britain. *ITE Research Publication No. 6*. NERC, London. [including data from this atlas held on the National Biodiversity Network Gateway: http://data.nbn.org.uk]

Atkinson, R.P.D., Macdonald, D.W. & Johnson, P.J. (1994) The status of the European mole *Talpa europaea* as an agricultural pest and its management. *Mammal Review*, 24: 73-90.

Aulagnier, S., Haffner, P., Mitchell-Jones, A.J., Moutou, F. & Zima, J. (2009) *Mammals of Europe, North Africa and the Middle East*. A & C Black, London.

Baines, D., Aebischer, N., MacLeod, A. & Woods, J. (2011) Assessing the activity of predators in relation to capercaillie hen densities and breeding performance. *Scottish Natural Heritage Commissioned Report 415*.

Baker, P.A. & Harris, S. (2008) Fox *Vulpes vulpes*. pp 407-423 in S. Harris & D.W. Yalden (eds.) *Mammals of the British Isles: Handbook 4th Edition*. The Mammal Society, Southampton.

Baker, P.J., Ansell, R.J., Dodds, P.A.A., Webber, C.E. & Harris S. (2003) Factors affecting the distribution of small mammals in an urban area. *Mammal Review*, 33: 95-100.

Baker, P.J., Bentley, A.J., Ansell, R.J. & Harris, S. (2005) Impact of predation by domestic cats *Felis catus* in an urban area. *Mammal Review*, 35: 302-312.

Balharry, D. & Daniels, M. (1998) Wild living cats in Scotland. *Scottish Natural Heritage Research, Survey and Monitoring Report. No 23*.

Balharry, E., Jefferies, D.J. & Birks, J.D.S. (2008) Pine Marten *Martes martes*. pp. 447-455 in S. Harris & D.W. Yalden (eds.) *Mammals of the British Isles: Handbook 4th Edition*. The Mammal Society, Southampton.

Balharry, E.A., McGowan, G.M., Kruuk, H. & Halliwell, E. (1996) Distribution of pine martens in Scotland as determined by field survey and questionnaire. *Scottish Natural Heritage Research, Survey and Monitoring Report. No. 48*.

Barlow, K.E. & Jones, G. (1999) Roosts, echolocation calls and wing morphology of two phonic types of *Pipistrellus pipistrellus*. *Zeitschrift fur Saugetierkunde*, 64: 257-268.

Barlow, K.E., Briggs, P.A., Haysom, K.A., Hutson, A.M., Lechiara, N.L., Racey, P.A., Walsh, A.L. & Langton, S.D. (2015) Citizen Science reveals trends in bat populations: The National Bat Monitoring Programme in Great Britain. *Biological Conservation*, 182: 14-26.

Barne, J.H., Robson, C.F., Kasnowska, S.S., Doody, J.P. & Davidson, N.C. (1996) *Coasts and Seas of the United Kingdom. Region 3, North-east Scotland: Cape Wrath to St Cyrus*. JNCC, Peterborough.

Barnett, C., Hossell, J., Perry, M., Procter, C. & Hughes, G. (2006) *A Handbook of Climate Trends across Scotland*. SNIFFER project CC03. Scotland and Northern Ireland Forum for Environmental Research.

Bat Conservation Trust (2010a) Brown long-eared *Plecotus auritus*. Factsheet: http://www.bats.org.uk/data/files/Species_Info_sheets/brownlongeared.pdf (accessed 13-12-16).

Bat Conservation Trust (2010b) Daubenton's Bat *Myotis daubentonii*. Factsheet: http://www.bats.org.uk/data/files/Species_Info_sheets/Daubentons_Bat.pdf (accessed 13-12-16).

Bat Conservation Trust (2016a) *Common Pipistrelle Population Trends*. http://www.bats.org.uk/pages/-common_pipistrelle-821.html (accessed 13-12-16).

Bat Conservation Trust (2016b) *Soprano Pipistrelle Population Trends*. http://www.bats.org.uk/pages/-soprano_pipistrelle-823.html (accessed 13-12-16).

Battersby, J. (ed.) & Tracking Mammals Partnership (2005) *UK Mammals: Species Status and Population Trends. First Report by the Tracking Mammals Partnership*. JNCC/Tracking Mammals Partnership, Peterborough.

Baumler, W. (1975) Activity of some mammals in the field. *Acta Theriologica*, 20: 365-379.

BCT/JNCC (2014) *The State of the UK's Bats 2014: National Bat Monitoring Programme Population Trends*. The Bat Conservation Trust, London.

Beck, A. (1995) Fecal analysis of European bat species. *Myotis*, 32-33: 109-119.

Bentley, E.W. (1964) A further loss of ground by *Rattus rattus* L. in the United Kingdom during 1956-61. *Journal of Animal Ecology*, 33: 371-373.

Berry, R.J., Tattersall, F.H. & Hurst, J. (2008) House Mouse *Mus domesticus*. pp. 141-149 in S. Harris & D.W. Yalden (eds.) *Mammals of the British Isles: Handbook 4th Edition*. The Mammal Society, Southampton.

Birks, J.D.S. (2008) *The Polecat Survey of Britain 2004-2006: A Report on the Polecat's Distribution, Status and Conservation*. Vincent Wildlife Trust, Ledbury.

Birks, J.D.S. (2015) *Polecats*. Whittet, Stansted.

Birks, J.D.S. & Kitchener, A.C. (eds.) (1999) *The Distribution and Status of the Polecat Mustela putorius in Britain in the 1990s*. Vincent Wildlife Trust, London.

Birks, J.D.S. & Kitchener, A.C. (2008) Polecat *Mustela putorius*. pp. 476-485 in S. Harris & D.W. Yalden (eds.) *Mammals of the British Isles: Handbook 4th Edition*. The Mammal Society, Southampton.

Bodey, T.W., Bearhop, S. & McDonald, R.A. (2010) The diet of an invasive non-native predator, the feral ferret, and implications for the conservation of ground-nesting birds. *European Journal of Wildlife Research*, 57: 107-117.

Bonesi, L., Chanin, P. & Macdonald, D.W. (2004) Competition between Eurasian otter *Lutra lutra* and American mink *Mustela vison* probed by niche shift. *Oikos*, 106: 19-26.

Bonesi, L., Dunstone, N. & O'Connell, M. (2000) Winter selection of habitats within intertidal foraging areas by mink (*Mustela vison*). *Journal of Zoology*, 250: 419-424.

Bonesi, L., Strachan, R. & Macdonald, D.W. (2006) Why are there fewer signs of mink in England? Considering multiple hypotheses. *Biological Conservation*, 130: 268-277.

Boursot, P., Auffray, J.C., Britton-Davidian, J. & Bonhomme, F. (1993) The evolution of house mice. *Annual Review of Ecology and Systematics*, 24: 119-152.

Brassey, R. & Tonkin, M. (2014) *Evaluation of Spring 2014 Squirrel Survey*. Saving Scotland's Red Squirrels unpublished report.

British Association (1963) *The North-East of Scotland*. British Association for the Advancement of Science. The Central Press, Aberdeen.

British Marine Life Study Society (2016) Bearded Seal *Erignathus barbatus* http://www.glaucus.org.uk/Bearded.htm (accessed 09-02-16).

Brown, R.W., Lawrence, M.J. & Pope, J. (2004) *Hamlyn Guide Animals Tracks, Trails & Signs*. Octopus Publishing Group, London.

Brownlow, A., Davison N. & ten Doeschate, M. (2015) Scottish Marine Animal Stranding Scheme *Annual Report 2014 1 January to 31 December 2014 for Marine Scotland, Scottish Government*. SRUC, Inverness.

Bruce, B. (2010) *Forth Islands Bird Report 2009*. Forth Seabird Group.

Bryce, R., Oliver, M.K., Davies, L., Gray, H., Urquhart, J. & Lambin, X. (2011) Turning back the tide of American mink invasion at an unprecedented scale through community participation and adaptive management. *Biological Conservation*, 144: 575-583.

Buckland, S.T., Bell, M.V. & Picozzi, N. (eds.) (1990) *The Birds of North-East Scotland*. North-East Scotland Bird Club, Aberdeen.

Bullock, D.J. (2008) Feral Goat *Capra hircus*. pp. 628-633 in S. Harris & D.W. Yalden (eds.) *Mammals of the British Isles: Handbook 4th Edition*. The Mammal Society, Southampton.

Butler, J.R.A., Middlemas, S.J., McKelvey, S.A., McMyn, I., Leyshon, B., Walker, I., Thompson, P.M., Boyd, I.L., Duck, C., Armstrong, J.D., Graham, I.M. & Baxter, J.M. (2008) The Moray Firth Seal Management Plan: an adaptive framework for balancing the conservation of seals, salmon, fisheries and wildlife tourism in the UK. *Aquatic Conservation: Marine and Freshwater Ecosystems*, 18: 1025-1038.

Byrne, A.W., Sleeman, D.P., O'Keeffe, J. & Davenport, J. (2012) The ecology of the European badger (*Meles meles*) in Ireland: a review. *Biology and Environment: Proceedings of the Royal Irish Academy*, 112B: 105-132.

Cairngorms National Park Authority (2015a) http://cairngorms.co.uk/caring-future/local-economy/tourism (accessed 23-01-16).

Cairngorms National Park Authority (2015b) Facts & Figures. http://cairngorms.co.uk/discover-explore/facts-figures/ (accessed 13-12-16).

Campbell, S. & Hartley, G. (2010) *Wild Boar Distribution in Scotland*. Poster Presentation - 8th International Symposium on Wild Boar and Other Suids.

Campos-Arceiz, A. & Takatsuki, S. (2005) Food habits of sika deer in the Shiranuka Hills, eastern Hokkaido: a northern example from the north-south variations in food habits in sika deer. *Ecological Research*, 20: 129-133.

Canning, S.J. (2007) *Cetacean Distribution and Habitat Use along the East Coast of Scotland*. PhD Thesis, University of Aberdeen.

Canning, S.J., Santos, M.B., Reid, R.J., Evans, P.G.H., Sabin, R.C., Bailey, N. & Pierce, G.J. (2008) Seasonal distribution of white-beaked dolphins (*Lagenorhynchus albirostris*) in UK waters with new information on diet and habitat use. *Journal of the Marine Biological Association of the United Kingdom*, 88: 1159-1166.

Capreolus Wildlife Consultancy (2005) The ecology and conservation of water voles in upland habitats. *Scottish Natural Heritage Commissioned Report No. 099 (ROAME No. F99AC320)*.

Carter, P. & Churchfield, S. (2006) Distribution and habitat occurrence of water shrews in Great Britain. *Environment Agency Science Report Science Report SC010073/SR*.

Caryl, F.M., Raynor, R., Quine, C.P. & Park, K.J. (2012) The seasonal diet of British pine marten determined from genetically identified scats. *Journal of Zoology*, 288: 252-259.

Chadwick, A.H., Ratcliffe, P.R. & Abernethy, K. (1996) Sika deer in Scotland: density, population size, habitat use and fertility - some comparisons with red deer. *Scottish Forestry*, 50: 8-16.

Chanin, P. (2003) *Ecology of the European Otter*. Conserving Natura 2000 Rivers Ecology Series No. 10. English Nature, Peterborough.

Cheney, B., Cockrey, R., Durban, J.W., Grellier, K., Hammond, P.S., Islas-Villanueva, V., Janik, V.M., Lusseau, S.M., Parsons, K.M., Quick, N.J., Wilson, B. & Thompson, P.M. (2014) Long-term trends in the use of a protected area by small cetaceans in relation to changes in population status. *Global Ecology and Conservation*, 2: 118-128.

Cheney, B., Thompson, P.M., Ingram, S.N., Hammond, P.S., Stevick, P.T., Durban, J.W., Culloch, R.M., Elwen, S.H., Mandleberg, L., Janik, V.M., Quick, N.J., Islas-Villanueva, V., Robinson, K.P., Costa, M., Eisfeld, S.M., Walters, A., Phillips, C., Weir, C.R., Evans, P.G.H., Anderwald, P., Reid, R.J., Reid, J.B. & Wilson, B. (2013) Integrating multiple data sources to assess the distribution and abundance of bottlenose dolphins *Tursiops truncatus* in Scottish waters. *Mammal Review*, 43: 71-88.

Churchfield, S. (1984) Dietary separation in three species of shrew inhabiting watercress beds. *Journal of Zoology, London*, 204: 211-228.

Churchfield, S. (1988) *Shrews of the British Isles*. Shire Publications, Princes Risborough.

Churchfield, S. (1998) Habitat use by water shrews, the smallest of amphibious mammals. pp 49-68 in N. Dunstone & M. Gorman (eds.) *Behaviour and Ecology of Riparian Mammals*. Symposia of the Zoological Society of London 71, Cambridge University Press, Cambridge.

Churchfield, S. (2002) Why are shrews so small? The costs and benefits of small size in northern temperate *Sorex* species in the context of foraging habits and prey supply. *Acta Theriologica*, 47, Suppl. 1: 169-184.

Churchfield, S., Barber, J. & Quinn, C. (2000) A new survey method for Water Shrews (*Neomys fodiens*) using baited tubes. *Mammal Review*, 30: 249-254.

Churchfield. S., Hollier, J. & Brown, V.K. (1991) The effects of small mammal predators on grassland invertebrates, investigated by field exclosure experiment. *Oikos*, 60: 283-290.

Churchfield, S., Rychlik, L. & Taylor, J.R.E (2012) Food resources and foraging habits of the common shrew, *Sorex araneus*: does winter food shortage explain Dehnel's phenomenon? *Oikos*, 121: 1593-1602.

Churchfield, S. & Searle, J.B. (2008a) Common Shrew *Sorex araneus*. pp. 257-265 in S. Harris & D.W. Yalden (eds.) *Mammals of the British Isles: Handbook 4th Edition*. The Mammal Society, Southampton.

Churchfield, S. & Searle, J.B. (2008b) Pygmy Shrew *Sorex minutus*. pp. 267-271 in S. Harris & D.W. Yalden (eds.) *Mammals of the British Isles: Handbook 4th Edition*. The Mammal Society, Southampton.

Clutton-Brock, T.H., Coulson, T. & Milner, J.M. (2004) Red deer stocks in the Highlands of Scotland. *Nature*, 429: 261-262.

CluttonBrock, T.H., Guinness, F.E. & Albon, S.D. (1982) *Red Deer: Behavior and Ecology of Two Sexes*. University of Chicago Press, Chicago.

Collier, R. (2013) *Wild Goats - Ray Colliers Wildlife in the North*. http://www.wildernesscottages.co.uk/blog/2013/12/wild-goats-ray-colliers-wildlife-north/ (accessed 04-11-15).

Collins, J. (ed.) (2016) *Bat Surveys for Professional Ecologists: Good Practice Guidelines*, 3rd Edition. The Bat Conservation Trust, London.

Cook, P. & L. and Partners (2008) *Agriculture in Aberdeenshire: looking to the future*. A study for NESAAG, Aberdeenshire Council and Scottish Enterprise, November 2008. Aberdeenshire Council.

Coope, R. (2007) A preliminary investigation of the food and feeding behaviour of pine martens *Martes martes* in productive forestry from an analysis of the contents of their scats collected in Inchnacardoch forest, Fort Augustus. *Scottish Forestry*, 61: 3-14.

Corbett, L.K. (1979) *Feeding Ecology and Social Organisation of Wildcats (Felis silvestris) and Domestic Cat (Felis catus) in Scotland*. PhD Thesis. University of Aberdeen.

Cosgrove, P. (2002) *The Cairngorms Local Biodiversity Action Plan*. Cairngorms Partnership Board, Grantown.

Cowan, D.P. & Hartley, F.G. (2008) Rabbit *Oryctolagus cuniculus*. pp. 201-210 in S. Harris & D.W. Yalden (eds.) *Mammals of the British Isles: Handbook 4th Edition*. The Mammal Society, Southampton.

Crawford, A. (2011) *Fifth Otter Survey of England 2009 - 2010*. The Environment Agency, Bristol.

Croose, E. (2016) *The Distribution and Status of the Polecat (Mustela putorius) in Britain 2014-2015*. Vincent Wildlife Trust, Ledbury.

Croose, E., Birks, J.D.S. & Schofield, H.W. (2013) Expansion zone survey of pine marten (*Martes martes*) distribution in Scotland. *Scottish Natural Heritage Commissioned Report No. 520*.

Croose, E., Birks, J.D.S., Schofield, H.W. & O'Reilly, C. (2014) Distribution of the pine marten (*Martes martes*) in southern Scotland in 2013. *Scottish Natural Heritage Commissioned Report No. 740*.

Daniels, M.J., Balharry, D., Hirst, D., Kitchener, A.C. & Aspinall, R.J. (1998) Morphological and pelage characteristics of wild living cats in Scotland: implications for defining the 'wildcat'. *Journal of Zoology*, 244: 231-247.

Daniels, M.J., Beaumont, M.A., Johnson, P.J., Balharry, D., Macdonald, D.W. & Barratt, E. (2001) Ecology and genetics of Wild-Living cats in the North-East of Scotland and the implications for the conservation of the wildcat. *Journal of Applied Ecology*, 38: 146-161.

Daniels, M.J. & Corbett, L.K. (2003) Redefining introgressed protected mammals: when is a wild cat a wild cat and a dingo a wild dog? *Wildlife Research*, 30: 213-218.

Daniels, M.J., Wright, T.C.M., Bland, K.P. & Kitchener, A.C. (2002) Seasonality and reproduction in wild-living cats in Scotland. *Acta Theriologica*, 47: 73-84.

Davidson, A., Birks, J.D.S., Brookes, R.C., Braithwaite, T.C. & Messenger, J.E. (2002) On the origin of faeces: morphological versus molecular methods for surveying rare carnivores from their scats. *Journal of Zoology*, 257: 141-143.

Davis, A.R. & Gray, D. (2010) The distribution of Scottish wildcats (*Felis silvestris*) in Scotland (2006-2008). *Scottish Natural Heritage Commissioned Report No. 360*.

De Nahlik, A.J. (1959) *Wild Deer*. Faber and Faber Ltd., London.

Dehnel, A. (1949) Studies on the genus Sorex L. *Annales Universitatis Mariae Curie-Sklodowska* Section C 4: 17-102. [In Polish with English summary]

Dodds, M. & Bilston, H. (2013) A comparison of different bat box types by bat occupancy in deciduous woodland, Buckinghamshire, UK. *Conservation Evidence*, 10: 24-28.

Doody, J. P., Johnston, C. & Smith, B. (eds.) (1993) *Directory of the North Sea Coastal Margin*. Joint Nature Conservation Committee, Peterborough.

Driscoll, C.A., Menotti-Raymond, M., Roca, A.L., Hupe, K., Johnson, W.E., Geffen, E., Harley. E.H., Delibes, M., Pontier, D., Kitchener, A.C., Yamaguchi, N., O'Brien, S.J. & Macdonald, D.W. (2007) The Near Eastern origin of cat domestication. *Science*, 317: 519-523.

R
162

Dunn, J., Still, R. & Harrop, H. (2012) *Britain's Sea Mammals. Whales, Dolphins, Porpoises and Seals and Where to Find Them*. Princetown University Press, Woodstock, Oxfordshire.

Dunstone, N. (1993) *The Mink*. T and A D Poyser Ltd, London.

Edlin, H. L. (ed.) (1963) *Forests of North-East Scotland*. Forestry Commission Guide. HMSO.

Edwards, C.A. & Lofty, J.R. (1972) *Biology of Earthworms*. Chapman & Hall, London.

Entwhistle, A.C., Racey, P.A. & Speakman, J.R. (1997) Roost selection of the brown long-eared bats *Plecotus auritus*. *Journal of Applied Ecology*, 34: 399-408.

Entwistle, A.C. & Swift, S.M. (2008) Brown Long-eared Bat *Plecotus auritus*. pp. 364-370 in S. Harris & D.W. Yalden (eds.) *Mammals of the British Isles: Handbook 4th Edition*. The Mammal Society, Southampton.

Evans, P.G.H. (1996) Whales, dolphins and porpoises. Chapter 5.15, pp. 131-134. In J.H. Barne, C.F. Robson, S.S. Kaznowska & J.P. Doody (eds.) *Coasts and Seas of the United Kingdom. Region 3. North-east Scotland: Cape Wrath to St Cyrus*. Joint Nature Conservation Committee, Peterborough.

Evans, P.G.H., Anderwald, P. & Baines, M.E. (2003) *UK Cetacean Status Review*. Final Report to English Nature & Countryside Council for Wales. Sea Watch Foundation, Oxford.

Fletcher, K., Aebischer, N.J., Baines, D., Foster, R. & Hoodless, A.N. (2010) Changes in breeding success and abundance of ground-nesting moorland birds in relation to the experimental deployment of legal predator control. *Journal of Applied Ecology*, 47: 263-272.

Floate, K.D., Wardhaugh, K.G., Boxall, A.B.A. & Sherratt, T.N. (2005) Faecal residues of veterinary parasiticides: Non-target effects in the pasture environment. *Annual Review of Entomology*, 50: 153-179.

Flowerdew, J.R. & Tattersall, F.H. (2008) Wood Mouse *Apodemus sylvaticus*. pp. 125-137 in S. Harris & D.W. Yalden (eds.) *Mammals of the British Isles: Handbook 4th Edition*. The Mammal Society, Southampton.

Flux, J.E.C. (1970) Life history of the mountain hare (*Lepus timidus scoticus*) in north-east Scotland. *Journal of Zoology London*, 161: 75-123.

Forman, J. (1954) Walrus at Collieston. *Scottish Naturalist*, 66: 56-57.

Francis, I. & Cook, M. (eds.) (2011) *The Breeding Birds of North-East Scotland*. Scottish Ornithologists' Club, Aberdeen.

Frantz, A.C., Massei, G. & Burke, T. (2012) Genetic evidence for past hybridisation between domestic pigs and English wild boars. *Conservation Genetics*, 13: 1355-1364.

Fraser, E.J., Lambin, X., McDonald, R.A. & Redpath, S.M. (2015a) Stoat (*Mustela erminea*) on the Orkney Islands - assessing risks to native species. *Scottish Natural Heritage Commissioned Report No. 871*.

Fraser, E.J., Lambin, X., Travis, J.M.J., Harrington, L.A., Palmer, S.C.F., Bocedi, G. & Macdonald, D.W. (2015b) Range expansion of an invasive species through a heterogeneous landscape - the case of American mink in Scotland. *Diversity and Distributions*, 21: 888-900.

French, B.I., Mezquita, F. & Griffiths, H.I. (2001) Habitat selection by *Neomys fodiens* (Mammalia, Insectivora) in Kent, UK. *Folia Zoologica*, 50: 99-105.

Frylestam, B. (1986) Agricultural land use effects on the winter diet of brown hares in southern Sweden. *Mammal Review*, 16: 157-161.

Gimingham, C. (ed.) (2002) *The Ecology, Land use and Conservation of the Cairngorms*. Packard Publishing Ltd., Chichester.

Goldenberg, N. & Rand, C. (1971) Rodents and the food industry: an in-depth analysis for a large British food handler. *Pest Control*, 39: 24-25.

Gorman, M. (ed.) (1997) *The Ythan: a festschrift for George Dunnet*. University of Aberdeen, Department of Zoology.

Gorman, M.L. (2008) Mole *Talpa europaea*. pp 250-255 in S. Harris & D.W. Yalden (eds.) *Mammals of the British Isles: Handbook 4th Edition*. The Mammal Society, Southampton.

Gorman, M.L. & Stone, R.D. (1990) *The Natural History of Moles*. Christopher Helm, London.

Goulding, M., Kitchener, A.C. & Yalden, D.W. (2008) Wild Boar *Sus scrofa*. pp. 561-564 in S. Harris & D.W. Yalden (eds.) *Mammals of the British Isles: Handbook 4th Edition*. The Mammal Society, Southampton.

Graham, I.M. & Lambin, X. (2002) The impact of weasel predation on cyclic field-vole survival: the specialist predator hypothesis contradicted. *Journal of Animal Ecology*, 71: 946-956.

Grampian Regional Council (1988) *Grampian Natural Habitats Survey*. Planning Department, GRC.

Gurnell, J. (1987) *The Natural History of Squirrels*. Christopher Helm, London.

Gurnell, J. (1994) *The Red Squirrel*. The Mammal Society.

Gurnell, J., Wauters, L.A., Lurz, P.W.W. & Tosi, G. (2004) Alien species and interspecific competition: effects of introduced eastern grey squirrels on red squirrel population dynamic. *Journal of Animal Ecology*, 73: 26-35.

Hailstone, M. (2012) The Great British Deer Survey. *Deer*, 16: 12-15.

Hall, A.J. (2008) Bearded Seal *Erignathus barbatus*. p. 549 in S. Harris & D.W. Yalden (eds.) *Mammals of the British Isles: Handbook 4th Edition*. The Mammal Society, Southampton.

Hammond, P.S., Berggren, P., Benke, H., Borchers, D.L., Collet, A., Heide-Jørgensen, M.P., Heimlich, S., Hiby, A.R., Leopold, M.F. & Øien, N. (2002) Abundance of harbour porpoise and other cetaceans in the North Sea and adjacent waters. *Journal of Applied Ecology*, 39: 361-376.

Hammond, P.S., Hall, A.J. & Prime, J.H. (1994) The diet of Grey Seals around Orkney and other island and mainland sites in north-eastern Scotland. *Journal of Applied Ecology*, 31: 340-350.

Hammond, P.S., Macleod, K., Berggren, P., Borchers, D.L., Burt, M.L., Cañadas, A., Desportes, G., Donovan, G.P., Gilles, A., Gillespie, D., Gordon, J., Hiby, L., Kuklik, I., Leaper, R., Lehnert, K., Leopold, M., Lovell, P., Øien, N., Paxton, C.G.M., Ridoux, V., Rogan, E., Samarra, F., Scheidat, M., Sequeira, M., Siebert, U., Skov, H., Swift, R., Tasker, M.L., Teilmann, J., Van Canneyt, O. & Vázquez, J.A. (2013) Cetacean abundance and distribution in European Atlantic shelf waters to inform conservation and management. *Biological Conservation*, 164: 107-122.

Hansson, L. & Henttonen, H. (1985) Regional differences in cyclicity and reproduction in Clethrionomys species: Are they related? *Annales Zoologici Fennici*, 22: 277-288.

Harrington, L.A., Harrington, A.L., Yamaguchi, N., Thom, M.D., Ferreras, P., Windham, T.R. & Macdonald, D.W. (2009) The impact of native competitors on an alien invasive: temporal niche shifts to avoid interspecific aggression. *Ecology*, 90: 1207-1216.

Harris, S. & Lloyd, H.G. (1991) Fox *Vulpes vulpes*. pp. 351-367 in G.C. Corbett & S. Harris (eds.) *Handbook of British Mammals*, 3rd edition. Blackwell Scientific Publications, Oxford.

Harris, S., Morris, P., Wray, S. & Yalden, D. (1995) *A Review of British Mammals: Population Estimates and Conservation Status of British Mammals other than Cetaceans*. Joint Nature Conservation Committee, Peterborough.

Harris, S. & Yalden, D.W. (eds.) (2008) *Mammals of the British Isles: Handbook 4th Edition*. The Mammal Society, Southampton.

Harris, S.J., Massimino, D., Newson, S.E., Eaton, M.A., Balmer, D.E., Noble, D.G., Musgrove, A.J., Gillings, S., Procter, D. & Pearce-Higgins, J.W. (2015) The Breeding Bird Survey 2014. *BTO Research Report 673*. British Trust for Ornithology, Thetford.

Harrison, A., Newey, S., Gilbert, L., Haydon, D.T. & Thirgood, S. (2010) Culling wildlife hosts to control disease: mountain hares, red grouse and louping ill virus. *Journal of Applied Ecology*, 47: 926-930.

Harrison, J., Winterbottom, S. & Johnson, R. (2001) *Climate Change and Changing Patterns of Snowfall in Scotland*. Scottish Executive Central Research Unit. Edinburgh.

Hart-Davis, D. (2002) *Fauna Britannica: The Practical Guide to Wild & Domestic Creatures of Britain*. Weidenfeld & Nicolson, London.

Hartmann, M. (2005) Reproduction and behaviour of European wildcats in species-specific enclosures. In M. Herrmann (ed.) *Biology and Conservation of the European wildcat (Felis silvestris silvestris)*. Symposium abstracts. Vosges du Nord - Pfälzerwald, Germany, Jan 21st-23rd.

Harwood, J. & Greenwood, J.J.D. (1985) Competition between British grey seal and fisheries. pp. 153-160 in J.R. Beddington, R.J.H. Beverton & D.M. Lavigne (eds.) *Marine Mammals and Fisheries*. George Allen & Unwin, London.

Hetherington, D. (2013) *Assessing the Potential for the Restoration of Vertebrate Species in The Cairngorms National Park: A Background Review*. Cairngorms National Park Authority Internal Report.

Hetherington, D. & Campbell, R.D. (2012) *The Cairngorm Wildcat Project. Final Report*. Report to Cairngorms National Park Authority, Scottish Natural Heritage, Royal Zoological Society of Scotland, Scottish Gamekeepers Association and Forestry Commission Scotland.

Hewison, A.J.M. & Staines, B.W. (2008) European Roe Deer *Capreolus capreolus*. pp. 605-617 in S. Harris & D.W. Yalden (eds.) *Mammals of the British Isles: Handbook 4th Edition*. The Mammal Society, Southampton.

Hewson, R. & Taylor, M. (1968) Movements of European hares in an upland area of Scotland. *Acta Theriologica*, 13: 31-34.

Hewson, R. & Watson, A. (1979) Winter whitening of Stoats (*Mustela erminea*) in Scotland and northeast England. *Journal of Zoology*, 187: 55-64.

Hulbert, I.A.R., Iason, G.R. & Mayes, R.W. (2001) The flexibility of an intermediate feeder: Dietary selection of mountain hares measured using faecal n-alkanes. *Oecologia*, 129: 197-205.

Hulbert, I.A.R., Iason, G.R. & Racey, P.A. (1996) Habitat utilization in a stratified landscape by two lagomorphs with different feeding strategies. *Journal of Applied Ecology*, 33: 315-324.

Hull, R. (2007) *Scottish Mammals*. Birlinn Limited, Edinburgh.

Hutchings, M.R. & Harris, S. (1996) *The Current Status of the Brown Hare (Lepus europaeus) in Britain*. JNCC, Peterborough.

Hutson, A.M. (1995) Recent Records. *Bat News*, 45: 6.

Hyvarinen, H. (1994) Brown fat and the wintering of shrews. pp 259-266 in J.A. Merritt, G.L. Kirkland & R.K. Rose (eds.) *Advances in the Biology of Shrews*. Carnegie Museum of Natural History, Special Publication 18, The Carnegie Museum of Natural History, Pittsburgh, USA.

Iason, G.R., Hulbert, I.A.R., Hewson, R. & Dingerkus, K. (2008) Mountain Hare/Irish Hare *Lepus timidus*. pp. 220-228 in S. Harris & D.W. Yalden (eds.) *Mammals of the British Isles: Handbook 4th Edition*. The Mammal Society, Southampton.

Iason, G.R. & Waterman, P.G. (1988) Avoidance of plant phenolics by juvenile and reproducing female mountain hares in summer. *Functional Ecology*, 2: 433-440.

Invasive Species Specialist Group (2015) Global Invasive Species Database: http://www.issg.org/database/species/search.asp?st=100ss (accessed 15-12-15).

IUCN (2015) *Red List of Threatened Species*. Version 2015-4. IUCN, Switzerland

Jefferies, D.J. & Woodroffe, G.L. (2008) Otter *Lutra lutra*. pp 437-447 in S. Harris & D.W. Yalden (eds.) *Mammals of the British Isles: Handbook 4th Edition*. The Mammal Society, Southampton.

Jenkins, D. (ed.) (1985) The *Biology and Management of the River Dee*. Institute of Terrestrial Ecology/NERC. ITE Banchory.

Jenkins, D. (ed.) (1988) *Land Use in the River Spey Catchment*. Aberdeen Centre for Land Use Symposium No. 1. ACLU, Department of Zoology, University of Aberdeen

Jennings, N. (2008) Brown Hare *Lepus europaeus*. pp. 210-220 in S. Harris & D.W. Yalden (eds.) *Mammals of the British Isles: Handbook 4th Edition*. The Mammal Society, Southampton.

Joint Nature Conservation Committee (2007) *Second Report by the UK under Article 17 on the implementation of the Habitats Directive from January 2001 to December 2006*. JNCC, Peterborough.

Jones, A.T. (1999) The Caledonian Pinewood Inventory of Scotland's native Scots pine woodlands. *Scottish Forestry*, 53: 237-242.

Jones, G. & van Parijs, S.M. (1993) Bimodal echolocation in pipistrelle bats: are cryptic species present? *Proceedings of the Royal Society B*, 251: 119-125.

Jones, K.E., Altringham, J.D. & Deaton, R. (1996) Distribution and population densities of seven species of bat in northern England. *Journal of Zoology*, 240: 788-798.

Jordan, N.R., Messenger, J., Turner, P., Croose, E., Birks, J.D.S. & O'Reilly, C. (2012) Molecular comparison of historical and contemporary pine marten (*Martes martes*) populations in the British Isles: evidence of differing origins and fates, and implications for conservation management. *Conservation Genetics*, 13: 1195-1212.

Judes, U. (1989) Analysis of the distribution of flying bats along line-transects. pp. 311-318 in V. Hanak, I. Horacek & J. Gaisler (eds.) *European Bat Research 1987*. Charles University Press, Prague, Czechoslovakia.

Kapteyn, K. (1993) Intraspecific variation in the echolocation calls of vespertilionid bats, and its implication for identification. pp. 45-57 in K. Kapetyn (ed.) *Proceedings of the First European Bat Detector Workshop*. Netherlands Bat Research Foundation, Amsterdam, Netherlands.

Keith, G.S. (1811) *A General View of the Agriculture of Aberdeenshire*; Drawn up under the direction of the Board of Agriculture.

Kilshaw, K., Johnson, P.J., Kitchener, A.C. & Macdonald, D.W. (2015) Detecting the elusive Scottish wildcat *Felis silvestris silvestris* using camera trapping. *Oryx*, 49: 207-215.

Kilshaw, K., Montgomery, R.A., Campbell, R.D., Hetherington, D.A., Johnson, P.J., Kitchener, A.C., Macdonald, D.W. & Millspaugh, J.J. (2016) Mapping the spatial configuration of hybridization risk for an endangered population of the European wildcat (*Felis silvestris silvestris*) in Scotland. *Mammal Research*, 61: 1-11.

Kitchener, A.C. & Birks, J. (2014) Categorising our 'cats': a case for pragmatism. *British Wildlife*, 25: 315-321.

Kitchener, A.C. & Birks, J.D.S. (2008) Feral Ferret *Mustela furo*. pp. 485-487 in S. Harris & D.W. Yalden (eds.) *Mammals of the British Isles: Handbook 4th Edition*. The Mammal Society, Southampton.

Kitchener, A.C., Yamaguchi, N., Ward, J.M. & Macdonald, D.W. (2005) A diagnosis for the Scottish wildcat (*Felis silvestris*): a tool for conservation action for a critically-endangered felid. *Animal Conservation*, 8: 223-237.

Kruuk, H. (1989) *The Social Badger: Ecology and Behaviour of a Group-living Carnivore (Meles meles)*. Oxford University Press, Oxford.

Kruuk, H. (2006) *Otters, Ecology, Behaviour and Conservation*. Oxford University Press.

Kruuk, H. (2014) Otters and Eels: Long-Term Observations on Declines in Scotland. *IUCN Otter Specialist Group Bulletin*, 31: 3-11.

Kuvikova, A. (1985) Zur Nahrung der Wasserspitzmaus, *Neomys fodiens* (Pennant 1771) in Slowakei. *Biologica, Bratislava*, 40: 563-572.

Lambin, X. (2008) Field Vole *Microtus agrestis*. pp. 100-107 in S. Harris & D.W. Yalden (eds.) *Mammals of the British Isles: Handbook 4th Edition*. The Mammal Society, Southampton.

Lambin, X., Aars, J., Piertney, S.B. & Telfer, S. (2004) Inferring patterns and process in small mammal metapopulations: insights from ecological and genetic data. pp 515-540 in I. Hanski & O.E. Gaggiotti (eds.) *Ecology, Genetics and Evolution of Metapopulations*. Elsevier Academic Press.

Lambin, X., Petty, S.J. & MacKinnon, J.L. (2000) Cyclic dynamics in field vole populations and generalist predation. *Journal of Animal Ecology*, 69: 106-118.

Langbein, J., Chapman, N.G. & Putman, R.J. (2008) Fallow Deer *Dama dama*. pp. 595-604 in S. Harris & D.W. Yalden (eds.) *Mammals of the British Isles: Handbook 4th Edition*. The Mammal Society, Southampton.

Langley, P.J.W. & Yalden, D.W. (1977) The decline of the rarer carnivores in Great Britain during the nineteenth century. *Mammal Review*, 7: 95-116.

Larkin, P.A. (1948) Ecology of Mole (*Talpa europaea* L.) Populations. *DPhil thesis*, University of Oxford.

Latham, J., Staines, B.W. & Gorman, M.L. (1982) Comparative feeding ecology of red (*Cervus elaphus*) and roe deer (*Capreolus capreolus*) in Scottish plantation forests. *Journal of Zoology*, 247: 409-418.

Leaper, G. (1999) *Biodiversity of the Cairngorms: assessment of priority habitats and species*. Cairngorms Partnership, Grantown.

Lees, A.C. & Bell, D.J. (2008) A conservation paradox for the 21st century: the European wild rabbit *Oryctolagus cuniculus*, an invasive alien and an endangered native species. *Mammal Review*, 38: 304-320.

Littlewood, N.A., Campbell, R.D., Dinnie, L., Gilbert, L., Hooper, R., Iason, G., Irvine, J., Kilshaw, K., Kitchener, A., Lackova, P., Newey, S., Ogden, R. & Ross, A. (2014) Survey and scoping of wildcat priority areas. *Scottish Natural Heritage Commissioned Report No. 768*.

Lurz, P. (2010) *Red Squirrels*. Naturally Scottish series, Scottish Natural Heritage.

MacDonald, D. & Barrett, P. (1993) *Mammals of Britain & Europe*. HarperCollins, London.

Macdonald, D.W., Daniels, M.J., Driscoll, C., Kitchener, A.C. & Yamaguchi, N. (2004) *The Scottish Wildcat: Analyses for Conservation and an Action Plan*. Wildlife Conservation Research Unit, University of Oxford.

Macdonald, D.W. & Harrington, L.A. (2003) The American mink: the triumph and tragedy of adaptation out of context. New Zealand. *Journal of Zoology*, 30: 421-441.

Macdonald, D.W., Tew, T.E., Todd, I.A., Garner, J.P. & Johnson, P.J. (2000) Arable habitat use by wood mice (*Apodemus sylvaticus*). 3. A farm-scale experiment on the effects of crop rotation. *Journal of Zoology*, 250: 313-320.

Mackey, E.C. & Shewry, M. (2006) Land cover change. pp. 61-69 in P. Shaw & D.B.A. Thompson (eds.) *The Nature of the Cairngorms: Diversity in a changing environment*. Scottish Natural Heritage/TSO, Edinburgh.

Mackey, E.C., Shewry, M.C. & Tudor, G.J. (1998) *Land cover change: Scotland from the 1940s to the 1980s*. Scottish Natural Heritage, The Stationery Office, Edinburgh.

Macpherson, J., Bavin, D. & Croose, E. (2015) Return of the native. *British Wildlife*, 26: 154-159.

Malo, A.F., Lozano, J., Huertas, D.L. & Virgos, E. (2004) A change of diet from rodents to rabbits (*Oryctolagus cuniculus*). Is the wildcat (*Felis silvestris*) a specialist predator? *Journal of Zoology*, 263: 401-407.

Mammal Society (2014) Full Species List. Downloaded from http://www.mammal.org.uk/species-hub/full-species-hub/full-species-hub-list/ (accessed 13-12-16).

Marques, F.F.C., Buckland, S.T., Goffin, D., Dixon, C.E., Borchers, D.L., Mayle, B.A. & Peace, A.J. (2001) Estimating deer abundance from line transect surveys of dung: sika deer in southern Scotland. *Journal of Applied Ecology*, 38: 349-363.

Marren, P. (1982) *A Natural History of Aberdeen*. R. Callander, Aberdeen People's Press, Aberdeen.

McConnell, B.J., Fedak, M.A., Lovell, P. & Hammond, P.S. (1999) Movements and foraging areas of grey seals in the North Sea. *Journal of Applied Ecology*, 36: 563-590.

R

164

McDonald, R. & Harris, S. (1997) *Stoats and Weasels*. The Mammal Society, London.

McDonald, R.A. & Harris, S. (2002) Population biology of stoats *Mustela erminea* and weasels *Mustela nivalis* on game estates in Great Britain. *Journal of Applied Ecology*, 39: 793-805.

McDonald, R.A. & King, C.M. (2008a) Stoat *Mustela erminea*. pp. 456-467 in S. Harris & D.W. Yalden (eds.) *Mammals of the British Isles: Handbook 4th Edition*. The Mammal Society, Southampton.

McDonald, R.A. & King, C.M. (2008b) Weasel *Mustela nivalis*. pp. 467-476 in S. Harris & D.W. Yalden (eds.) *Mammals of the British Isles: Handbook 4th Edition*. The Mammal Society, Southampton.

McDonald, R.A., Webbon, C. & Harris, S. (2000) The diet of Stoats (*Mustela erminea*) and Weasels (*Mustela nivalis*) in Great Britain. *Journal of Zoology*, 252: 363-371.

Meerburg, B.G. & Kijlstra, A. (2007) Role of rodents in transmission of Salmonella and Campylobacter. *Journal of the Science of Food and Agriculture*, 87: 2774-2781.

Melero, Y. & Palazón, S. (2011) Visón americano--Neovison vison (Schreber, 1777) In A. Salvador & J. Cassinello (eds.) *Enciclopedia Virtual de los Vertebrados Españoles*.

Melero, Y., Palazón, S. & Lambin, X. (2014) Invasive crayfish reduce food limitation of alien American mink and increase their resilience to control. *Oecologia*, 174: 427-434.

Melero, Y., Robinson, E. & Lambin, X. (2015) Density- and age-dependent reproduction partially compensates culling efforts of invasive non-native American mink. *Biological Invasions*, 17: 2645-2657.

Merritt, J. & Leslie, G. (2009) *Northeast Scotland: a landscape fashioned by Geology*. SNH/BGS, Battleby.

Meteorological Office (1989) *The Climate of Scotland: Some Facts and Figures*. HMSO, London.

Micol, T., Doncaster, C.P. & Mackinlay, L.A. (1994) Correlates of local variation in the abundance of hedgehogs, *Erinaceus europaeus*. *Journal of Animal Ecology*, 63: 851-860.

Milner, C. & Ball, D.F. (1970) Factors affecting the distribution of the mole (*Talpa europaea*) in Snowdonia (North Wales). *Journal of Zoology*, 162: 61-69.

Montgomery, W., Montgomery, S. & Reid, N. (2015) Invasive alien species disrupt spatial and temporal ecology and threaten extinction in an insular, small mammal community. *Biological Invasions*, 17: 179-189.

Moores, R. (2007) *Where to Watch Mammals in Britain and Ireland*. A & C Black, London.

Moorhouse, T.P., Macdonald, D.W., Strachan, R. & Lambin, X. (2015) What does conservation research do, when should it stop, and what do we do then? Questions answered with water voles. pp 269-290 (Chapter 15) in D.W. Macdonald & R.E. Feber (eds.) *Wildlife Conservation on Farmland. Managing for Nature on Lowland Farms*. Oxford University Press.

Morecroft, M.D., Bealey, C.E., Beaumont, D.A., Benham, S., Brooks, D.R., Burt, T.P., Critchley, C.N.R., Dick, J., Littlewood, N.A., Monteith, D.T., Scott, W.A., Smith, R.I., Walmesley, C. & Watson, H. (2009) The UK Environmental Change Network: emerging trends in terrestrial biodiversity and the physical environment. *Biological Conservation*, 142: 2814-2832.

Morris, P. (1993) *A Red Data Book for British Mammals*. The Mammal Society. London.

Morris, P., Alderson, L., Beebee, T., Chapman, N. & Harris, S. (1989) *Readers Digest Nature Lover's Library Field Guide to the Animals of Britain*. Readers Digest Association Limited, London.

Morris, P.A. & Reeve, N.J. (2008) Hedgehog *Erinaceus europaeus*. pp. 241-249 in S. Harris & D.W. Yalden (eds.) *Mammals of the British Isles: Handbook 4th Edition*. The Mammal Society, Southampton.

Murray, I. & Watson, A. (2015) *Place Name Discoveries on Upper Deeside and the Far Highlands*. Paragon Publishing, Rothersthorpe, Northants.

National Records of Scotland (2015) Aberdeen City Council Area - demographic factsheet. https://www.nrscotland.gov.uk/statistics-and-data/statistics/stats-at-a-glance/council-area-profiles (accessed 23-01-16).

Neal, E. (1948) *The Badger*. Collins, London.

Neal, E. & Cheeseman, C. (1996) *Badgers*. T & A D Poyser, London.

Nethersole-Thompson, D. & Watson, A. (1974) *The Cairngorms: Their Natural History and Scenery*. Collins, London.

Nethersole-Thompson, D. & Watson, A. (1981) *The Cairngorms*. 2nd edition. The Melven Press, Perth.

Newey, S., Willebrand, T., Haydon, T., Dahl, F., Aebischer, N.J., Smith, A.A. & Thirgood, S.J. (2007) Do mountain hare populations cycle? *Oikos*, 116: 1547-1557.

North East Scotland Biodiversity Steering Group Partnership (2000) *North East Scotland Local Biodiversity Action Plan*. The Moray Council.

Nyholm, E.S. (1965) Zur Okologie von *Myotis mystacinus* (Leisl) und *M. daubentonii* (Leisl.) (Chiroptera). *Annales Zoologici Fennici*, 2: 77-123.

Office for National Statistics (2012) 2011 Census, Population and Household Estimates for the United Kingdom. http://www.ons.gov.uk (accessed 23-01-16).

Office for National Statistics (2015) Mid-year population estimates for the UK 2014. http://www.ons.gov.uk (accessed 23-01-16).

Oliver, M.K., Piertney, S.B., Zalewski. A. & Lambin, X. (2016) The compensatory potential of increased immigration following intensive American mink population control is diluted by male-biased dispersal. *Biological Invasions*, 18: 3047-3061.

O'Meara, D., Harrington, A., O'Neill, D., Morris, C., O'Reilly, C., Turner, P. & Strachan, R. (2012) *A Study of the Spring Diet of Otters in the Comeragh Mountains, Co. Waterford*. Otter Diet Workshop - Waterford November 24th, 2012. The Mammals in a Sustainable Environment (MISE) Project, Waterford Institute of Technology, Waterford.

O'Neill, D., Turner, P., O'Meara, D., Chadwick, E., Coffey, L. & O'Reilly, C. (2013) Development of novel real-time TaqMan PCR assays for the species and sex identification of otter (*Lutra lutra*) and their application to noninvasive genetic monitoring. *Molecular Ecology Resources*, 13: 877-833.

Palmer, S.C.F. & Truscott, A.M. (2003) Seasonal habitat use and browsing by deer in Caledonian pinewoods. *Forest Ecology and Management*, 174: 149-166.

Patton, V., Ewald, J.A., Smith, A.A., Newey, S., Iason, G.R., Thirgood, S.J. & Raynor, R. (2010) Distribution of mountain hares *Lepus timidus* in Scotland: results from a questionnaire. *Mammal Review*, 40: 313-326.

Pérez-Espona, S., Pemberton, J.M. & Putman, R. (2009) Red and sika deer in the British Isles, current management issues and management policy. *Mammalian Biology*, 74: 247-262.

Pocock, M.J.O., Hauffe, H.C. & Searle, J.B. (2005) Dispersal in house mice. *Biological Journal of the Linnean Society*, 84: 565-583.

Polunin, O. & Walters, M. (1985) *A Guide to the Vegetation of Britain and Europe*. Oxford University Press, Oxford.

Pounds, C.J. (1981) *Niche Overlap in Sympatric Populations of Stoats and Weasels in North-east Scotland*. University of Aberdeen PhD thesis.

Putman, R. (2012) Scoping the economic benefits and costs of wild deer and their management in Scotland. *Scottish Natural Heritage Commissioned Report No. 526*.

Putman, R.J. (1986) Foraging by roe deer in agricultural areas and impact on arable crops. *Journal of Applied Ecology*, 23: 91-99.

Putman, R.J. (2008) Sika *Cervus nippon*. pp. 587-594 in S. Harris & D.W. Yalden (eds.) *Mammals of the British Isles: Handbook 4th Edition*. The Mammal Society, Southampton.

Putman, R.J. & Moore, N.P. (1998) Impact of deer in lowland Britain on agriculture, forestry and conservation habitats. *Mammal Review*, 28: 141-163.

Quy, R.J. & Macdonald, D.W. (2008) Common Rat *Rattus norvegicus*. pp 149-155 in S. Harris & D.W. Yalden (eds.) *Mammals of the British Isles: Handbook 4th edition*. The Mammal Society, Southampton.

Racey, P.A., Barratt, E.M., Burland, T.M., Deaville, R., Gotelli, D., Jones, G. & Piertney, S.B. (2007) Microsatellite DNA polymorphism confirms reproductive isolation and reveals differences in population genetic structure of cryptic pipistrelle bat species. *Biological Journal of the Linnean Society*, 90: 539-550.

Racey, P.A. & Swift, S.M. (1986) The residual effects of remedial timber treatments on bats. *Biological Conservation*, 35: 205-214.

Racey, P.R., Swift, S.M., Rydell, J. & Brodie, L. (1998) Bats and insects over two Scottish rivers, with contrasting nitrate status. *Animal Conservation*, 1: 195-202.

Rainey, E., Butler, A., Bierman, S. & Roberts, A.M.I. (2009) *Scottish Badger Distribution Survey 2006-2009: Estimating the Distribution and Density of Badger Main Setts in Scotland*. Scottish Badgers and Biomathematics and Statistics Scotland.

Rao, S.J., Iason, G.R., Hulbert, I.A.R., Daniels, M.J. & Racey, P.A. (2003a) Tree browsing by mountain hares (*Lepus timidus*) in establishing Scots pine (*Pinus sylvestris*) and birch (*Betula pendula*) woodland. *Forest Ecology and Management*, 76: 459-471.

Rao, S.J., Iason, G.R., Hulbert, I.A.R. & Racey, P.A. (2003b) The effect of establishing native woodland on habitat selection and ranging of moorland mountain hares (*Lepus timidus*), a flexible forager. *Journal of Zoology*, 260: 1-9.

R

165

Ratcliffe, P.R. (1987) Distribution and current status of sika deer, *Cervus nippon*, in Great Britain. *Mammal Review*, 17: 39-58.

RCAHMS (Royal Commission on the Ancient and Historical Monuments of Scotland) (2008) *In the Shadow of Bennachie: a field archaeology of Donside, Aberdeenshire*. 2nd edition. RCAHMS, Edinburgh.

Reid, J., Evans, P.G.H. & Northridge, S.P. (2003) *Atlas of Cetacean Distribution in Northwest European Waters*. Joint Nature Conservation Committee, Peterborough.

The Reindeer Company Ltd (1993) Reindeer *Rangifer tarandus*. The Reindeer Company Ltd.

Rhyan, J.C. & Saari, D.A. (1995) A comparative study of the histopathologic features of bovine tuberculosis in cattle, fallow deer (*Dama dama*), sika deer (*Cervus nippon*), and red deer and elk (*Cervus elaphus*). *Veterinary Pathology*, 32: 215-220.

Richardson, P.W., Waters, D. & Waters, R. (2008) Daubenton's Bat *Myotis daubentonii*. pp. 319-323 in S. Harris & D.W. Yalden (eds.) *Mammals of the British Isles: Handbook 4th Edition*. The Mammal Society, Southampton.

Robinson, K.P., Baumgartner, N., Eisfeld, S.M., Clark, N.M., Culloch, R.M., Haskins, G.N., Zapponi, L., Whaley, A.R., Weare, J.S. & Tetley, M.J. (2007) The summer distribution and occurrence of cetaceans in the coastal waters of the outer southern Moray Firth in northeast Scotland (UK). *Lutra*, 50: 19-30.

Robinson, K.P., Tetley, M.J. & Mitchelson-Jacob, E.G. (2009) The distribution and habitat preference of coastally occurring minke whales (*Balaenoptera acutorostrata*) in north-east Scotland. *Journal of Coastal Conservation*, 13: 39-48.

Roer, H. (1995) 60 years of bat-banding in Europe - results and tasks for future research. *Myotis*, 32-33: 251-261.

Roos, S., Johnston, A. & Noble, D. (2012) UK Hedgehog Datasets and their Potential for Long-Term Monitoring. *BTO Research Report 598*.

Roper, T.J. (2010) *Badger*. HarperCollins, London.

Russ, J. (2012) *British Bat Calls: A Guide to Species Identification*. Pelagic, Exeter.

Russ, J.M., Hutson, A.M., Montgomery, W.I., Racey, P.A. & Speakman, J.R. (2001) The status of Nathusius' pipistrelle (*Pipistrellus nathusii* (Keyserserling & Blasius, 1839)) in the British Isles. *Journal of Zoology*, 254: 91-100.

Russ, J.M., O'Neill, K. & Montgomery, W.I. (1998) Nathusius' pipistrelle (*Pipistrellus nathusii* (Keyserserling & Blasius, 1839)) breeding in Ireland. *Journal of Zoology*, 245: 345-349.

Rydell, J., Catto, C. & Racey, P.A. (1993) Observations of Leisler's bat *Nyctalus leisleri* in northern Scotland. *Scottish Bats*, 2: 5-6.

SAC Consulting (2015) *Farm Management Handbook*, 2015/16 Edition.

Santulli, G., Palazon, S., Melero, Y., Gosalbez, J. & Lambin, X. (2014) Multi-season occupancy analysis reveals large scale competitive exclusion of the critically endangered European mink by the invasive non-native American mink in Spain. *Biological Conservation*, 176: 21-29.

SCOS (2014) *Scientific Advice on Matters Related to the Management of Seal Populations: 2014*. Natural Environment Research Council, Swindon.

Scott, R. (ed.) (2011) *Atlas of Highland Land Mammals*. Highland Biological Recording Group. Inverness.

Scott, R., Easterbee, N. & Jeffries, D. (1992) A radio-tracking study of wildcats in Scotland. pp. 94-97 in *Council of Europe Seminar on the Biology and Conservation of the Wildcat (Felis silvestris)* 22-25 Sept. 1992.

Scottish Enterprise (2008) *Aberdeen City and Shire Economic Review*. Scottish Enterprise, Aberdeen.

Scottish Executive (2001) *Economic Report on Scottish Agriculture 2001 Edition*. Scottish Executive Environment and Rural Affairs Department - Economics and Statistics.

Scottish Executive (2004) *Scotland's Biodiversity - It's in your Hands*. Scottish Executive, Edinburgh.

Scottish Government (2015a) *Scotland's Biodiversity - a Route Map to 2020*. The Scottish Government, Edinburgh.

Scottish Government (2015b) *Economic Report on Scottish Agriculture 2015 Edition*. Scottish Government Directorate for Environment and Forestry, Rural and Environment Science and Analytical Services.

Scottish Natural Heritage (2002) *Natural Heritage Futures - Cairngorms Massif; North East Glens; North East Coastal Plain; Eastern Lowlands; Moray Firth*. Scottish Natural Heritage, Battleby. (5 booklets).

Scottish Natural Heritage (2006) *A Guide to Best Practice for Watching Marine Wildlife*. Scottish Natural Heritage, Inverness.

Scottish Natural Heritage (2010) *Creag Dhubh Site of Special Scientific Interest. Site Management Statement*. https://gateway.snh.gov.uk/sitelink/index.jsp (accessed 04-11-15).

Scottish Natural Heritage (2015) Protected Mammal Species in Scotland. http://www.snh.gov.uk/protecting-scotlands-nature/protected-species/which-and-how/mammals (accessed 22-08-16).

Senn, H.V., Barton, N.H., Goodman, S.J., Swanson, G.M., Abernethy, K.A. & Pemberton, J.M. (2010a) Investigating temporal changes in hybridization and introgression in a predominantly bimodal hybridizing population of invasive sika (*Cervus nippon*) and native red deer (*C. elaphus*) on the Kintyre Peninsula, Scotland. *Molecular Ecology*, 19: 910-924.

Senn, H.V. & Pemberton, J.M. (2009) *Red-sika hybridisation in the Western Cairngorms National Park*. Unpublished report to the Cairngorms National Park Authority.

Senn, H.V., Swanson, G.M., Goodman, S.J., Barton, N.H. & Pemberton, J.M. (2010b) Phenotypic correlates of hybridisation between red and sika deer (genus *Cervus*). *Journal of Animal Ecology*, 79: 414-425.

Shaw, P. & Thompson, D.B.A. (2006) *The Nature of the Cairngorms: Diversity in a changing environment*. Scottish Natural Heritage/TSO, Edinburgh.

Sheail, J. (1971) *Rabbits and Their History*. David & Charles Ltd, Newton Abbot.

Sheehy, E. & Lawton, C. (2014) Population crash in an invasive species following the recovery of a native predator: the case of the American grey squirrel and the European pine marten in Ireland. *Biodiversity and Conservation*, 23: 753-774.

Sheehy, E., O'Meara, D.B., O'Reilly, C., Smart, A. & Lawton, C. (2013) A non-invasive approach to determining pine marten abundance and predation. *European Journal of Wildlife Research*, 60: 223-236.

Shiel, C.B., Jones, G. & Waters, D. (2008) Leisler's Bat *Nyctalus leisleri*. pp. 334-338 in S. Harris & D.W. Yalden (eds.) *Mammals of the British Isles: Handbook 4th Edition*. The Mammal Society, Southampton.

Shirihai, H. (2006) *Whales, Dolphins and Seals. A Field Guide to the Marine Mammals of the World*. A & C Black, London.

Shore, R.F. & Hare, E.J. (2008) Bank Vole *Myodes glareolus*. pp. 88-99 in S. Harris & D.W. Yalden (eds.) *Mammals of the British Isles: Handbook 4th Edition*. The Mammal Society, Southampton.

Shore, R.F., Myhill, D.G. & Lhotsky, R. (1995) Capture success for pygmy and common shrews (*Sorex minutus* and *S. araneus*) in Longworth and pitfall traps on upland blanket bog. *Journal of Zoology*, 237: 657-662.

Shuttleworth, C.M., Lurz, P.W.W. & Halliwell, E.C. (eds.) (2015) *Shared Experience of Red Squirrel Conservation Practice*. European Squirrel Initiative.

Signorile, A.L., Wang, J., Lurz, P.W.W., Bertolino, S., Carbone, C. & Reuman, D.C. (2014) Do founder, size, genetic diversity and structure influence rates of expansion of North American grey squirrels in Europe? *Diversity and Distributions*, 20: 918-930.

Silva, A.P., Kilshaw, K., Johnson, P.J., Macdonald, D.W. & Rosalino, L.M. (2013) Wildcat occurrence in Scotland: food really matters. *Diversity and Distributions*, 19: 232-243.

Sim, G. (1903) *The Vertebrate Fauna of "Dee"*. D. Wyllie & Son, Union Street, Aberdeen.

Sleeman, P. (1989) *Stoats & Weasels, Polecats & Martens*. Whittet Books.

Smith, P.G. & Rivers, N.M. (2008) Natterer's Bat *Myotis nattereri*. pp 323-328 in S. Harris & D.W. Yalden (eds.) *Mammals of the British Isles: Handbook 4th Edition*. The Mammal Society, Southampton.

Somers, N., D'Haese, B., Bossuyt, B., Lens, L. & Hoffmann, M. (2008) Food quality affects diet preference of rabbits: experimental evidence. *Belgian Journal of Zoology*, 138: 170-176.

Staines, B.W. & Crisp, J.M. (1978) Observations on food quality in Scottish red deer (*Cervus elaphus*) as determined by chemical-analysis of rumen contents. *Journal of Zoology*, 185: 253-259.

Staines, B.W., Langbein, J. & Burkitt, T.D. (2008) Red Deer *Cervus elaphus*. pp. 573-587 in S. Harris & D.W. Yalden (eds.) *Mammals of the British Isles: Handbook 4th Edition*. The Mammal Society, Southampton.

Stebbings, R.E. (1995) Why should bats be protected? A challenge for conservation. *Biological Journal of the Linnean Society*, 56: 103-118.

Stewart, A. (2012) *Wildlife & The Law*. Argyll Publishing, Glendaruel.

Strachan, C., Strachan, R. & Jefferies, D.J. (2000) *Preliminary Report on the Changes in the Water Vole Population of Britain as shown by the National Survey of 1989-1990 and 1996-1998*. The Vincent Wildlife Trust, Ledbury.

Strachan, R. (2007) National survey of Otter *Lutra lutra* distribution in Scotland 2003-2004. *Scottish Natural Heritage Commissioned Report No.211 (ROAME No. F03AC309)*.

Strachan, R., Jefferies, D.J. & The Vincent Wildlife Trust (1993) *The Water Vole Arvicola terrestris in Britain 1989-1990: Its Distribution and Changing Status*. The Vincent Wildlife Trust, Ledbury.

Swift, S.M. (1997) Roosting and foraging behaviour of Natterer's bats (*Myotis nattereri*) close to the northern border of their distribution. *Journal of Zoology*, 242: 375-384.

Swift, S.M. & Racey P.A. (1983) Resource partitioning in two species of vespertilionid bats (chiroptera) occupying the same roost. *Journal of Ecology*, 200: 249-259.

Tapper, S.C. & Barnes, R.F.W. (1986) Influence of farming practice on the ecology of the brown hare (*Lepus europaeus*). *Journal of Applied Ecology*, 23: 39-52.

Tattersall, F.H., Avundo, A.E., Manley, W.J. Hart, B.J. & Macdonald, D.W. (2000) Managing set-aside for field voles (*Microtus agrestis*). *Biological Conservation*, 96: 123-128.

Tattersall, F.H., Smith R.H. & Nowell, F. (1997) Experimental colonisation of contrasting habitats by house mice. *Zeitschrift Fur Saugetierkunda*, 62: 350-358.

Telfer, S., Holt, A., Donaldson, R. & Lambin, X. (2001) Metapopulation processes and persistence in remnant water vole populations. *Oikos*, 95: 31-42.

Telfer, S., Piertney, S.B., Dallas, J.F., Stewart, W.A., Marshall, F., Gow, J.L. & Lambin, X. (2003) Parentage assignment reveals widespread and large-scale dispersal in water voles. *Molecular Ecology*, 12: 1939-1951.

Tetley, M.J., Mitchelson-Jacob E.G. & Robinson, K.P. (2008) The summer distribution of coastal minke whales (*Balaenoptera acutorostrata*) in the southern Moray Firth, northeast Scotland, in relation to co-occurring mesoscale oceanographic features. *Remote Sensing of Environment*, 112: 3449-3454.

Thompson, P.M., Tollit, D.J., Greenstreet, S.P.R., Mackay, A. & Corpe, H.M. (1996) Between year variations in the diet and behaviour of harbour seals (*Phoca vitulina*) in the Moray Firth: causes and consequences. pp. 44-52 in S.P.R. Greenstreet & M.L. Tasker (eds.) *Aquatic Predators and Their Prey*. Blackwell Scientific, Oxford.

Thulin, C.-G. (2003) The distribution of mountain hares *Lepus timidus* in Europe: a challenge from brown hares *L. europaeus*? *Mammal Review*, 33: 29-42.

Tollit, D., Greenstreet, S.P.R. & Thompson, P.M. (1997) Prey selection by harbour seals, *Phoca vitulina*, in relation to variations in prey abundance. *Canadian Journal of Zoology*, 75: 1508-1518.

Toms, M.P., Siriwardena, G.M. & Greenwood, J.J.D. (1999) Developing a mammal monitoring programme for the UK. *BTO - Research Report 223*.

Trees for Life (2013) *Caledonia Wild!* Trees for Life Members' Magazine, Autumn 2013.

Trout, R.C. & Harris, S. (2008) Harvest Mouse *Micromys minutus*. pp 117-125 in S. Harris & D.W. Yalden (eds.) *Mammals of the British Isles: Handbook 4th edition*. The Mammal Society, Southampton.

Twigg, G.I., Buckle, A.P. & Bullock, D.J. (2008) Ship Rat *Rattus rattus*. pp 155-158 in S. Harris & D.W. Yalden (eds.) *Mammals of the British Isles: Handbook 4th edition*. The Mammal Society, Southampton.

Vaughan, N. (1997) The diets of British bats (Chiroptera). *Mammal Review*, 27: 77-94.

Vaughan, N., Jones, G. & Harris, S.M. (1997) Habitat use by bats (Chiroptera) assessed by means of a broad-band acoustic method. *Journal of Applied Ecology*, 34: 16-18.

Vaughan, T.A., Ryan, J.M. & Czaplewski, N.J. (2015) *Mammalogy* (6th edition). Jones & Bartlett Learning, Burlington, MA, USA.

Velander, K.A. (1983) *Pine Marten Survey of Scotland, England and Wales 1980-1982*. The Vincent Wildlife Trust, London.

Vincent Wildlife Trust (1998) *The Polecat*. Vincent Wildlife Trust, Ledbury.

Vincent Wildlife Trust (2002) *Polecats and Ferrets: How to Tell Them Apart*. Vincent Wildlife Trust, Ledbury.

Visit Scotland (2005) *The Official Guide to Golf in Aberdeen & Grampian Highlands*. Produced for Visit Scotland Aberdeen & Grampian and the Golf Tourism Partnership. Visit Scotland 2005

Vogel, P., Bodmer, C., Spreng, M. & Aeschimann, H. (1998) Diving capacity and foraging behaviour of the water shrew (*Neomys fodiens*). pp 31-47 in N. Dunstone & M. Gorman (eds.) Behaviour and Ecology of Riparian mammals. *Symposia of the Zoological Society of London 71*. Cambridge University Press, Cambridge.

Voigt, C.C., Popa-Lisseanu, A.G., Niermann, I. & Kramer-Schadt, S. (2012) The catchment area of wind farms for European bats: A plea for international regulations. *Biological Conservation*, 153: 80-86.

Volkova, V., Savill, N.J., Bessell, P.R. & Woolhouse, M.E.J. (2008) *Report on Seasonality of Movements and Spatial Distribution of Sheep, Cattle and Pigs in Scotland*. Centre of Excellence in Epidemiology, Population Health & Infectious Disease Control (EPIC), University of Edinburgh.

Ward, A.I., White, P.C.L., Smith, A. & Critchley, C.H. (2004) Modelling the cost of roe deer browsing damage to forestry. *Forest Ecology and Management*, 191: 301-310.

Watson, A. (1992) *The Cairngorms*. Scottish Mountaineering Club District Guidebook. Scottish Mountaineering Club, Edinburgh.

Watson, A. (2013) *Mammals in North-East Highlands*. Paragon Publishing, Rothersthorpe, Northants.

Watson, A. & Hewson, R. (1973) Population densities of mountain hares (*Lepus timidus*) on Western Scottish and Irish moors and on Scottish hills. *Journal of Zoology London*, 170: 151-159.

Webbon, C.C., Baker, P.J. & Harris, S. (2004) Faecal density counts for monitoring changes in red fox numbers in rural Britain. *Journal of Applied Ecology*, 41: 768-779.

Weir, C.R. & Stockin, K.A. (2001) *The occurrence and distribution of bottlenose dolphins (Tursiops truncates) and other cetacean species in the coastal waters of Aberdeenshire, Scotland*. Sea Watch Foundation, Aberdeen. 68pp.

Weir, C.R., Stockin, K.A. & Pierce, G.J. (2007) Spatial and temporal trends in the distribution of harbour porpoises, white-beaked dolphins and minke whales off Aberdeenshire (UK), north-western North Sea. *Journal of Marine Biological Association U.K.*, 87: 327-338.

Wembridge, D. & Langton, S. (2016) Living with mammals: an urban study. *British Wildlife*, 27: 188-195.

Werner, R. (1998) *'The Exmoor Pony of the Goat World'. Breed Points of the British Native Goat*. http://goatresearch.yolasite.com (accessed 04-11-15).

Werner, R. (2010) *'Wild Goats of Britain' - A commentary on an article by David Watkins, source and date undetermined*. http://goatresearch.yolasite.com (accessed 04-11-15).

White, A. & Lurz, P.W.W. (2014) A modelling assessment of control strategies to prevent/reduce Squirrelpox spread. *Scottish Natural Heritage Commissioned Report No. 267*.

Wilson, A., Fenton, B., Malloch, G., Boag, B., Hubbard, S. & Begg, G. (2014) Coexisting small mammals display contrasting strategies for tolerating instability in arable habitat. *European Journal of Wildlife Research*, 60: 811-820.

Wilson, C.J. (2014) The establishment and distribution of feral wild boar (*Sus scrofa* L.) in England. *Wildlife Biology in Practice*, 10: 1-6.

Wilson, D.E. & Reeder, D.M. (editors) (2005) *Mammal Species of the World. A Taxonomic and Geographic Reference* (3rd ed). Johns Hopkins University Press, Baltimore, USA.

Wilson, G., Harris, S. & Jefferies, D.J. (1997) *Changes in the British Badger Population 1988-1997*. People's Trust for Endangered Species, London.

Woods, M., McDonald, R.A. & Harris, S. (2003) Predation of wildlife by domestic cats *Felis catus* in Great Britain. *Mammal Review*, 33: 174-188.

Wolton R.J. & Flowerdew J.R. (1985) Spatial distribution and movements of wood mice, yellow-necked mice and bank voles. *Symposia of the Zoological Society of London*, 55: 249-275.

Wray, S. & Harris, S. (1994) Brown hares in commercial forestry in Great Britain. *Quarterly Journal of Forestry*, 88: 217-224.

Wright, L.J., Newson, S.E. & Noble, D.G. (2014) The value of a random sampling design for annual monitoring of national populations of larger British terrestrial mammals. *European Journal of Wildlife Research*, 60: 213-221.

Yalden, D. (1999) *The History of British Mammals*. T & A D Poyser Ltd., London.

R

167

A | Annex

1. Acknowledgements and funders

2. Recorders' names

3. Scientific names of species mentioned in the text

4. Glossary of terms

5. Gazetteer of sites mentioned in the text

6. Atlas facts and figures

Image: Brown Hares, Dinnet. Ian Francis

ANNEX 1. ACKNOWLEDGEMENTS AND FUNDERS

First and foremost, this atlas would not have been possible without the efforts and commitment of an army of biological recorders that took time to accurately note and submit mammal records, either directly to NESBReC or to other recording schemes whose data are used here. These recorders range from lifelong naturalists to those who have never before submitted a biological record and we hope that all will think the final product a worthy output from their recording activities. We thank Johnny Birks for writing the foreword and providing many useful comments on the draft.

The authors of the species accounts are individually named on the respective pages and we are very grateful to them for their work on the accounts. They include some of the nationally acknowledged experts on the species covered as well as dedicated and experienced local mammal enthusiasts. A range of people assisted with compiling the species accounts or gave assistance in other ways and we are grateful to them all for sharing their time and expertise: Nicholas Aebischer, Therese Alampo, Karen Birkby, Johnny Birks, Hebe Carus, Derek Crawley, Lizzie Croose, Douglas Darling, Isobel Davidson, Annabel Drysdale, Peter Evans, Gillian Forbes, Dave Goffin, John Haddow, Stephen Harris, David Hetherington, Iain Hope, Jimmy Irvine, Justin Irvine, Glyn Jones, Alan Knox, Hans Kruuk, Willie Lamont, Ewan Laurie, Murdo Macdonald, Ken Neil, Beverley O'Lone, Ian Perks, Paul Racey, Harry Scott, Helen Senn, Emma Sheehy, Mahboobeh Shirkhorshidi, Tilly Smith, Susan Swift, Mel Tonkin and Anne Youngman.

The book is enlivened with images freely provided by photographers from within the region and beyond. Photographers are credited with each image used but we are grateful to all who made photographs available, whether used in the book or not: Therese Alampo, Elizabeth Bacon, Paul Cameron, Marrianna Cammack, Roo Campbell, Paul Chapman, James Common, Isobel Davidson, John Dixon, Ed Duthie, Adam Francis, Ian Francis, Hilary Gaunt, Stephen Goodall, Martyn Gorman, Duncan Goulder, John Haddow, Ian Halliday, Ian Hay, Kevin Hepworth, Mark Howes, Glyn Jones, Kerry Kilshaw, John Langdale, Ruari Law, Raymond Leinster, Genevieve Leaper, Nick Littlewood, Beverley O'Lone, Mary Laing, Catriona Low, Nicola Mack, Sandy Main, John Malster, Tim Marshall, Jill Matthews, Ian Perks, Charlie Phillips, Dan Puplett, Stuart Rae, Katie Rewston, Annie Robinson, Alan Ross, Aileen Salway, Emma Schofield, Harry Scott, Mark Shewry, Alan J Sinclair, Bee Smith, Tilly Smith, Helen Taylor, Beverley Thain, Yzanne Turbett, Andy Wakelin, Alistair Watson, Toni Watt, Jenny Weston, Steve Willis, Amanda Wilson, Fenneke Wolters-Sinke, Rick Wood and Karol Zub.

We extend great thanks to Sunil Vishin of OpenBoxDesign (www.openboxdesign.co.uk) for his creativity and patience in designing this book during such a lengthy process of decision making.

Such is the nature of this project, with input from an extensive base of contributors, that many more people have made tangible contributions to the final publication than we have been able to note above. We are thankful to all and apologise to those whose contribution has not been individually acknowledged.

Finally, we give thanks to the following organisations for their continued financial support of NESBReC: Aberdeenshire Council, Aberdeen City Council, Cairngorms National Park Authority, Forestry Commission Scotland, RSPB Scotland and Scottish Natural Heritage. The logos of those organisations that provided funds specifically for this atlas project are shown below.

ANNEX 2. RECORDERS' NAMES

A. Allison · A. Anderson · A. Burnham · A. Campbell · A. Henrici · A. Kelly · A. MacColl · A. Petrie · A. Smith · A. Start · A. Watson · A.B. Cooper · A.C. Leonard · A.C. Newton · A.C. Wilson · A.F. Mussellwhite · A.G. Blunt · A.G. Duff · A.G. Stewart · A.J. Gaston · A.J. Taylor · A.M. Tittensor · A.R. Meade-Briggs · A.S. Cooke · Abby Harman-Wilson · Aberdeen Bat Group · Aberdeen City Council · Aberdeenshire Council · Aberdeenshire Rangers · Adam Styles · Adam Whitton · Aden Ranger · Adrian Scott · Adrian T. Sumner · Aftab Majeed · Aileen Meek · Aileen Salway · Aimee Gow · Ainoa Pravia · Aisling Gribbin · Al Macdonald · Alan Bodman · Alan Braddock · Alan Campbell · Alan Dobie · Alan Duncan · Alan Edward · Alan Gaskin · Alan Giles · Alan J. McNaughton · Alan Knox · Alan Linee · Alan Rogers · Alan Ross · Alan Souter · Alasdair Hosking · Alastair Fullwood · Alastair Watt · Albert Brittan · Alec Paterson · Alex Gray · Alex Pakeman · Alexander Craig · Alexander Crow · Alexandra Hendry · Alford Academy · Alford Cubs · Ali Robertson · Alisha Reeve · Alison Allan · Alison Alphonse · Alison Currie · Alison Espie · Alison Greggans · Alison Haggan · Alison Hawkins · Alison Owens · Alison Sutherland · Alison Wilson · Alistair Allan · Alistair Beeley · Alistair Ewen · Alistair Jeffs · Alistair Stott · Alistair Summers · Alistair Watson · Alister Clunas · Alister Riddell · Allan Bantick · Allan Macleod · Allan Perkins · Amanda Biggins · Amanda Bonner · Amanda Proud · Amanda Wilson · Amy Muir · Amy Withers · Ana Maia MacLellan · Andrea Williams · Andrew Duncan · Andrew Francis · Andrew Harrold · Andrew Heaver · Andrew Irvine · Andrew Kinghorn · Andrew Leonard · Andrew McCarry · Andrew McConnachie · Andrew Mckerron · Andrew Miller · Andrew Milne · Andrew Mitchell · Andrew Simpson · Andrew Stalker · Andrew Taylor · Andrew Thorpe · Andrew Turner · Andrew Wilson · Andy Burroughs · Andy Coventry · Andy Devine · Andy Ferguson · Andy Wilkins · Angela Maycox · Angela Slater · Angie Smith · Angus Beacom · Angus Miller · Ann Miles · Ann Woodfin · Anna Allan · Anna Ross · Annabel Drysdale · Anne Hay · Anne Moffat · Anne Mowat · Anne Phillips · Anne Rigg · Anne Sullivan · Anne Walker · Anne Wilkins · Anne Williamson · Anne-Marie Gauld · Annette Murray · Annie Lamb · Annie Robinson · Annie Sturgeon · Annika Samland · Anthony Chamberlain · Anthony Hay · Antony Hilton · Asha Gupta · Ashley Hamilton · Asol Ouwendijk · Audrey Blair · Audrey Turner · Ava Wallis Harper · Avril M. Vaagenes · AWPR Survey Team · B. Philp · B. Stewart · B.B. Rae · B.D. Eastcott · Bailies of Bennachie · Ballogie Estate · Balmoral Ranger Service · Banchory-Devenick Primary School · Barbara Taylor · Barnaby Simpkin · Barrie English · Barry Caudwell · Barry Cheyne · Barry Foster · Bat Conservation Trust · BEAR Scotland · Ben Freeman · Ben Notley · Benedict Mellor · Bertrand Couillens · Beryl Coope · Beryl McKenzie · Beth Umstead · Bethel Smith · Beverley Ridyard · Beverley Thain · Bill Burns · Bill Cuthbert · Bill Halliday · Bill Mearns · Bill Mohr · Bill Murray · Bill Quirrie · Bill Richardson · Bill Williams · Birnie Roberts · Blair Bank · Bob Daly · Bob Davis · Bob Palmer · Bob Proctor · Bob Turner · Brenda Potts · Brenda Turner · Brian Blagden · Brian Haigh · Brian Hill · Brian Jenner · Brian Mitchell · Brian Stacey · Brian Stewart · Bridget Freeman · Britt Taylor · Brittish Dragonfly Society · Brona Keenan · Bruce Anderson · C. Andrews · C. Campbell · C. Gibson · C. McKibbin · C. Pirie · C. Placido · C. Roberts · C.A. Foster · C.H. Bouck · C.V. Cuthbert · Callum Gilhooley · Calum McRoberts · Calum Ross · Cameron Beattie · Cameron Murray · Cara Stevens · Carmel Gilchrist · Carol Davidson · Carol Pudsey · Caroline Argo · Caroline Dempsey · Caroline Hood · Caron Hunter · Catherine Isherwood · Catherine Macleod · Catherine McLeod · Catherine Sharp · Catherine Young · Catriona Lawson · Catriona Reid · Cattie Anderson · Cdr Norris · Cecilia Rogers · Charles Leggat · Charles Weatherly · Charlie Morrison · Charlotte Milburn · Chris Bailey · Chris Bingham · Chris Bollen · Chris Cathrine · Chris Cook · Chris Cowley · Chris Curry · Chris Foster · Chris Gleed-Owen · Chris Leclare · Chris Redmond · Chris Ryan · Chris Stamp · Chris Stephen · Chris Sydes · Chris Taylor · Chris Wilson · Christina Anderson · Christina Oliver · Christine Farquhar · Christine Foster · Christine Hall · Christine Pert · Christine Ross · Christine Searle · Christopher Bailey · Claire Carrigan · Claire Herbert · Clare Ballinger · Clare Fulker · Clare Scanlan · Claudia Garratt · CNP Wild Living Cats Project · Colin Booth · Colin Castle · Colin Hardacre · Colin Harvey · Colin McLeod · Colin Miller · Colin Mowat · Colin Whyte · Connor Wilson · Craibstone Rural Ski Club · Craig Davis · Craig Gray · Craig Thomson · Craig Westlake · Craigievar Primary School · D. Ashley · D. Bruce · D. Dey · D. Grant · D. Hetherington · D. Jenkins · D. Law · D. Leslie · D. Meston · D. Saunders · D. Savage · D. Simpson · D.B. Newland · D.C. Jardine · D.C. Thornycroft · D.E. Hanson · D.I. Chapman · D.J. Jefferies · D.J. Schafer · D.J. Selbie · D.M. Herdson · D.M. Stoddart · D.W. Yalden · Dan Puplett · Danestone Primary School · Daniel Arnold · Daniel Ward · Danny Heptinstall · Daryl Short · Dauna Matheson · Dave Batty · Dave Braiden · Dave Gill · Dave Kilbey · Dave Macdonald · Dave Marshall · Dave Sutherland · David Bale · David Bell · David Bova · David Brown · David Chessor · David Clark · David Dunstan · David Elston · David Farrell · David Genney · David Gill · David

Hansen · David Henderson · David Kerr · David Law · David Leslie · David Maguire · David Maisels · David Murray · David Newland · David Parnaby · David Plant · David Potter · David Ramsay · David Reid · David Ross · David Shannon · David Simmons · David Sutherland · David Tosh · David Welch · Davie Beauly · Davy Brand · Dawn Tatton · Dawn Trundle · Debbie Fielding · Debra Campbell · Del Smith · Deni Sarafimoski · Denise Martin · Deon Roos · Derek Dickson · Derek Jennings · Derek Leiper · Derek Sutherland · Derek Wedderburn · Desmond Dugan · Diana Robertson · Diana Spencer · Dianne Stokes · DJW Cults Courier · Dominic Funnell · Donald Junnier · Donald Ross · Dorena Battaglino · Dot Ralli · Doug Collins · Doug Thorn · Douglas Blease · Douglas Cameron · Douglas Gooday · Douglas Ross · Drummuir 21 · Duncan Emsley · Dundee Museum · E. Farquharson · E. Smith · E.J. Lenton · E.J.N.T. Coghill · E.W. Ellis · Ed Grace · Elaine Bryson · Elaine Findlay · Elaine Roft · Eleanor Hutchins · Eleanor Munro · Eleanor Shield · Elisabeth Legg · Elizabeth Bacon · Elizabeth Hall · Elizabeth Russell · Elizabeth Strath · Ellie Watts · Ellis Milton · Elton Foister · Emily Alsford · Emily Little · Emily Taylor · Emma Chapman · Emma Godwin · Emma Rawling · Emma Sheehy · Emma Williams · Emma Wilson · Enid Black · Eric Hart · Eric Jensen · Eric Meek · Erica Hollis · Ern Emmett · Estelle Duncan · Esther Taylor · Esther Woodward · Euan Cameron · Eva Sparreboom · Evril Nicola · Ewan Lawrie · Ewan McHenry · Ewan Pearce · Ewan Shilland · Ewan Sutton · Ewen Cameron · F. Rawsthorne · F.G. Reeman · F.H. Perring · FCS Grampian Conservancy · Fearghal McCartan · Fergus Cumming · Findlay Ecology Services · Fiona Anderson · Fiona Bain · Fiona Barclay · Fiona Cruickshank · Fiona Everingham · Fiona Gordon-Duff · Fiona Milne · Fiona Montgomery · Fiona Oldroyd · Fiona Prior · Fiona Smith · Fiona Webster · Fiona Yarrow · Fordyce Primary School · Forest Enterprise Tay · Forestry Commission Scotland · Francesco Germi · Frank Robertson · Frank Tomlinson · Fraser Green · Fred Gordon · Friends of Denlethen Wood · Fyvie Primary School P3 · G. Ghillies · G. Ramsay · G. Rose · G.K. Whitehead · G.M. Dunnet · G.R. Hill · G.W. Rebecca · Gabriele Longo · Gareth Clingan · Gary Flynn · Gary Morris · Gavin Forest · Gavin O'Neill · Ged Connell · Gemini Explorer · Gemma Laing · Gemma Nixon · Genevieve Jones · Genevieve Leaper · Geoff Collinson · Geoff Johnson · Geordie Roberts · George Cheyne · George Robertson · Georgia Moody · Georgie Bain · Georgina Cook · Geva Blackett · Gibby Kirwan · Gill Grant · Gillian Crawford · Gillian Leith · Gillian Mitchell · Gillian Taylor Shaw · Gina Ford · Gina Scanlan · Glasgow Museum · Glenn Iason · Glenn Roberts · Glyn Jones · Gordon Bryan · Gordon Corbet · Gordon Green · Gordon Haughton · Gordon McRuvie ·

Gordon Ridley · Gordon Smith · Grace Banks · Grace Chau · Graeme Cumming · Graeme Henderson · Graeme Morison · Graeme Rose · Graham Christer · Graham Johnston · Graham Marr · Graham McNicol · Graham Morrison · Grant Anderson · Greg Fullarton · Gregor McAbery · Gulia Grazianai · Gus Jones · Gus Routledge · H. Young · H.I. Leitch · H.R. Arnold · H.V. Thompson · Hamilton Hinton · Hancock Museum · Hannah Low · Harry Scott · Harry Smith · Hayley Douglas · Hayley Wiswell · Hazel Davidson · Hazel Hartley · Hazel Lawrie · Hazel Riddell · Head Greenkeeper Covesea · Head Greenkeeper Lossiemouth · Heather Bantick · Heather Barclay · Heather Manning · Heather Mullan · Heather Paul · Heather Wyllie · Hebe Carus · Helen Fitch · Helen Gray · Helen Kelly · Helen Lumsden · Helen Rowe · Helen Taylor · Helen Watts · Helen Webb · Helen Wells · Helen Williamson · Helen Young · Helena Dalgleish · Helena Holland · Henry Cox · Henry Hall · Hill of Banchory P6 & P7 Class · Hinton Barret · Hollie Walker · Huberta Robinson · Hugh Addlesee · Hugh Insley · Hywel Maggs · I. Alcock · I. Duncan · I. Ridge · I.S. Rowie · I.S. Suttie · Iain Gillespie · Iain Kelly · Iain Lawrie · Iain Mitchell · Ian Annan · Ian Barnett · Ian Broadbent · Ian Brodie · Ian Brownlow · Ian Francis · Ian Grant · Ian Green · Ian Harkiss · Ian Hill · Ian Macpherson · Ian Mitchell · Ian Pirie · Ian Talboys · Ian Tanner · Ian Tillett · Ilse Elders · Indy Mair · Innes Smith · Insh Marshes RSPB Observations · Inverness Museum Records Centre · Iona MacGregor · Irene McKinnie · Iris Walker · Isobel Davidson · Isobel MacDonald · Ivor Simpson · J. Adams · J. Allan · J. Blenkin · J. Carter · J. Christie · J. Christie · J. Douglas · J. Duncan · J. Green · J. Haddow · J. Henderson · J. Herman · J. Humprey · J. Keith · J. Knowles · J. MacKay · J. Macnab · J. Mair · J. Mojsiewicz · J. Morrison · J. Newby · J. Smith · J.A. Love · J.B. Searle · J.E. Gaffney · J.H. Cuthbert · J.H. Taylor · J.J. Rowe · J.J.D. Greenwood · J.L.Finlay Fergusson · J.M. Almond · J.M. Butterworth · J.M. Duncan · J.M. Fletcher · J.P. Winn · J.T.R. Sharrock · Jack Ibbotson · Jackie Brawley · Jackie Cumberbirch · Jackie Lawrie · Jackie Maskall · Jackie Webley · Jacqueline Chapman · Jacqueline Holland · James Addison · James Common · James Davidson · James Harding · James Lister · James Reid · James Ross · James Wood · Jamie Shepherd · Jamie Sneddon · Jamie Urquhart · Jan Dunbar · Jan Lythgoe · Jan Morse · Jan Regulski · Jane Sears · Jane Sim · Janet Ash · Janet Imlach · Janette Taylor · Jason Hon · Jason Hysert · Jean Johnson · Jeff Banks · Jeff Waddell · Jen Heatley · Jenni Stockan · Jennifer Bates · Jennifer Heatley · Jennifer Mclaren · Jennifer Polson · Jenny Allen · Jenny Bryce · Jenny Weston · Jerry Cobb · Jessica Philip · Jessica Scott · Jessica Wood · Jill Birch · Jill Matthews · Jill Stables · Jim Bacon · Jim Ferguson · Jim Gillies · Jim Hendry · Jim Lister · Jim Mackenzie · Jim Macrae · Jim Manthorpe · Jim McNair · Jim McRae · Jim Taylor · Jimmy Johnston · Jo Bagguley · Jo

Smith · Jo Whyte · Joanna Dick · Joanna Stewart · Joanne Davidson · Joanne Harper · Joanne Webb · Jodie Rhodes · Joe Bilious · Joe Walsh · Johanna Pelling · John Allison · John Black · John Chapman · John Coyne · John Derbyshire Consultants · John Duncan · John Flux · John Hansford · John Hitchon · John Kearns · John Kennedy · John Kirk · John Lamb · John Lang Wilson · John Latham · John Leishman · John Lennox · John MacKay · John Malster · John McLem · John Milne · John Morton · John Thompson · John Thomson · John Thorpe · John Tweddle · John Watt · John Wills · Johnny Birks · Jon Bailey · Jonathan Appleby · Jonathan Bailey · Jonathan Fenton · Jonathan Groom · Jonathan Hughes · Jonathan Jones · Jonathan Willet · Jos Milner · Joshua Goldfarb · Joyce Murphy · Judith Bale · Judith Binney · Judith Bullivant · Judith Cox · Julia Duncan · Julia Mackay · Julia Ricketts · Julia Spencer · Julia Truscott · Julie Currie · Julie White · Julie Wyness · K. Bailey · K. Gordon Smith · K. Malster · K. Ogilve · K.M. Berry · K.P. Bland · Karen Connon · Karen Couper · Karen Cunningham · Karen McDonald · Karen Paterson · Karen Piper · Karen Smith · Karin de Rijck · Kat Regulski · Kath Hamper · Katherine Househam · Kathy Ader · Kathy Dale · Kathy Fallowfield · Kathy Fletcher · Katrina Davie · Katy Astell · Katy Brayshaw · Keig School · Keith Brockie · Keith Cromar · Keith Duncan · Keith Hopps · Keith Kingham · Kemnay Wildlife Explorers · Ken Ireland · Ken Macrae · Ken McEwen · Ken Taylor · Ken Watson · Kenn Watt · Kenneth Kite · Kenny Buchan · Kenny MacKintosh · Kerry Kilshaw · Kevin Bell · Kevin Greensall · Kevin Hepworth · Kevin Lynch · Kevin Strathdee · Kevin Wright · Kingswells Eco Group · Kirkwall Boys Brigade · Kirsten O'Sullivan · Kirsten West · Kirstie Ross · Kirsty Duncan · Kirsty McAbery · Konstantinos Sideris · L.V. Fleming · Laura Campbell · Laura Cannicott · Laura Lucas · Laura Mann · Laura Taylor · Lauren Horncastle · Lauren Macgregor · Laurie Corbett · Leah Jackson · Leanne Barnes · Leanne Donochie · Leo du Feu · Leon Black · Lesley Blackhall · Lesley Craig · Lesley Ellis · Lesley McKinlay · Lesley Naylor · Leslie Cheyne · Lewis Murray · Lina-Elvira Back · Linda Mathieson · Linda McLaren · Linda Robertson · Linda Vickers · Linda Washington · Lisa Wood · Lisette Degioanni · Liz Bishop · Liz Bracegirdle · Liz Cooper · Liz Galley · Liz Hall · Liz Holden · Liz Marchant · Liz Wilson · Lizzie Croose · Lorna Dow · Lorna Edey · Lorna Haugh · Lorna Murray · Lorna Oldershaw · Lorna Wilkie · Lorna Williamson · Louise Simpson · Lucinda Robinson · Lucy Dunn · Lucy Gunn · Lyn Wells · Lynda Maddrick · Lynn Powell · Lynn Purvis · M. Clarkson · M. Dawson · M. Faulkner · M. Ferguson · M. Gregory · M. Innes · M. Ketcher · M. McLeod · M. Nichol · M. Nicoll · M. Ramirez · M. Richardson · M. Rodgers · M. Rotheroe · M. Thompson · M. Walker · M. Wilson · M. Winsch · M. Wright · M.A. Freeman · M.C. Meston · M.D. Marsh · M.F. Drake · M.H. Port · M.J.

Cotton · M.J. Richardson · M.K. Williams · M.R. Taylor · Maggie Evans · Maggie Laws · Mairi Stewart · Malcolm Hardwick · Malcolm Hobson · Malcolm MacGarvin · Malcolm Smith · Mandy Tulloch · Marc Campbell · Margaret Cinderey · Margaret Cowie · Margaret Cramb · Margaret Macpherson · Margaret Mitchell · Margaret Riddell · Maria Dawson · Maria Rinke · Marie Donald · Marie Fish · Marie Shore · Marion Anderson · Marion Grant · Marion Malcolm · Marion Webb · Marius Anderson · Mark Antcliff · Mark Cauvin · Mark Cubitt · Mark Hall · Mark Johnston · Mark Johnstone · Mark Jones · Mark Lewis · Mark Melville · Mark Shewry · Mark Tasker · Mark Woodfin · Mark Young · Marka Rifat · Marsaili Aspinall · Martin Cook · Martin Duncan · Martin Hacket · Martin Robinson · Martin Sinclair · Martyn Brett · Martyn Gorman · Mary Brown · Mary Laing · Matt Crofts · Matt Harding · Matt Millington · Matthew Buist · Matthew Mace · Matthew Smith · Matthew Wallace · Maureen Corley · Mearns Academy Eco Club · Melanie Clouston · Melanie Findlay · Melissa Noble · Mhairi Mackintosh · Mhairi McRae · Michael Adams · Michael Buchan · Michael Casey · Michael Cuff · Michael Dawson · Michael Fifield · Michael Fotheringham · Michael Goldie · Michael Harris · Michael Neely · Michael Taylor · Michael Whyte · Michelle Kemp · Michelle McPartlain · Mick Bestwick · Mike Barnetson · Mike Carson-Rowland · Mike Casey · Mike Chandler · Mike Coleman · Mike Duguid · Mike Hanlin · Mike Harris · Mike Hume · Mike Innes · Mike Martin · Mike Mathers · Mike Smith · Mike Sullivan · Mike Taylor · Mike Wheeler · Mike Whitcombe · Mike Woodcock · Moira Moran · Moray Mackay · Moray Souter · Moyra Gray · Mr Cruickshank · Mr Gillan · Mr Hewson · Mr Jones · Mr MacKinnon · Mr McNaughton · Mr Riley · Mr Taylor · Mrs Campbell · Mrs Marshall · Mrs Moir · Mrs Sheriden · Mrs Smith · Murdo Macdonald · Myles Brownhill · N. Bullivant · N. Taylor · N. Theodoreson · N.D. Redgate · N.G. Chapman · Nancy Cuthbert · Natalie Goodlad · National Game Census · National Trust for Scotland · Natural Power · Natural Retreats Rangers · Nava Tintarev · NE Scotland Water Vole Project · Neil Lowther · Neil Taylor · Neil Theodoreson · Neil Walker · NESBATS · NESBReC · Nethy Bridge Ranger · Neville Duncan · New Machar Primary School · Niall Currie · Nichola Hepburn · Nick A. Littlewood · Nick Dadds · Nick Davis · Nick Downs · Nick Picozzi · Nick Stewart · Nick Williams · Nick Young · Nicky Dancer · Nicky Penford · Nicola Dixon · Nicola Seal · Nicola Spalding · Nigel Fallon · Nigel Scriven · Nigel Webster · Nik Robinson · NORCET · Norman Defoe · Norman Elkins · Oscar Campbell · Otter Survival Fund · P. Barr · P. Cairney · P. Chanin · P. Cullington · P. Graham · P. Jarvis · P. MacDonald · P. Morris · P.A. Neville · P.C. Tinning · P.G. Webb · P.G.H. Evans · P.K.

Page 170 | Image: Grey Seal, Peterhead. Paul Chapman

Page 171 | Image: Mountain Hare, Glen Muick. Ian Francis

Page 172 | Image: Red Deer, Mar Lodge. Ian Francis

Page 173 | Image: Otters, River Don, Aberdeen. Andy Coventry

ANNEX 3. SCIENTIFIC NAMES OF SPECIES MENTIONED IN THE TEXT

BIRDS

Barn Owl	*Tyto alba*
Buzzard	*Buteo buteo*
Capercaillie	*Tetrao urogallus*
Chough	*Pyrrhocorax pyrrhocorax*
Curlew	*Numenius arquata*
Kestrel	*Falco tinnunculus*
Pheasant	*Phasianus colchicus*
Red Grouse	*Lagopus lagopus*
Red Kite	*Milvus milvus*
Stone-curlew	*Burhinus oedicnemus*
Tawny Owl	*Strix aluco*
Woodlark	*Lullula arborea*

MARINE SPECIES

Cod	*Gadus morhua*
European Eel	*Anguilla anguilla*
Herring	*Clupea harengus*
Salmon	*Salmo salar*
Sandeel	Ammodytidae
Sprat	*Sprattus sprattus*
Squid	Loliginidae

INVERTEBRATES

Earthworm	Lumbricidae
Large Blue	*Phengaris arion*

MAMMALS

Brown Bear	*Ursus arctos*
Dog	*Canis lupus familiaris*
Eurasian Beaver	*Castor fiber*
Lynx	*Lynx lynx*
Polar Bear	*Ursus maritimus*
Wolf	*Canis lupus*

VASCULAR PLANTS

Alder	*Alnus glutinosa*
Ash	*Fraxinus excelsior*
Aspen	*Populus tremula*
Barley	*Hordeum vulgare*
Beech	*Fagus sylvatica*
Birch	*Betula* spp.
Blackberry	*Rubus fruticosus* agg.
Bracken	*Pteridium aquilinum*
Broom	*Cytisus scoparius*
Common Reed	*Phragmites australis*
Corsican Pine	*Pinus nigra*
Deergrass	*Trichophorum* spp.
Douglas Fir	*Pseudotsuga menziesii*
Dwarf Bamboo	*Pleioblastus* spp.
European Larch	*Larix decidua*
Flag Iris	*Iris pseudacorus*
Gorse	*Ulex europaeus*
Hare's-tail Cottongrass	*Eriophorum vaginatum*
Heather	*Calluna vulgaris*
Japanese Larch	*Larix kaempferi*
Juniper	*Juniperus communis*
Lodgepole Pine	*Pinus contorta*
Meadowsweet	*Filipendula ulmaria*
Norway Spruce	*Picea abies*
Oak	*Quercus* spp.
Oil-seed Rape	*Brassica napus*
Pignut	*Conopodium majus*
Potato	*Solanum tuberosum*
Scots Pine	*Pinus sylvestris*
Sitka Spruce	*Picea sitchensis*
Sycamore	*Acer pseudoplatanus*
Willow	*Salix* spp.

ANNEX 4. GLOSSARY OF TERMS

Bolt - to insert a captive predatory animal, such as a Ferret, into a burrow to force animals such as Rabbits to leave so they can be caught or shot

Cervid - a mammal of the deer family (Cervidae)

Cetaceans - marine mammals such as dolphins, porpoises and whales

Citizen science - gathering of scientific data by members of the public

Congener - a member of the same taxonomic genus

Dorsal - pertaining to the back of an animal

Echolocation - emitting calls and using their echoes to locate objects and prey items

Emergent vegetation - plants that grow in water and emerge above the surface

Eutrophic - referring to water bodies that have a high, sometimes excessive, mineral content

Hectad - a square measuring 10 km x 10 km

Hybridisation - crossbreeding between different species

Intergrading - gradual merging of species through evolution

Introgression - where repeated hybridisation leads to the blurring of genetic distinction between species

Keepered - land managed by gamekeepers associated with shooting estates

kHz - kilohertz, a unit of soundwave frequency

Mesotrophic - referring to water bodies that have a moderate mineral content

Monoculture - growing a single species crop in a given area

Mustelid - a mammal of the weasel family (Mustelidae), including Badger, Otter, Pine Marten, Stoat, Weasel, Feral Ferret and American Mink

Myxomatosis - infectious viral disease in Rabbits that causes inflammation of the eyes and is fatal

Natal area - location of an individual's birth

NESBReC - North East Scotland Biological Records Centre

Oligotrophic - referring to water bodies that have a low mineral content

Pelage - the coat of a mammal

Pellets - droppings (as in Rabbit)

Pelt - the skin of a mammal

Predation - where one animal kills and eats another animal

Rank grassland - ungrazed, tall, coarse grassland

Recording bias - the distribution of records being strongly influenced by where recorders are active, e.g. human settlements, well-visited locations

Riparian habitat - vegetation along river margins and banks

Scats - droppings, referring particularly to carnivores such as Fox and Pine Marten

Scrape - a shallow depression in the ground used as a basic nest or resting place

Spraint - droppings of an Otter

Stratified random survey - a survey in which survey sites are selected randomly within sub-sets of possible sites that are based on variables such as location, altitude or habitat, etc.

Tetrad - a square measuring 2 km x 2 km, comprising four 1 km squares

Image: Hedgehog, Aboyne. Harry Scott

ANNEX 5. GAZETTEER OF SITES MENTIONED IN THE TEXT

A 6 figure grid reference represents a notional, central point for the site name. For larger areas and features, a 10 km square or range of squares is used to identify the approximate location.

SITE NAME	GRID REFERENCE
ABERDEEN (CITY)	NJ935065
ABERNETHY	NJ020150
ABOYNE	NO528984
ALFORD	NJ576161
ALLTCAILLEACH (GLEN MUICK)	NO335925
AN TORC (THE BOAR OF BADENOCH)	NN621763
ANGUS GLENS	NO27-NO48
ATHOLL	NN87 area
AVIEMORE	NH895125
BADENOCH	NN59-NH80
BALLATER	NO368958
BALLOCHBUIE	NO200900
BALLOGIE	NO570955
BALMEDIE	NJ976180
BANCHORY	NO698955
BANFF	NJ685645
BANFF AND BUCHAN	NJ95 area
BEINN A' GHLO	NN970732
BEN AVON	NJ135015
BEN MACDUI	NN989989
BENNACHIE	NJ682223
BENNACHIE CENTRE	NJ698216
BIRKHALL	NO349936
BIRSE	NO59 area
BLAIR ATHOLL	NN875653
BOGTURK	NO554910
BRAEMAR	NO149914
BRIDGE OF DON	NJ946094
BUCHAN	NJ94 area
BUCKIE	NJ425657
BURGHEAD	NJ115690
CABRACH	NJ385270
CAIRN GORM	NJ005040
CAIRN TOUL	NN960972
CAIRNGORMS	NJ000000
CAIRNWELL PASS	NO139780
CARN AN TUIRC	NO175805
CARN NAN GABHAR	NN970732
CARRBRIDGE	NH906228
CLASHINDARROCH	NJ445325
COLLIESTON	NK040283

SITE NAME	GRID REFERENCE
CRAIBSTONE	NJ873107
CRAIG MASKELDIE	NO392797
CRATHES CASTLE	NO734968
CREAG DHUBH	NN678972
CREAG NAN GABHAR	NO155841
CRUDEN BAY	NK092363
CULBIN (SANDS)	NH965627
CULLEN HOUSE	NJ506663
DALNACARDOCH	NN690740
DEESIDE	NO09-NJ90
DINNET	NO459987
DINNET LOCHS	NJ4400 area
DONMOUTH	NJ954095
DONSIDE	NJ20-NJ90
DRUMOAK	NO785985
DRUMOCHTER PASS	NN632760
DURRIS FOREST	NO795925
DYCE	NJ890126
ELGIN	NJ215625
FETTERESSO	NO760870
FINDHORN BAY	NJ045625
FOREST OF BIRSE	NO525905
FORMARTINE	NJ82 area
FORRES	NJ035585
FOUDLAND	NJ605345
FOWLSHEUGH	NO881803
FRASERBURGH	NJ995665
GAICK FOREST	NN78 area
GARBH-CHOIRE, BRAEMAR	NO175787
GIGHT WOODS	NJ823393
GIRDLE NESS	NJ973053
GLEN CALLATER	NO175845
GLEN CLUNIE	NO147866
GLEN DYE	NO635835
GLEN ESK	NO48-NO57
GLEN EY	NO090860
GLEN GARRY	NN67-NN86
GLEN MUICK	NO310851
GLEN QUOICH	NO080930
GLEN SHEE	NO139782
GLEN TANAR	NO465940
GLEN TILT	NN97 area
GLENBERVIE	NO766806

SITE NAME	GRID REFERENCE
GLENBUCHAT	NJ3617 area
GLENFESHIE	NN845933
GLENLIVET	NJ22 area
GLENMORE	NH980090
GORDON DISTRICT	NJ72 area
GOURDON	NO825705
GRANTOWN (ON-SPEY)	NJ031276
HADDO HOUSE	NJ868347
HOWE OF THE MEARNS	NO67-NO77
INSH MARSHES	NH7700-NH8103
INVERBERVIE	NO833725
INVERCAULD	NO19 area
INVERMARK	NO437806
INVERUGIE	NK103484
INVERURIE	NJ774216
KEITH	NJ430510
KEMNAY	NJ735160
KINCARDINE	NO78 area
KINGSTON	NJ337655
KINLOSS	NJ065618
KINVEACHY	NH880180
LAGGAN	NN615944
LAICH OF MORAY	NJ26 area
LECHT	NJ248125
LESLIE, INSCH	NJ597247
LOCH ETCHACHAN	NJ005005
LOCH GARTEN	NH973180
LOCH INSH	NH832044
LOCH KINORD, DINNET	NO442995
LOCH MUICK	NO285825
LOCH OF STRATHBEG	NK074590
LOCH SPYNIE	NJ235665
LOCHINDORB	NH975365
LOCHNAGAR	NO250855
LOSSIEMOUTH	NJ235710
LYNTURK	NJ598122
MAR	NO070910
MAR LODGE	NO100900
MARR (HISTORICAL AREA OF UPPER DEESIDE AND DONSIDE)	NN98-NJ41 area
MARYCULTER	NO856991
MEARNS	NO67-NO77
MONADHLIATH	NN59-NH81 area
MORAY FIRTH	NJ07 area
MORVEN	NJ380040
MOSSET BURN, FORRES	NJ048568

SITE NAME	GRID REFERENCE
MOUNTH	NN98-NO68
MUCHALLS	NO895910
MUIR OF DINNET	NO4399 area
MULBEN FOREST	NJ356506
NEWBURGH	NJ999252
NEWTONMORE	NN713990
OLDMELDRUM	NJ809273
PETERHEAD	NK133464
PITLOCHRY	NN938581
RATTRAY HEAD	NK105580
RED MOSS OF NETHERLEY	NO857938
RHYNIE	NJ498271
RIVER DEE	NO09-NJ90
RIVER DEVERON	NJ32-NJ66
RIVER DON	NJ20-NJ90
RIVER GARRY	NN67-NN86
RIVER LOSSIE	NJ04-NJ27
RIVER NORTH ESK	NO48-NO76
RIVER SOUTH ESK	NO27-NO37
RIVER SPEY	NN59-NJ36
RIVER UGIE	NK04 area
RIVER YTHAN	NJ63-NK02
ROSEHEARTY	NJ932675
ROTHES	NJ275495
ROTHIEMURCHUS	NH927078
SAND LOCH	NK034284
SANDS OF FORVIE	NK023278
SANDHAVEN	NJ965675
SGOR AN LOCHAIN UAINE	NN954976
SCORS BURN, BLACKWATER FOREST	NJ325222
SLOCHD	NH840250
SPEY BAY	NJ354653
SPEY VALLEY	see Speyside
SPEYSIDE	NN59-NJ36
ST CYRUS	NO747648
ST FERGUS	NK097520
STONEHAVEN	NO874856
STRATHAVON	NJ00-NJ13
STRATHDON	NJ351129
STRATHSPEY	NH91-NJ02
TARLAND	NJ482046
TILLYFOUR	NJ594103
TOWIE, DONSIDE	NJ460127
TROUP HEAD	NJ825674
UATH LOCHANS, INSHRIACH	NH836020
YTHAN ESTUARY	NK005243

ANNEX 6. ATLAS FACTS AND FIGURES

43 MAMMAL SPECIES MAPPED

NUMBER OF HECTADS **146** INCLUDING PART HECTADS AT THE ATLAS BOUNDARY

LARGEST NUMBER OF SPECIES RECORDED IN A SINGLE TETRAD **27** FROM TETRAD **NO73I**: CRATHES CASTLE AND SURROUNDINGS

THE MOST WIDELY RECORDED SPECIES ROE DEER **1,353** TETRADS

RECORDS RECIEVED FROM **1,472** OBSERVERS

77,496 RECORDS USED IN COMPILING THE MAPS

LAND AREA **11,629** km² 15% OF SCOTLAND 5% OF UK

NUMBER OF TETRADS **3,101** INCLUDING PART TETRADS AT THE ATLAS BOUNDARY

77 MAMMAL SPECIES COVERED IN TOTAL

THE MOST FREQUENTLY REPORTED SPECIES RED SQUIRREL **13,473** RECORDS

INDEX OF MAMMAL SPECIES

A

Alpacas **130**

American Bison **130**

American Mink 23, 44 **102–103**, 134, 139,141, 144, 147, 148, 150, 154, 175

Apodemus sylvaticus **46–47**

Arvicola amphibius **44–45**

Atlantic White-Sided Dolphin **127**

B

Badger 8, 20, 22, 24, 28, 35, **88–89**, 133,134,139, 140, 142, 146, 147, 148, 175

Balaenoptera acutorostrata **127**

Balaenoptera physalus **128**

Bank Vole 20, 21, 24, **40–41**, 42, 43, 134, 140

Bearded Seal **108–109**, 134, 139, 140

Beaver 124, 150, 178

Bison bison **130**

Black Rat 124, 125, 139

Bos taurus **130**

Brown Bear 124, 153, 174

Brown Hare 24, 26, **54–55**, 56, 57, 133, 134, 139, 140,141, 147, 154, 155

Brown Long-Eared Bat 28, 71, **80–81**, 71, 133, 134, 140

Brown Rat 23, 24, 29, **50–51**, 45, 94, 125, 134, 140, 148, 154

C

Canis lupus 174

Canis lupus familiaris 174

Capra hircus **120–121**, 130

Capreolus capreolus **118–119**

Castor fiber 174

Cattle 19, 24, 74, 122, 129, 130

Cervus elaphus **112–113**

Cervus nippon **114–115**

Cetaceans 2, 3, 33, 35, 126, 127, 139, 144, 146, 175

Common Bottlenose Dolphin **127**

Common Pipistrelle 24, 28, 29, **74–75**, 76, 77, 134, 139, 140

Common Seal 32, 33, **104–105**, 107, 134, 140

Common Shrew 19, 24, 30, 31, **62–63**, 64, 65, 134, 140

Coypu **125**, 139

Cystophora cristata **125**

D

Dama dama **116–117**

Daubenton's Bat 23, **68–69**, 134, 139, 140, 159

Delphinus delphis **127**

Dog 52, 60, 86, 147

Domesticated horse 130

Domestic Cat 60, 75, 77, 82, 83, 84, 96, 156

Domestic Cattle 130

Domestic Goat 120, 130

Domestic Pig 110, 130

Domestic Reindeer 150

Domestic Sheep 130

E

Equus caballus ferus 130

Erignathus barbatus **108–109**

Erinaceus europaeus **58–59**

F

Fallow Deer **116–117**, 134, 140

Felis catus **82–83**

Felis silvestris **82–83**, 84

Feral Cat 11, 35, **82–83**, 84, 134, 140, 153, 156

Feral Ferret 11, 35, **98–99**, 100, 101, 134, 140

Feral Goat 21, 35, **120–121**, 131, 134, 140

Field Vole 24, 26, 30, 40, **42–43**, 45, 86, 96, 122, 134, 140

Fin Whale **128**

Fox 8, 20, 24, 28, 29, 31, 32, 52, 54, **86–87**, 133, 134, 137, 139, 140, 142, 147, 148, 153, 154, 175

G

Globicephala melas **128**

Grampus griseus **127**

Grey Seal 31, 32, 105, **106–107**, 108, 134, 139, 140, 141, 147

Grey Squirrel 2, 28, 29, 36, 37, **38–39**, 92, 133, 134, 139, 140,141, 143, 147, 148, 149, 150, 155

H

Halichoerus grypus **106–107**

Harbour Porpoise 32, **127**

Harbour Seal **104**

Harp Seal **125**

Harvest Mouse **125**, 139

Hedgehog 24, 29, 35, **58–59**, 88, 134, 139, 140, 175

Homo sapiens **122–123**

Hooded Seal **125**

House Mouse 29, 47, **48–49** 134, 140

Human 2, 5, 15, 32, 35, 46, 48, 61, 63, 64, 75, 77, 82, 86, 88, 91, 104, 116, **122–123**, 135, 139, 140, 144, 147, 150, 153, 154, 175

Humpback whale **127**

Hyperoodon ampullatus **128**

K

Killer Whale **127**

Kuhl's Pipistrelle **125**

L

Lagenorhynchus acutus **127**

Lagenorhynchus albirostris **127**

Lama glama **130**

Leisler's Bat 24, **72–73**, 139, 140

Lepus europaeus **54–55**

Lepus timidus **56–57**

Llamas **130**

Long-Finned Pilot Whale **128**

Lutra lutra **90–91**

Lynx 124, 153, 174

Lynx lynx 174

M

Martes martes **92–93**

Megaptera novaeangliae **127**

Meles meles **88–89**

Mesoplodon bidens **128**

Micromys minutus **125**

Microtus agrestis **42–43**

Minke Whale **127,** 128

Mole 5, 8, 9, 24, 35, **60–61**, 96, 133, 134, 140, 147

Mountain Hare 2, 18, 19, 55, **56–57**, 134, 138, 139, 140, 142, 143 147, 155

Muskrat **125**, 139

Mus musculus **48–49**

Mustela erminea **94–95**

Mustela furo **98–99**

Mustelo furo x putorius **98–99**

Mustela nivalis **96–97**

Mustela putorius **98–99**

Myocastor coypus **125**

Myodes glareolus **40–41**

Myotis daubentonii **68–69**

Myotis nattereri **70–71**

N

Nathusius' Pipistrelle 23, **78–79**, 134, 139, 140

Natterer's Bat 23, 28, **70–71**, 134, 139, 140

Neomys fodiens **66–67**

Neovison vison **102–103**

Noctule 73, **125**

Northern Bottlenose Whale **128**

Nyctalus leisleri **72–73**

Nyctalus noctula **125**

O

Odobenus rosmarus **125**

Ondatra zibethicus **125**

Orcinus orca **127**

Oryctolagus cuniculus **52–53**

Otter 4, 7, 8, 23, 24, 27, 31, 32, **90–91**, 103, 134, 140, 141, 143, 144, 146, 175

Ovis aries **130**

P

Pagophilus groenlandicus **125**

Phoca vitulina **104-105**

Phocoena phocoena **127**

Physeter macrocephalus **128**

Pine Marten 2, 3, 8, 20, 22, 28, 46, 51, **92-93**, 102, 134, 139, 140, 141, 142, 143, 146, 147, 148, 153, 154, 175

Pipistrellus kuhlii **125**

Pipistrellus nathusii **78-79**

Pipistrellus pipistrellus **74-75**

Pipistrellus pygmaeus **76-77**

Plecotus auritus **80-81**

Polecat **98-99**, 101

Polecat-Ferret **98-99,** 100

Pusa hispida **125**

Pygmy Shrew 18, 19, 26, 62, **64-65**, 134, 140

R

Rabbit 5, 9, 24, 30, 31, **52-53**, 82, 86, 94,95, 97, 98, 99, 134, 139, 140, 147, 150, 154, 157, 175

Rangifer tarandus **125**

Rattus norvegicus **50-51**

Rattus rattus **125**

Red Deer 12, 18, 20, **112-113**, 114, 115, 117, 120, 130, 134, 139, 140, 141, 150, 151, 153, 156

Red Squirrel 2, 20, 21, 22, 28, 29, **36-37**, 38, 39, 92, 133, 134, 139, 140, 142, 143, 145, 146, 155, 157

Reindeer **125**, 150

Ringed Seal **125**

Risso's Dolphin **127**

Roe Deer 20, 21, 22, 24, 29, **118-119**, 133, 134, 139, 140, 142, 184

S

Sciurus carolinensis **38-39**

Sciurus vulgaris **36-37**

Scottish Wildcat 2, 8, 11, 20, 22, 35, 46, 52, 82, 83, 84, 85, 110, 134, 139, 140, 142, 145, 146, 153, 156, 157

Short-Beaked Common Dolphin **127**

Sika 112, **114-115**, 134, 139, 140, 156

Soprano Pipistrelle 23, 28, 29, 74, 75, **76-77**, 78, 79, 81, 134, 139, 140

Sorex araneus **62-63**

Sorex minutus **64-65**

Sowerby's Beaked Whale **128**

Sperm Whale **128**

Stoat 19, 24, 30, 31, 52, 60, **94-95**, 96, 97, 134, 139, 140, 142, 147, 153, 157, 175

Sus scrofa **110-111**

Sus scrofa domesticus **130**

T

Talpa europaea **60-61**

Tursiops truncatus **127**

U

Ursus arctos 174

V

Vicugna pacos **130**

Vulpes vulpes **86-87**

W

Walrus **125**

Water Shrew 23, 26,27, 62, **66-67**, 134, 140

Water Vole 7, 9, 18, 23, **44-45**, 94, 102, 134, 140, 145, 146, 147, 148, 150, 154, 157

Weasel 19, 24, 26, 34, 35, 63, 95, **96-97**, 134, 140, 142, 147, 148, 153, 175

White-Beaked Dolphin **127**

Wild Boar 2, 35, **110-111**, 130, 134, 139, 140, 150,

Wildcat see Scottish Wildcat

Wild Goat **120**

Wolf 124, 153, 174

Wood Mouse 20, 21, 22, 24, 29, **46-47**, 48, 49, 86, 134, 140

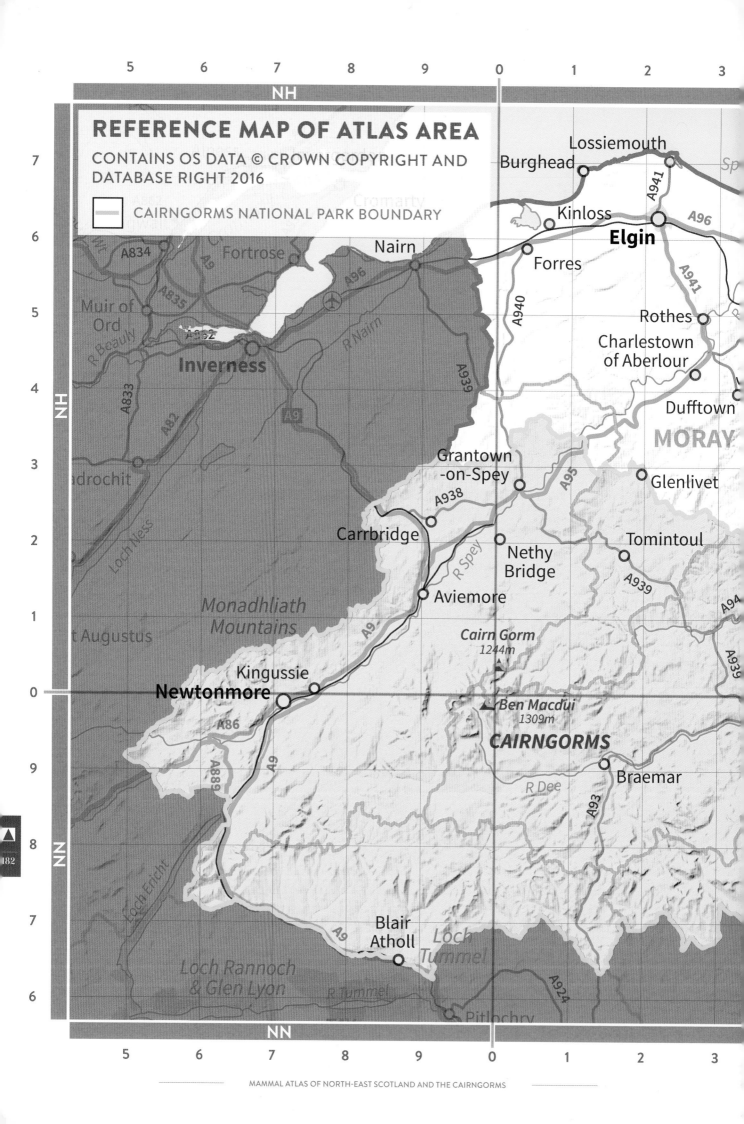

REFERENCE MAP OF ATLAS AREA

CONTAINS OS DATA © CROWN COPYRIGHT AND
DATABASE RIGHT 2016

CAIRNGORMS NATIONAL PARK BOUNDARY

Lossiemouth
Burghead
Kinloss
Elgin
Forres
Rothes
Charlestown
of Aberlour
Dufftown
MORAY
Cromarty
Fortrose
Nairn
Muir of
Ord
Inverness
Grantown
-on-Spey
Glenlivet
Carrbridge
Nethy
Bridge
Tomintoul
Monadhliath
Mountains
Aviemore
Cairn Gorm
1244m
Kingussie
Newtonmore
Ben Macdui
1309m
CAIRNGORMS
Augustus
Braemar
R Dee
Loch Ness
adrochit
Blair
Atholl
Loch
Tummel
Loch Rannoch
& Glen Lyon
R Tummel
Pitlochry

MAMMAL ATLAS OF NORTH-EAST SCOTLAND AND THE CAIRNGORMS

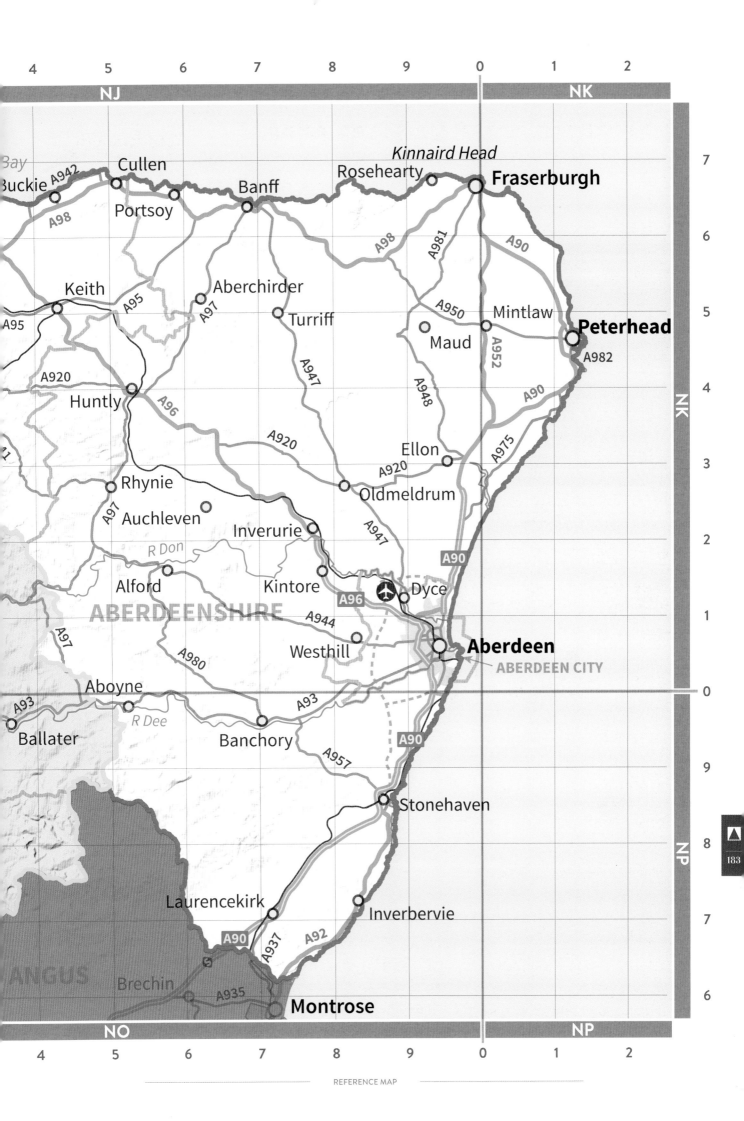

THIS IS A CARBON NEUTRAL PUBLICATION
USING FSC CERTIFIED PAPER

Image: Roe Deer, Birse. Rick Wood